FEEDING AND NUTRITION

THE MAKING OF A CHAMPION

August 1992   Birubi Pacific, PO Box 86, Rouse Hill, NSW 2153, Australia

ISBN No. 0 9589339 6 0

KOHNKE, John Russell BVSc, RDA

Special acknowledgments:
The author acknowledges the contribution by the thousands of horse owners and clients who over the years have provided details of their horse diets and feeding practices as a practical basis for this book. Special thanks are given to Barbara Kelly for typing the manuscript, Melanie Reynolds for typesetting layout and patiently incorporating the many improvements, Carmel Boudib for tedious hours of editing and re-editing, and to Richard Atkin for the design concept, and supervision of publication and printing. The contribution to the scientific and practical content for US conditions by the consultant DVM editor is also gratefully acknowledged. And lastly to my wife Kaye, and children Philippa and Peter, for their understanding, encouragement and family support during the prolonged gestation of this book.

The author appreciates the financial assistance given by Vetsearch International in the publication of this book.

NOTICE

FEEDING AND NUTRITION

THE MAKING OF A CHAMPION

John Kohnke B.V.Sc., R.D.A.

BIRUBI PACIFIC

PUBLISHED 1992

The Author
John Russell Kohnke, BVSc (Hons), RDA (Hons)

John Kohnke grew up on a farm in South Australia, where horses were part of his way of life. He studied Agriculture at Roseworthy Agricultural College, served in Vietnam, and then went on to Sydney University to study Veterinary Science, where he graduated with First Class Honors in 1975.

During a period in private practice, John's interest in horses developed further, and he later joined Lindsay Park Stud as resident veterinarian. Lindsay Park, one of Australia's leading studs, has produced a long string of prize-winning thoroughbred racehorses.

John is currently the equine consultant to Vetsearch International, Australia's premier manufacturer of specialist equine pharmaceuticals and supplements, whose products are now used in over 30 countries around the world.

Over recent years, John has been involved in various research projects on lameness and other common problems. More recently his research interests have included feeding and nutrition, and respiratory conditions in horses. John travels widely overseas, and has many contacts that keep him well informed on any new research findings and treatments.

John has contributed as a co-author of a number of scientific papers, including the initial studies to evaluate isoxsuprine as a treatment for navicular disease. As well, he has contributed to books and texts, most recently "Handbook of Equine Practice" (Saunders, Phil) by Professors R J Rose & D R Hodgson. John also has a specialist knowledge of greyhound and camel nutrition and performance, and presented a paper on The Practical Feeding of the Racing Camel at the First International Camel Symposium in Dubai in early 1992.

From a strong theoretical and research base has emerged a love of communicating in user-friendly terms, with the most important audience of all, the horse owner and trainer. John is author of over 500 articles on veterinary topics and management of all types of horses - he is a regular columnist for many popular horse magazines and journals. He has a reputation for providing practical down-to-earth information in an easy to read style.

John travels widely, giving lectures and seminars on all aspects of horse care. He is much in demand as a speaker, because of his up-to-date practical knowledge, and his entertaining and easy to follow advice.

This book, written in the same helpful style, represents the culmination of months of dedicated study and work, to give you, the horse owner, a practical and useful guide on feeding your horses based on extensive experience and the latest research findings.

AUTHOR'S PREFACE

Perhaps one of the most common queries raised by horse owners and trainers is how to best feed their horses. Most want their horses to perform better, some seek a shiny coat and good condition, many wish for a quieter, less playful animal, and a few are concerned about a particular horse's eating habits.

Many times, after giving practical advice on feeding, the most common parting comment is "Hey, doc, is that information in a book somewhere?"

There are quite a few books on horse feeding and nutrition, but the simple ones often only give the basics with which most horse owners are familiar. Others provide excellent practical and scientific information, but the average horse owner is still left wondering how much of each feed to provide a particular horse, and how to avoid many of the common problems related to feeding.

Most of the horse owners I meet are looking for a recipe type guideline to make-up their horse's rations. My immediate reaction - too many variables, not scientific enough; a lot of work; relegate to the "too hard" feed bin!. But, with the challenge clearly there I carried out a survey of successful horse trainers and competitors on their feed mixes and recipes.

This really opened a can of worms! Some just fed grain and hay, others fed a complicated blend of feeds - overall the outcome was the same - their horses looked healthy and performed well. Everyone considered their feeding program was the best.

In my profession as an equine veterinarian and adviser, and during my travels as a consultant to Australia's leading manufacturer of feed supplements and horse care products, I started to compile a list of questions raised at seminars, during phone calls, and from letters written for advice. It was surprising how many of these queries related to practical aspects of feeding horses.

I have included a selection of some of the most frequently asked questions preceding the index of this handbook with page references given for advice or an answer. You may have similar questions on feeding your horses too!

This handbook was written to give you, as a horse owner, a background to the basic nutrition of horses, and above all, practical guidelines on how to feed and get the best out of your horses.

The recommendations are based on my own experience and observations, books and scientific papers on horse nutrition, and practical advice obtained over years of feedback from horse owners just like yourselves.

I trust you will find this handbook of practical interest and help in feeding and caring for your horses. Not everyone is going to agree with the recommendations, but they are a blend of the art and science of feeding horses - and it is up to you to make the final adjustments to suit your own horses.

COMMON QUESTIONS ON FEEDING HORSES

Horse owners often have queries on the types of feed, amounts to feed and other aspects of practical feeding of their horses. Here are some common queries and the reference page you'll find a hint or an answer.

CONTENTS

SECTION TWO

SECTION THREE

SECTION FOUR

SECTION FIVE

SECTION SIX

SECTION SEVEN

SECTION EIGHT

SECTION NINE

THE SCIENCE AND ART OF FEEDING

With the increase in popularity of the horse as an athletic and recreational animal, and the economic return on the breeding of performance horses, more time, money and effort is being spent researching their nutritional needs. There has been an explosion of scientific knowledge related to the specific nutrient requirement of the horse.

Although horse feeding has been traditionally regarded as an art rather than a science, in today's world of show and performance horses, where presentation and performance are paramount, the scientific aspects of nutrition are becoming more recognised. Owners and trainers of pleasure and performance horses want their horses not only to look their best, but to perform to their maximum genetic capability.

In many cases, a combination of scientific training and feeding can give a horse a competitive advantage. However, the science of feeding cannot be applied without practical knowledge of the art of feeding.

The science of feeding (nutrition) is ensuring an adequate nutrient intake to meet the needs of a particular horse by feeding a well balanced ration. It is knowing the nutritional value and the quality of feeds, what combination is best for specific types of horses, and how to correct likely deficiencies or imbalances.

The art of feeding is the practical knowledge and experience gained from catering to an individual horse's needs, likes and dislikes, and feeding habits. It is being able to select good quality feeds, and knowing how and when to feed. Regular and close observation is required to determine a horse's individual needs and to assess the benefits or otherwise of the ration. A good ration must also be complemented by correct feeding management to ensure the best results of any feeding program.

This handbook gives an overview and update on the practical nutrition and feeding of performance and pleasure horses. It provides scientifically based, but practical guidelines, to the feeding of horses of all ages, breeds and athletic activity under a variety of seasonal and climatic conditions. Most horse owners, whether experienced or new, like to follow established practices with sample guidelines of practical rations. Ration mixes, or feed recipes, have been formulated to give a convenient guideline to feeding the average horse. Hints on feeding management, feed alternatives, and catering for individual needs are also included.

BASIC NUTRITIONAL REQUIREMENTS

It is well known that horses must be provided with an adequate supply of energy, protein, vitamins and minerals, and have access to clean fresh water. Generally, mature adult horses can maintain themselves and perform moderate exercise for short periods on good quality pasture. For these horses, supplementary feed, usually as good quality hay, may only be required when pasture is sparse, short, or of poor nutritional quality.

However, extra nutrients will be required by growing horses, breeding horses, and particularly stabled horses used for equine athletic competition or in the show ring. It is necessary to feed a balanced and adequate ration to maintain health and vitality, as well as match the requirements of growth, performance, and reproduction.

Until recently, the nutritional requirements of horses were based on the known dietary needs of other grazing animals. However, recent research into the specific needs of horses has provided more accurate information on both the nutrient content of feeds, and the dietary needs for exercise, growth, pregnancy and lactation. Scientific calculations can give an estimate of the relative composition, amount to feed and adequacy of a ration made up from available feeds.
The cost and availability of feeds are important factors that can influence the final composition of the ration. Not all horse owners are able to purchase or select the best quality feed for their horses, particularly when seasonal conditions influence the availability, quality and cost. There is also a limit to the horse feeding budget, making many owners compromise in their selection of feeds to achieve the most economical and palatable ration for their horses.

The practical side of feeding requires careful and regular observation and assessment, with occasional adjustments to the ration to ensure the horse looks and performs as required. Overfeeding must be avoided, with feed intake related to the demands of growth and exercise.

It is important to understand the basic layout and function of the horse's digestive system, how to control internal parasites, and the quality and digestibility of feeds, to ensure that horses obtain maximum benefit from their rations. A knowledge of equine eating behavior and feeding patterns are the basis of careful feeding management and help to avoid feed related problems.

THE HORSE'S DIGESTIVE SYSTEM

Unlike many other grazing animals, horses have a very adaptive digestive system that enables them to utilize a wide variety of feeds. Knowledge of the basic structure and function of the digestive system of the horse enables a better understanding of the feeding required to maintain health and performance. On average, it takes 65-76 hours for feed to pass through the digestive tract when horses are fed a grain/hay ration.

THE MOUTH AND TEETH

Horses have very mobile lips, and sharp forward-curved incisor teeth that enable them to selectively feed and graze on short pasture. Some horses use their lips to select and sift out unpalatable feeds and granulated medications.

Compared to other grazing animals horses take relatively small amounts of food at each bite. They grind and crush their food very thoroughly by repeated jaw sweeps to prepare it for digestion in the small intestine, as fermentation and breakdown of fiber does not occur until the feed mass reaches the large hind gut. As a result, horses slowly and carefully chew their food using about 60,000 jaw movements per day when grazing, taking about 1,000 jaw sweeps to chew 2lb (about 1kg) of grain, and more than 3,000 to prepare a similar quantity of hay prior to swallowing. Ponies chew even more thoroughly than horses.

> **HINT**
> *Horses that bolt their feed, or are unable to chew it properly or comfortably due to teeth problems, are more prone to digestive upset and weight loss.*

Regular Teeth Care

Efficient digestion starts when the food is taken in and chewed, and routine attention to the teeth is an important part of feeding management. The most common problem that can reduce the efficiency of mastication (chewing) is the development of sharp edges on the *cheek* or large pre-molar and molar teeth on the upper and lower jaws. This occurs because the bottom jaw is narrower than the top jaw. In order to bring the molar teeth in apposition to grind, a side-to-side sweeping action is required to chew food efficiently. Consequently, after some time, if the hard tooth enamel is not worn away evenly at the completion of the jaw movement, sharp edges develop on the <u>outside</u> border of the top cheek teeth, and the <u>inside</u> border of the bottom teeth.

> **HINT**
> *Horses at pasture rarely develop sharp-edged teeth to a degree that interferes with chewing. However, horses on concentrated rations containing grains or hay that require more grinding, or soft damp feeds that are chewed with less jaw sweep action, are more likely to develop sharp edges.*

Signs of Sharp Edges

Sharp-edged molar teeth can lacerate the mouth membranes, inside the cheeks and tongue, causing pain and discomfort as the horse chews. Affected horses may slobber excessively, "quid" or drop lumps of partly chewed food around the food bin, and take longer to finish their feed because they are avoiding discomfort by careful, slow chewing.

> **HINT**
> *Press on the sides of the mouth along the teeth edges above the level of the corners of the mouth - the horse will show discomfort and pull away if sharp-edged teeth are present.*

Sharp-edged molar teeth may also cause resistance to the bit in hack and show horses, as the tongue and oral membranes are pulled back onto the back teeth by the bit during turning or stopping. This results in pain, with head tossing, twisting the head away on the painful side when turning, and lugging to one side. Horses can fight the bit, grab the bit and pull hard because of sharp-edged teeth.

> **HINT**
> *Although a rubber sleeved bit can help counteract this problem, it is best to first check the teeth for sharp edges, as they are often the underlying cause of the behavior.*

Many veterinarians consider that the teeth should be checked in any horse working on the bit that has an altered head carriage, or an uneven or shifting lameness in the front legs.

In severe cases, digestion may be impaired, resulting in weight loss, a fall away in condition, and poor performance because the food is not efficiently digested.

Young horses aged between two and five years that are fed whole, dry grains and hay that require a lot of chewing often develop sharp-edged molar teeth. Some authorities believe horses develop a habit of lazy chewing, or restricted jaw sweep action on easy to chew, soft concentrate rations as youngsters. Later in life they tend to be more prone to sharp-edged teeth as they grind feed using only the inside surfaces of their top cheek teeth.

Teeth Rasping

Young Horses: *(2-5 years of age)*

It is important to have the teeth checked and sharp edges filed off (rasped or floated) with a tooth rasp every six months in horses 2-5 of age, particularly those fed on concentrate feeds in training.

Older Horses: *(5-20 years of age)*

The teeth should be checked routinely when any horse is brought into work, and at least once yearly in older horses on concentrate feeds.

For convenience, teeth can be checked by your veterinarian at the time of de-worming, vaccination and general health check when a horse first comes into work.

NOTE: If you rasp the teeth yourself, remove only the sharp points on the cheek teeth until the rasp slides freely over the teeth. Over-rasping is detrimental and reduces the grinding efficiency of the teeth. Any abnormalities (stepped teeth, loose caps) should be referred to your vet or horse dentist. Wolf teeth present in geldings and stallions should be removed if the gum is inflamed over the area. However, some horse owners have the wolf teeth routinely removed in horses that are turned or stopped on the rein during competition. Consult your vet for advice.

Aged Horses (25 years or older)

During the horse's lifetime, the teeth do not grow, but continue to be pushed out of the bony jaw as they wear away. Eventually, old horses over 20-25 years of age bite or chew on the remaining root portion of their teeth, or may lose them altogether. If a horse's teeth problems cannot be corrected, or are due to old age, then crushed grains, soaked grains and other soft foods or pellets, and dampened or chopped hay, should be fed so that minimal chewing is required. (See Diets for Aged Horses, page 47.)

Abnormal Teeth Wear

Unfortunately, horses that develop chewing habits such as crib-biting, rail chewing and windsucking often wear their front incisor teeth abnormally. Generally these vices develop due to boredom when confined to stables or corrals. However some horses appear to like the taste of soft wood, such as pine, as they gnaw or crib on rails, doors etc. If the wood has been treated with preservatives to prolong its weathering properties, this may lead to toxicity in avid wood chewers.

When purchasing a horse, always check its mouth to confirm its approximate age, and look for abnormally worn incisor teeth. This can give a clue to the horse's chewing vices.

Saliva

Horse's secrete about 1 gallon (4 liters) of saliva for every 5 gallons (20 liters) of dry feed consumed; or roughly 3 gallons (12 liters) of saliva each day. Horse saliva has a buffering action, with little direct digestive function, and the high mucus content helps to lubricate the food bolus for swallowing.

HINT

It is important that blood samples for electrolyte analysis be collected before exercise, when a horse is at rest, and before it is fed. When a horse eats, relatively large volumes of fluid and electrolytes (potassium, bicarbonate etc) are secreted in saliva to help to buffer stomach digestion. Although they are re-absorbed 1-4 hours later in the lower gut,

the blood level of potassium salt may be artificially lowered if blood is collected within two hours of feeding, or 4-6 hours after exercise, and it may appear that a blood deficiency is present. (For full details refer to Health Care and Common Problems Booklet Edition 8 1992-USA.)

THE DIGESTIVE SYSTEM

Stomach
Mixing of food. Secretion of gastric juices. Partial digestion of protein.
Passage Time:
Food: 20 minutes (small meal) to 3 hours (large meal).
Water: High proportion bypasses along stomach wall into small intestine.

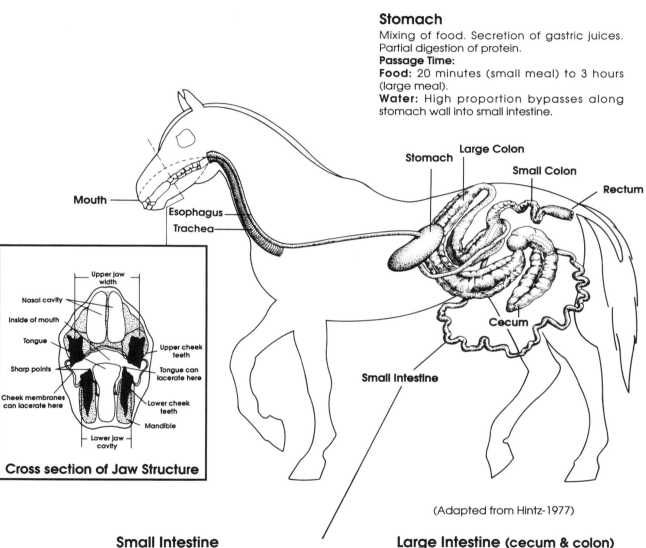

(Adapted from Hintz-1977)

Small Intestine
Major digestion and absorption of proteins, fats and carbohydrates to glucose. Absorption site for CALCIUM, IRON, and other minerals, ELECTROLYTES, B-COMPLEX vitamins.
Passage Time: 45 minutes - 8 hours.
Most food in cecum within 3 hours.

Large Intestine (cecum & colon)
Bacterial fermentation of fiber, cellulose and carbohydrates. Bacterial synthesis of vitamins and protein. Water absorption.
Passage Time:
Food: Pellets, concentrates and fresh grass 24-36 hours. Hay 50-60 hours.

THE STOMACH

The horse's stomach capacity is small as compared to other grazing animals, being only about 8% of the total digestive tract volume, or about 8 liters in a 1100lb (500kg) horse. Stomach capacity of the young foal is relatively larger than that of the adult horse. This is because the stomach plays an important part in digesting milk, and the large bowel itself is not developed to ferment fibrous food. Both saliva and gastric juice are secreted with the actual presence of food in the mouth or stomach, rather than by sight or smell of food (as in some other animals): horses do not drool or dribble saliva in anticipation of receiving food at feed time.

Liquids pass rapidly through the stomach, and food is retained for about 20 minutes, during which time it is mixed and partly digested. Although the food mass is only held for a short time, the stomach never really empties, as small amounts of residual food stay for up to three hours. Liquids often rapidly by-pass the stomach content by travelling along folds in the wall, and are able to rapidly rehydrate the small bowel after a drink, even if the horse has a full stomach.

Horses have evolved as continuous eaters like the rat and deer, grazing or feeding for up to ten hours a day. They have little storage capacity in the stomach and no gall bladder, so bile is secreted continuously as the food mass moves through the gut. Because of their limited stomach capacity, horses eat slowly, and over-feeding must be avoided as it may lead to colic or even rupture of the stomach.

HINT
When stabled or confined to corrals or pens, horses should be provided with small feeds on a regular basis. Stabled horses should be fed at least twice daily, and where high grain rations are given, such as in performance horses, 3-4 feeds daily are recommended. (See Do's and Don'ts of Feeding page 39.)

THE SMALL INTESTINE

The small intestine occupies about 27% of the digestive tract volume (about 30 liters in a 1100lb (500kg) horse). The small intestine is approximately 70 feet (21 meters) long in an adult horse, and food moves through it at up to 1 foot (30cm) per minute. The food mass reaches the large bowel within three hours after a meal. However, it takes up to eight hours for most of the food to pass through the small intestine. The small bowel is the primary site of digestion for most protein to amino acids, fats to fatty acids, and about half the soluble carbohydrates to sugars. This is the section where much of the cereal grain content of the ration is digested.

The small intestine contains about 90% fluid. Many soluble minerals, particularly calcium, zinc, copper, manganese, iron and magnesium are absorbed primarily from the small intestine. Phosphorus, sodium, potassium and chloride are absorbed from both the small and large intestine.

Large amounts of phosphorus (phosphates), or calcium-binding compounds (eg phytates in wheat bran, oxalates in tropical grass) can significantly reduce absorption of calcium in the relatively restricted length of the small intestine. (See page 149.)

HINT
Additional calcium should be added to high grain, high wheat bran or high oxalate containing rations to ensure adequate absorption from the small bowel. (See Individual Ration Guidelines for specific advice.)

Most vitamins in the feed, particularly the B-complex vitamins, are absorbed from the small intestine.

HINT
In horses under stress, (eg performance horses) it may be beneficial to provide oral B-Complex vitamins (eg 2oz (60ml) Pulse-8 over the tongue) 4-6 hours prior to strenuous exercise to help maintain the appetite (see Ration Guidelines).

The remaining fibrous portion of the feed, undigested food starch and protein is passed on to be digested in the large bowel.

THE LARGE INTESTINE

The large intestine consists of the cecum, various sections of the large and small colon, and finally the rectum. It contributes about 65% of the total digestive tract 16-18 gallons (65-72 liters) in a 1100lb (500kg) horse), as fermentation of fiber requires larger capacity. The passage of liquids and feeds is slow and takes 50-60 hours to pass through this area of the gut. This is necessary to allow effective bacterial fermentation and digestion of the fibrous portion of the feed, undigested protein and remaining carbohydrates. The first part, or the cecum (which corresponds to the human appendix) contains large populations of bacteria and protozoa which digest fiber, cellulose and the remainder of the soluble carbohydrates.

The large intestine expands in capacity and activity from foal to yearling age to allow digestion of more fibrous food. There are no digestive enzymes secreted into the large bowel, although mucus is released to lubricate the passage of the food mass.

Studies have shown that pelleted type foods move faster than fresh grass through the large intestine, and hay has the slowest passage of all. Very young horses do not have the digestive capacity to ferment large amounts of fiber, so more concentrated feedstuffs (eg grains) should be included in foal and weanling rations. (See individual Ration Guidelines.)

Although the bacteria themselves metabolize nitrogen and produce bacterial protein, only limited amounts of this protein are actually absorbed from the large intestine and used as a protein source by the horse. More than half the dried weight of the manure is, in fact, composed of bacterial cells.

Generally, the absorption of food protein from the small intestine accounts for the major protein uptake in the adult horse. The bacteria also synthesize many B-Complex vitamins, particularly Vitamins B1, B2 and B5, and limited amounts of these can be absorbed and utilized by the horse. Horse manure contains higher levels of some B-Complex vitamins than were present in the original feed. Studies have indicated that bacterial protein and vitamin absorption and utilization is reduced when horses are fed highly concentrated feeds, or are under stress of strenuous exercise. Horses in this case may benefit from protein and vitamin supplements added to their feeds.

Water is absorbed mainly from the large intestine, with the manure of a healthy horse containing only about 60% moisture. Horses grazing lush pasture, or those that have diarrhea have more fluid feces. However some young stabled horses, bored by confinement, may occupy time by sipping water, overloading their digestive system, and hence passing more fluid manure. Wet bedding around the water trough, or water dribbled over the floor or doors is a sure sign. Restricting the water intake, or turning them out as often as possible, will often help to control this habit.

> **HINT**
>
> *Horse owners occasionally observe that the manure balls passed out in the droppings are drier and have a thicker coating of slimy mucus. This is most commonly due to fluid uptake from the bowel following heavy sweating during exercise, or consumption of large amounts of dry fibrous food, such as stalky hay, particularly if horses do not drink sufficient water to maintain bowel fluid levels. It can also be due to bowel wall irritation from heavy worm burdens; or starvation, when a horse is sick and not eating or drinking regularly. Consult your veterinarian for advice if necessary.*

For further discussion on the importance and quality of water, see pages 27.

CONTROL OF PARASITES

Heavy worm burdens can cause a horse to lose condition and lack vitality despite an adequate and balanced ration. Heavy infection with *external* parasites may also affect health and condition, sap vitality and cause a horse to spend time itching and rubbing itself, interrupting its feeding time.

Regular control of internal parasites is an important management procedure to ensure proper digestive efficiency and freedom from worm-related conditions. Heavy worm burdens should be considered as a cause of recurring colics, poor condition, lack of thrift, chronic or acute diarrhea, poor stamina and coat condition, and sub-optimal performance in horses of all ages.

In simple terms, the lifecycle of the common internal parasites of horses can be divided into a parasitic phase and an environmental phase.

Parasitic Phase

Horse worms living in the tissues and the gut are true parasites, using the horse's body as a source of nutrition and lodging. Initially, minute larval stages migrate through the gut wall and undergo developmental stages (moults) within the abdominal tissues, blood vessels and organs. Even a small number of worms in these stages can cause severe and permanent internal damage, with symptoms of colic and ill-thrift. Unfortunately, during this often extended migratory period (up to 6 months for Bloodworms), the larval stages are not controlled by many worming compounds. Adult worms have a range of harmful effects: they interfere with digestion, irritate the bowels, and sap blood and nutrients, thus reducing vitality.

> **HINT**
>
> *Worming compounds, or anthelmintics, are used to control these internal forms, with some chemicals controlling only the adult form, others removing migratory larval stages as well.*

Although modern worming compounds are highly effective, regular worming alone will not safeguard horse health. Careful attention to dosing technique to avoid under dosing and wastage will ensure the full dose is delivered and swallowed; rotation of worming compounds every 12-18 months will reduce likelihood of resistance to a worming compound; timing of wormings to suit seasonal conditions; as well as monitoring of fecal egg counts for efficiency of worming and recontamination rates, will achieve the best overall control of these internal parasites. Consult your veterinarian for advice on a worming program best suited to your stocking rate and management system, rate and level of recontamination (as indicated by fecal egg count results), and seasonal conditions.

Environmental Phase

The major worms do not multiply within the horse's body, but through microscopic eggs passed in the manure.

Studies have shown that up to 99% of a worm population exists as eggs or larval forms on the pasture at any one time. Worm eggs either hatch to produce minute mobile larvae or develop into infective eggs on the pasture. Manure becomes infective with Strongyle larvae about seven days after it has been passed, and in this way these worms spread to all horses grazing the pasture or eating contaminated feed. (See Lifecycle of Worms, page 21.)

> **HINT**
>
> *Regular collection of manure to reduce contamination in stalls, corrals and small paddocks, and careful grazing and pasture management to reduce egg and larval uptake and limit worm survival on pasture, are essential to limit worm burdens.*

Good pasture hygiene will complement regular worming in providing effective, long-term control of worms. Provision of hay racks and feed bins will reduce the uptake of worm larvae and eggs from contaminated pasture or soil.

> **HINT**
>
> *Recent research confirms the importance of pasture hygiene in worm control. Twice weekly removal of manure from corrals and small paddocks was 5-10 times more effective in reducing worm burdens than treatment with wormers alone. Worm levels on uncleaned pasture were 18 times higher than on regularly cleaned pastures, and since 99% of worm populations exist on the pasture, pasture hygiene is an important adjunct to worm control. Suitable methods to control or remove worm larval build-up in pastures include follow-up grazing with sheep or cattle, harrowing etc. or vacuuming and sweeping to remove manure. Machines are now available to clean pasture.*

The Small Strongyle species of worms (Small Redworms or Cyathostomes) are now considered to be one of the major causes of worm related ill-thrift, reduced vitality, and poor growth and performance in horses. Although regular 6-8 weekly worming intervals have assisted control of other major worms, including the artery Bloodworm (Strongylus vulgaris), the shorter adult maturity time of 4-5 weeks to egg laying stage, presence of hybiotic or encysted resting stages in the gut wall, and resistance build-up against older generation Benzimidazole (B-Z) worming compounds, have resulted in an increase of Small Strongyle worm populations on the pasture and heavy burdens in horses.

THE COMMON PROBLEM WORMS

		Migratory Stages	Developing Adult/ Adult Forms	Adult Location
LARGE STRONGYLES Bloodworms	Harmful Effect	(S.vulgaris as example) Migrate in blood vessel walls. Damage to main gut supply vessels - swelling, blood clots, damage to internal organs.	Suck on plugs of bowel wall- erosion, bleeding, blood loss. Interfere with digestion.	Large bowel
	Symptoms	Loss of appetite. Fever. Mild to severe colic. Occasional nervous signs, lameness. Permanent long term damage to blood vessels.	Weight loss, rough coat, poor condition, weakness, ill-thrift, anemia, diarrhea, colic, death.	
SMALL STRONGYLES Redworms Cyathostomes	Harmful Effect	Enter bowel wall - can remain dormant in "resting" form in nodules for 2.5 years. Interfere with nutrient absorption.	Interfere with digestion, complete for nutrients, blood loss.	
	Symptoms	Seasonal release of large burdens can cause severe diarrhea, weight loss, death. Increased risk of sand colic on sandy pastures.	Ill-thrift, loss of vitality, anemia, weight loss, poor performance.	
ASCARIDS Large Roundworm	Harmful Effect	Most common in foals. Damage to lungs as larvae enter airways.	Heavy burdens interfere with digestion, and may obstruct bowels with dead worms after worming.	Small bowel
	Symptoms	Coughing, nasal discharge. Fever, loss of appetite in severe infections.	Diarrhea, depression, ill-thrift, rough coat, "pot bellied" appearance, poor growth.	
OXYURIS spp Pinworms	Harmful Effect	No migratory stage. Compete for nutrients during feed digestion.	Interfere with digestion. Compete for nutrients during feed digestion	Cecum and Large Bowel
	Symptoms	Developing adults - some ulceration of gut in heavy burdens only.	Main symptoms from eggs around anus. Rubs tail-butt to relieve itch, hair loss, interrupts feeding, loss of condition.	
GASTERO- PHILUS spp Bot Larvae	Harmful Effect	Migrate initially in tongue and mouth tissues. Attach to stomach wall by hooks.	Pupa in soil for 1-3 months. Bot flies emerge in summer.	Bot flies
	Symptoms	Pain on chewing, reduced appetite, "resistance to bit". Ulceration and perforation of stomach possible in heavy infections.	Annoyance by bot flies. Fright and injury risk. Interrupts feeding, loss of condition. Eggs on legs detract from appearance.	
ANO- PLOCEPHALA spp. Tapeworm	Harmful Effect	No migratory stage.	Erosion of Ilio-cecal valve junction area, irritation to large bowel. Severe infections may cause death due to obstruction/ perforation.	Ilio- cecal junction. Large bowel
	Symptoms	Heavy burdens of immatures may cause colic and diarrhea	Ill-thrift, diarrhea, sporadic colic, sign often 4-5 days after routine worming. More serious in yearlings.	

LIFECYCLE OF COMMON HORSE WORMS

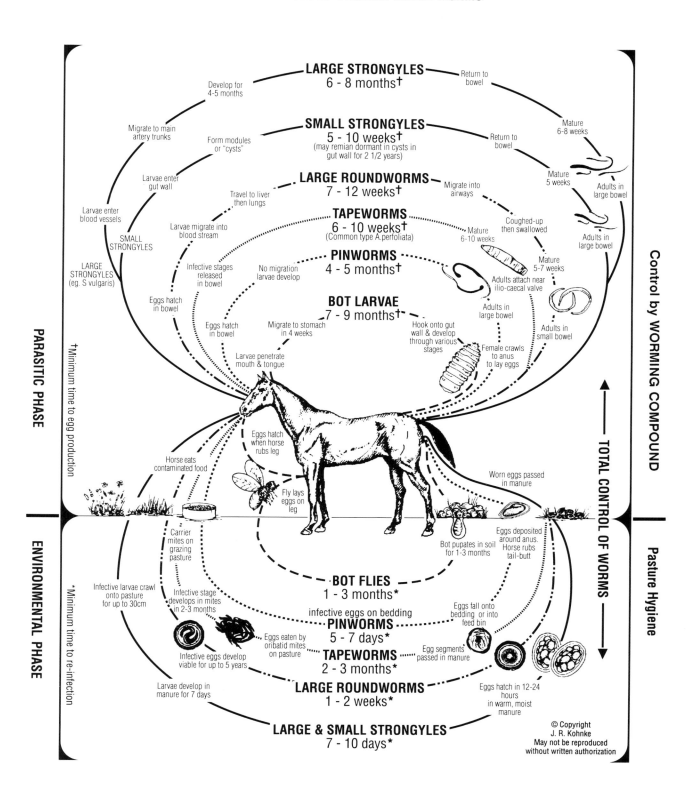

PARASITIC PHASE

†Minimum time to egg production

ENVIRONMENTAL PHASE

*Minimum time to re-infection

LARGE STRONGYLES
6 - 8 months†

Develop for 4-5 months

Return to bowel

Mature 6-8 weeks

Migrate to main artery trunks

Form modules or "cysts"

Return to bowel

SMALL STRONGYLES
5 - 10 weeks†
(may remian dormant in cysts in gut wall for 2 1/2 years)

Mature 5 weeks

Adults in large bowel

Larvae enter gut wall

Larvae enter blood vessels

LARGE ROUNDWORMS
7 - 12 weeks†

Migrate into airways

Travel to liver then lungs

SMALL STRONGYLES

Larvae migrate into blood stream

TAPEWORMS
6 - 10 weeks†
(Common type A.perfoliata)

Coughed-up then swallowed

Adults in large bowel

LARGE STRONGYLES (eg. S vulgaris)

Infective stages released in bowel

No migration larvae develop

PINWORMS
4 - 5 months†

Mature 6-10 weeks

Mature 5-7 weeks

Eggs hatch in bowel

Adults attach near ilio-caecal valve

Adults in large bowel

BOT LARVAE
7 - 9 months†

Eggs hatch in bowel

Migrate to stomach in 4 weeks

Hook onto gut wall & develop through various stages

Adults in small bowel

Larvae penetrate mouth & tongue

Female crawls to anus to lay eggs

Eggs hatch when horse rubs leg

Horse eats contaminated food

Fly lays eggs on leg

Worn eggs passed in manure

Carrier mites on grazing pasture

Bot pupates in soil for 1-3 months

Eggs deposited around anus. Horse rubs tail-butt

BOT FLIES
1 - 3 months*

Infective larvae crawl onto pasture for up to 30cm

Infective stage develops in mites in 2-3 months

infective eggs on bedding

Eggs fall onto bedding or into feed bin

PINWORMS
5 - 7 days*

Eggs eaten by oribatid mites on pasture

Infective eggs develop viable for up to 5 years

TAPEWORMS
2 - 3 months*

Egg segments passed in manure

Larvae develop in manure for 7 days

LARGE ROUNDWORMS
1 - 2 weeks*

Eggs hatch in 12-24 hours in warm, moist manure

LARGE & SMALL STRONGYLES
7 - 10 days*

Control by WORMING COMPOUND

TOTAL CONTROL OF WORMS

Pasture Hygiene

Poor teeth and worm burdens must always be considered as possible causes for lack of thrift or loss of condition in horses on an otherwise adequate diet. A teeth check and an initial worming, with a follow-up worming in three weeks, (to help control release of Small Redworms) are important aspects of routine health care when a horse is brought into work to ensure the best response to an improved ration.

It is beyond the scope of this handbook to outline the pasture management procedures, and selection and use of worming compounds in a worm control program for specific types of horses. (For an overview, refer to Health Care and Common Problems booklet; Edition 8-1992 - USA.)

However, as most horse owners use paste or liquid worming preparations for routine control of worms in horses, it is worthwhile including some helpful hints on the technique to ensure the full dose of wormer is administered.

Steps to Ensure Accuracy of Paste Dosing

Paste wormers are convenient and easy to use. However, underdosing and wastage may be problems which could increase likelihood of resistance build-up, even in the newer worming compounds. Take time -- read label directions and dosage rate.

- **Step 1** - Ensure horse's mouth is empty.

HINT
If necessary, wash mouth out with a hose.

- **Step 2** - Give the full recommended dose rate.

HINT
Estimate weight of horse using a girth tape or other measurement method, or weigh on scales. (See Estimating Bodyweight, page 163.)

- **Step 3** - Deposit the paste over the back of the tongue (ie at rear of main mouth cavity).

HINT
Do not deposit paste between inside of cheeks and teeth as paste may become trapped and irritate the mucosal lining, or be more easy for the horse to slobber out.

- **Step 4** - Hold the horse's head up for 15-20 seconds to ensure the full dose is swallowed.

- **Step 5** - Keep accurate records of worming dates/worming compounds used etc. for future reference.

HINT
It is not advisable to work or exercise a horse within a few hours of worming. Worm on a rest day.

- **Step 6** - On breeding farms, or where large populations of horses are grazed on pasture, carry out fecal egg counts on 10% of the horse population every 6 months, about 6 weeks after the last worming, to monitor recontamination rates. Consult your veterinarian for advice.

THE FEEDS AND FEEDERS

Horses are able to adapt to a wide variety of feeds. The selection and blend of feeds is most important when horses are stabled, have little free choice, or have restricted access to pasture to overcome minor nutritional imbalances and deficiencies in their concentrated rations.

The common feeds are often grouped into basic sources of energy, protein, fat, and fiber, each overlapping to some degree, and contributing various amounts to the mineral, electrolyte, and vitamin requirements of the horse. Horses need a daily supply of these nutrients, as well as an adequate intake of clean, fresh water.

> **HINT** *Horses will normally consume 1.5-2.5% of their bodyweight (1½-2½lb per 100lb or 1.5kg-2.5kg/100kg) daily, depending on the frequency of feeding, appetite and amount of work and exercise. (See page 172 for guidelines for individual classes of horses.)*

ENERGY

Energy is supplied by carbohydrates (sugars and starches), protein and fat. Carbohydrate is the main source of energy, and in working horses supplies 80-90% of the energy requirement. Cereal grains contribute the major source of carbohydrate for exercising horses. Over recent years, vegetable oils containing fats have become a popular energy dense feed for racing, hard-working and long distance riding horses.

Energy is required to fuel the body processes and maintain body temperature. Whenever a horse is required to be productive, either to grow, reproduce or work, more energy is required.

> **HINT** *The energy needs of an individual horse are also influenced by its temperament, the speed and duration of exercise, temperature, humidity, the weight and ability of the rider, type of working surface, and general metabolic efficiency of the breed. The ration may have to be adjusted to suit the individual horse. Nervy or high strung horses can expend up to twice as much energy during exercise as their calm counterparts. Fretting during confinement to a stall or corral also uses more energy than grazing in pasture.*

Horses at Rest

Recent studies have indicated that the energy requirement for horses at rest (non working, or maintenance) is proportional to the horse's bodyweight. Therefore, in theory, the requirement for a 500lb (225kg) pony is about half that of a 1000lb

(450kg) adult horse. Obviously, variations in activity, environmental conditions, and even temperament, will influence the energy requirement. Certain breeds of ponies and horses appear to have a higher metabolic efficiency in utilizing energy than other breeds. As a guideline, horses at rest can be maintained with an amount of feed equal to about 1.5-2% of their bodyweight.

Energy for Exercise

The energy required for work is related to the duration, speed and intensity of exercise, and relative fitness of the horse. Estimates indicate that galloping expends twice as much energy as a fast trot, and five times more than a slow trot or walk. Recent studies have shown that energy expenditure is increased in proportion to the combined weight of the horse and rider. As the horse has a limit to the volume of feed it can consume, the calorific value or energy density should be increased to reduce the bulk of the ration to meet high energy demands of hard or prolonged exercise. This is usually done by adding extra grain, and reducing the overall bulk or roughage content of the ration.

> **HINT** *Small framed horses or picky eaters, or horses in hard or fast work, often need less bulky rations than easy keepers or good doers.*

Therefore, reducing bulk of feeds, for example, by replacing some of the oats with more energy dense feeds, such as corn or fat (as vegetable oil), will often enable those horses to eat sufficient to meet their energy needs.

The relative requirements for individual classes of horses are discussed under the Individual Feeding Guidelines. The contribution of various feeds to supply energy is summarized in tables on page 173.

PROTEIN

Proteins provide the "building blocks" or amino acids for growth and repair of body tissues. When protein in food is digested, it is split up into its constituent amino acids. These amino acids are then recombined during metabolism to provide the specific proteins for muscle, blood, skin, hair and other tissues of the horse's body.

Some amino acids are synthesized by the horse, others are termed essential amino acids, and must be supplied in the diet. Cereal grains are imbalanced or deficient in some amino acids, whereas oil seed meals, such as soybean meal, have a more balanced amino acid profile for growth. Horses require increased amounts of protein during periods of growth, pregnancy, lactation and hard work.

HINT
Although excess protein can be converted into energy, feeding protein meals is an expensive way of providing energy, compared to cereal grains and fat.

Exercising Horses

Exercise generally increases the daily requirement for protein. Studies of human athletes indicate that an increase in protein levels may help in early stages of training, as muscle mass and blood cell production is increased. A higher protein diet may also be beneficial when fed the day after a hard race or competition to aid repair of muscle tissue damaged by strenuous exercise.

In performance horses, an increase in cereal grain content (eg oats, corn and barley) to satisfy energy needs also provides a proportional increase in protein to meet protein requirements at the exercise level. Where alfalfa or mixed hay is used as roughage, it boosts the energy and protein content of the ration to above that required, whereas grass hay based rations often have to be boosted with a protein supplement, such as soybean meal.

Recent evidence suggests that excessive protein levels may increase heart and respiratory rates, and increase sweat output in horses performing slow, endurance type exercise. Some riders consider a horse secretes white foamy sweat when unfit or on a high protein diet.

HINT
Horses consuming excessive protein will usually urinate more and increase their water intake. Many trainers believe excess protein in the diet can increase ammonia smell in the urine of a stabled horse.

One study suggested that protein intake above relative needs may affect the performance of young racehorses, slowing the race time by 1-3 seconds for every 2¼lb (about 1kg) of excess protein consumed daily.

Other studies have shown that there is no advantage in feeding rations greater than 10-12% crude protein to working horses. Provided adequate energy is available, working and racing horses can perform on rations of 9-12% protein. This level is usually supplied by rations composed of grains and good quality hay.

HINT
Poorly muscled horses in early training may benefit from an additional 8-12oz (230-340g) of protein meal (eg soybean, linseed etc.) daily, to help their body develop in response to exercise. (See Individual Ration Guidelines.)

NOTE: A low blood protein level in a racing horse does not indicate a dietary deficiency, except perhaps when the albumin:globulin ratio is decreased. As albumin is formed in the liver, then low protein diets in horses under stress may reduce albumin synthesis. The protein level in the blood usually decreases by up to 4g/liter during the training period. A higher than normal level of blood protein (elevated total plasma protein reading) usually indicates hemo-concentration due to dehydration. (See Health Care & Common Problems, Edition 8 1992 (USA) for further details.)

Growing Horses

A recent study in 4-month old weanlings fed a 14-20% protein diet for a period of 140 days, resulted in daily weight gains of about 1½lb (700g). However, another similar group of weanlings, fed a 9% protein diet, only put on about 2½oz (70g) daily and feed intake and utilization was depressed. When the low protein group was then fed the 20% protein diet for a further 140 days, they caught up in growth rate and development with no significant differences in weight, height, or cannon bone thickness to other treatment groups.

Another study, carried out over a two year period, indicated that growing horses, if exercised regularly, with adequate levels of energy in a ration, could develop normally on a 6-8% protein diet. As exercise stimulates the appetite and feed consumption, the overall intake of protein is increased to meet growth requirements. Therefore it appears that, provided energy and exercise needs are met with grains and hays, and exercise is given to encourage development, young horses will grow adequately on a relatively low protein diet. Higher protein diets do not increase growth rates, but over an extended time, may actually be harmful. Studies have shown that excess energy, combined with normal or high protein diets, can lead to developmental orthopedic disease (DOD) and bone problems in young horses. (See page 73 for preventative hints.)

Although cereal grains provide adequate levels of protein for working horses, most are deficient in essential amino acids required for growth, particularly lysine, methionine, tryptophan and cystine. Small amounts of oil seed meals (eg soybean meal) and provision of legume hays for roughage (eg alfalfa and clover hays) can be fed to boost the protein quality in growing and young working horses. (See Individual Feeding Guidelines for details.) The contribution of various feeds is summarized on pages 173-177.

FIBER

Fiber, consisting of cellulose and lignin, is essential for efficient digestion in the horse. Fiber tends to open-up the digestive mixture, thus allowing more efficient action of digestive juices, enzymes and fermentation bacteria on the feed particles. An adequate level of fiber is essential to maintain the flow of digestive material through the bowel. Excessive intake of fiber, as in poor quality hay, distends the digestive tract and leads to "hay belly". Fiber also helps retain water and electrolytes in the digestive mass of the large bowel, acting as a valuable reserve of fluid for horses that sweat heavily when working in hot weather or during long distance or strenuous exercise. Adequate fiber helps to combat the effects of dehydration and tucking up in the belly. Inadequate roughage in highly concentrated grain or pellet based rations increases the risk of digestive upsets and vices in stabled horses, such as wood chewing and eating bedding.

Horses in training on high grain diets may develop a low grade diarrhea with "cow pat" manure, often with a sour, acidic smell and a yellowish-green paste consistency. It is often a result of feeding excessive amounts of grain relative to hay. In this case, reduce the grain by 50% and feed double the volume of fiber for 3-5 days. If the digestive upset persists, consult your vet for advice. A drench of live culture yogurt 3½oz (100ml) over the tongue daily for 2-3 days may help re-establish fiber-digesting bacteria in the large bowel.

HINT
Fiber is fermented in the large bowel by cellulose-digesting bacteria, a process that produces heat and warmth within the body. Additional hay in cold weather will help keep horses warm at pasture. (See Feeding Horses in Cold Weather page 50.)

The contribution of various feeds is summarized on pages 173-177.

FAT

Although most horse feeds contain less than 5% fat, additional fat can be used to provide energy and essential fatty acids to improve coat and skin condition.

HINT
Feeding up to 3oz (90ml) of polyunsaturated corn oil or cooking oil a day provides essential fatty acids to improve skin and coat condition in racing and show horses.

Over recent years, the feeding of extra vegetable oil as a source of energy for both low and high intensity exercise, is one of the most significant advances in performance horse nutrition. Some horses will reduce their feed intake for a few days, but if adequate bulk is provided, they will usually accept a fat boosted diet once they are conditioned to it.

Consumption of fat boosted diets increases both liver and muscle energy (glycogen) stores. Conditioning a horse by training also increases muscle energy levels in fit horses.

Fats contain about 2¼ times more energy per unit weight than carbohydrates and proteins. Traditional grains and hays contain very little fat (3-5%). Reports indicate that horses are capable of digesting and utilizing up to 30% of their energy need as fat, without developing digestive complications, providing it is slowly introduced to allow the digestive and metabolic systems to adapt. In practice, 10-12% of total energy as fat in the diet seems to be a safe and beneficial level.

Horses that are fed on energy dense diets containing fat generally have to eat less food to meet their energy needs. High fat diets reduce the bulk of gut contents, and hence the overall bodyweight carried during exercise. As energy demand is proportional to bodyweight, reduced gut weight may give a significant competitive edge in racing horses competing over short distances. However, in endurance and other horses working over long distances or for extended times, then adequate fiber intake by feeding good quality hay is important to sotre

electrolytes and water. (See guidelines for endurance horses.) Small framed horses, fussy or picky horses, or those with poor appetites, are more likely to consume the reduced bulk of a fat boosted diet.

It has been well established that fats can be efficiently utilized for slow, low intensity exercise, such as endurance, jumping and hacking activities. However, recent reports suggest racetime in thoroughbred racehorses running over 1600 meters was improved by 2.5 seconds (2.1%) after consuming a diet containing 12% of its energy contributed by corn oil, compared to a grain diet with 2% energy from fat. Feeding the fat diet did not increase the rate of muscle energy depletion during exercise. However, more research is needed.

Metabolism of Fats

Fats have a slower rate of mobilization and conversion to energy than carbohydrates. Some grains such as oats, tend to make horses hot and playful, which is usually a result of overfeeding energy relative to the exercise requirement and more rapid availability of the starch on digestion. However, many horse owners claim that feeding barley and fat as energy sources results in less heating and nervy type behaviour on equivalent energy intakes. More research is needed on this, but in my experience substitution of grain with part fat seems to make nervy horses easier to handle.

The total amount of digestive and metabolic heat "waste" produced per unit of energy of fat is lower than fermentable feeds such as roughages and carbohydrates. For example, about 75% of the energy in roughage is lost during fermentation as heat waste, 40% from proteins, 30% from oats, 23% from barley, 20% from corn, and only 15% from fats.

HINT
Feeding extra fats may be suited to horses working in hot climates to reduce overall heat stress and sweat loss. However, adequate fiber intake to retain a reserve of water and electrolytes must be maintained.

Fats also contribute a higher amount of water as a by-product from metabolism than carbohydrates and proteins. This may benefit endurance and heavily sweating horses by helping to prevent dehydration. (See Feeding in Hot Weather, page 48.)

Recent studies have suggested that horses prefer corn oil (90% digestible), although soybean, sunflower or blended oils are all accepted if introduced in a step-wise manner. Although horses will eat warm liquid tallow (rendered animal fats) mixed into feed, once the tallow cools they will not readily consume the solidified form of fat.

Fats to Replace Grains

If fat (eg corn oil or vegetable cooking oil) is to be fed as an energy source to working horses, then 8oz (240ml) daily is about the minimum that makes its addition worthwhile. When feeding polyunsaturated oil (eg corn oil, soybean oil, blended cooking oil) introduce in stepwise increases over a period of 2-3 weeks. This is essential to ensure acceptance of the added fat, and also adapt metabolic pathways to digest and utilze fat as an energy source during exercise. Commence on volumes of 3oz (90ml) once daily, then 3oz (90ml) twice daily, increasing over 10-14 days to 8oz (240ml or 2 teacups) in the morning and evening feeds. One 8oz measure (240ml) of polyunsaturated oil provides approximately the same amount of digestible energy as 1½lb (700g) of whole oats or 1¼lb (600g) of cracked corn.

The energy contributed by fats and oils is outlined in a table on pages 173, 177.

When substituted on an energy basis for grain (eg oats), fat, containing a higher density of energy, helps to reduce the volume of the ration. Smaller feeds are beneficial in small framed horses or in performance and hard working horses where their appetite may be depressed by the affects of stress or fatigue.

NOTE: Polyunsaturated vegetable or blended cooking oils are subject to oxidation or rancidity during storage and use. Many horses will reduce their intake if the oil tastes stale or has bittered through rancidity. It is essential that you seal the containers well after use, store in a cool place and avoid shaking prior to measuring out the required dose. Shaking mixes and traps air bubbles in the oil and increases the likelihood of oxidation and rancidity.

Fats and Vitamin E

Studies have indicated that as the level of polyunsaturated fats is increased in the diet, the requirement of Vitamin E and selenium increases. In selenium deficient areas, selenium status should be evaluated prior to adding extra fat to the diet. Consult your vet for advice.

THEORY: *Vitamin E prevents the initial oxidation of polyunsaturated fats to peroxides in muscle cell walls and blood. Peroxides can reduce the efficiency of muscle function and overall performance. Selenium, contained in the enzyme glutathionine peroxidase, helps prevent further oxidation of peroxides to harmful superoxide radicals. These can cause irritation, inflammation, and damage to muscle and other cells. A dietary selenium deficiency can lead to muscle weakness and degeneration (with white muscle disease in severe cases in foals and growing horses) and reduced performance. In diets high in fat, it is important to protect against oxidation by adding Vitamin E (such as in White-E), and in selenium deficient areas, a supplement of selenium (such as in Feramo-H).*

As a guideline, extra Vitamin E should be supplemented at the rate of 100iu Vitamin E per 3½oz (100ml) of added corn oil or vegetable fat in addition to the standard daily recommended dose of 1000iu Vitamin E for racing and working horses.

Fat and Protein Needs

Fat does not contribute a source of protein in the same way as grains that are included for energy in rations. Therefore, if the protein contribution from grains is reduced by replacing some of the grain with fat, then the overall protein content of the ration may fall short of requirements, especially on grass hay based diets. Extra protein meal should be added to meet protein needs.

As a guideline, replacing some of the grain with up to 8oz (240ml or 2 teacups) of fat should not cause a shortfall in protein even on grass hay based diets. However, for each additional 4oz (120ml or 1 teacup) of fat (eg corn oil) substituted for grain in the diet, it is recommended to add one extra teacup of protein meal (eg soybean meal) to the ration.

Fat and Calcium/Phosphorus

When fat is substituted for grain as an energy source, then the intake of calcium, and particularly phosphorus, is reduced as grain is removed from the ration. Cereal grains are a major source of phosphorus in grain based high energy diets. These

essential minerals may fall short of daily requirements in fat boosted diets, and lead to risk of musculo-skeletal and metabolic problems.

As a guideline, for each 8oz (2 teacups) of fat substituted for grain, add ½oz (15g or 1 tablespoon) of dicalcium phosphate to help ensure adequate intake and balance of calcium and particularly phosphorus.

WATER

Horses must have an ample supply of clean, fresh water at all times. It is especially important that horses have adequate water during growth, work and lactation. The amount needed and consumed is dependent on the moisture content of the feed, (pasture 75-80% moisture, grains and hays 12-15% moisture), the temperature and humidity, the digestibility of the feed, level of exercise, sweat output, and milk production in mares. At the peak of lactation, where a 1100lb (500kg) mare may produce up to 35 pints (approximately 20 liters) of milk per day, consumption of water can increase by 50-70%, or an extra 5 gallons (20 liters) per day.

Water is lost in urine and manure, as well as by moisture evaporation from lungs (panting) and skin (sweating) during exercise which help cool the body (thermo-regulation) in working horses.

A resting horse in a cool environment needs at least half a gallon per 100lb (roughly 2 liters per 50kg bodyweight). Volumes of up to 16 gallons (70 liters) or more are required by heavily sweating horses in work.

Horses at rest will drink from 1½-2 pints per pound (or 2 liters/kg) of feed. They will consume almost double the amount of water when fed on coarse hay or pasture, than when given a more digestible ration of grains and good quality hay.

In hot weather, at an ambient temperature of 100°F (38°C), horses can consume up to four times as much water to dry matter [equivalent to about 6½ pints per lb (8 liters/kg)] than they will at cooler temperatures of 65°F (18°C).

Lack of Water

Although horses can survive for up to six days without water, normally they stop eating and develop colicky signs after two days. A lack of water reduces feed intake and growth, and leads to dehydration that hampers physical activity and performance. Nutrients absorbed from the gut must be in solution, and a deficiency of water decreases this drainage effect, and slows the passage of feed through the gut. Both water and electrolytes are stored in the fibrous digesta in the large bowel, and an adequate intake of fiber is essential to maintain a reserve of water to combat sweat loss in hot weather, or during extended periods of exercise in horses. If the digestive mass dries out due to inadequate water intake, digestion may be decreased, resulting in colic, food impaction, reduced ability to work and risk of dehydration in heavily sweating horses. It is especially important to have an adequate supply of water when horses are given electrolytes, as salts stimulate the thirst response and horses will seek water to drink.

Water Quality

Drinking water should be clean, good quality and not contaminated by decomposing organic matter, algae and sediment, or have high salt content which can render it less palatable.

> **HINT**
>
> *Most horses prefer to drink cool water below about 75°F (25°C). In the warmer weather, water troughs and buckets should be located in a cool, shady area, and cleaned regularly.*

The level of total dissolved solids a horse will regularly accept in drinking water is 1000ppm (1g/liter), with a maximum of 3000ppm (3g/liter).

Water containing greater than 5000-7000ppm (5g-7g/liter) of total dissolved solids will affect performance and rate of growth in horses.

> **HINT**
>
> *When you are adding electrolytes or concentrated rehydration solutions to drinking water, the total concentration should not exceed this maximum level. In most cases, allowing for the natural mineral content of domestic water, it is best to avoid adding more than one ounce per 4 gallons (or 30g or 1½ tablespoons per 18 liters) of salt, or electrolyte mix, to drinking water.*

A salt mix should not be added to well or pond water which has a high natural mineral content. If in doubt, have the water supply on your farm or to your stable tested for total dissolved solid content. Your veterinarian or local County Agricultural Agent will be able to arrange testing, and give advice on water suitability. Studies have shown that water containing high levels of mineral salts, (eg bore water) - provided horses will drink it - is unlikely to cause build-up of kidney stones or calculi.

Time of Watering

Where troughs and self waterers are not available, horses should be watered at regular times, ensuring that adequate quantities are offered, depending on the ration, temperature and type of work. Horses may be watered before, during or after feeding, without interfering with digestion or absorption of feed.

If horses are to be worked hard, it is preferable that they are offered water before feeding. Horses should not be allowed to drink large volumes of water while they are still hot. Large amounts of very cold water given to hot, tired horses can result in colic (water gripes), and on rare occasions laminitis (water founder). After hard exercise, many horse owners allow a horse to graze or eat dampened hay for 15-20 minutes to cool down, and then provide water to drink. Alternatively, others offer only 1-2 pints of water intially (if it is very cold, they add warm water to take the chill off), then allow free access to water after 15 minutes.

> **HINT**
>
> *During long distance competition, such as trail and endurance riding, horses may be watered at creeks, pools, dams or troughs, provided exercise is immediately continued after the drink. However, it is best not to allow a hot and thirsty horse to drink an excessive amount of cold water too quickly.*

> **HINT**
>
> *At endurance vet checks, experience has shown that horses will satisfy their thirst rapidly by drinking as much water as they want, then rest to recover, without evident complications. It is essential that water is not withheld at any time during an endurance ride if the horse is thirsty. Fluid and electrolyte levels, as provided by a rehydration formulation (such as Recharge) must be maintained to combat dehydration at every opportunity.*

NOTE: If the water or rehydration drink is very cold, such as when stored overnight in drums, then the chill should be taken off by adding a small amount of warm water before offering large volumes to a hot, thirsty horse.

Waterers

Always locate the watering bucket or automatic waterer in a cool, shady area. Automatic waterers for stabled horses are preferred to buckets because water is not wasted and less time is spent cleaning and refilling. However, daily water consumption cannot be monitored with self waterers. Self waterers should be checked at least twice daily to ensure they are operating efficiently. In the winter, automatic waterers in yards may need to be heated to prevent freezing over, and troughs located in a protected area. Although horses will consume snow as a source of water for a short time, water is preferred. Electrolytes or salt mixes should not be added to self waterers, as it is difficult to judge the quantities to avoid an excessively salty taste. Salt added to water may corrode metal fittings in drinking vessels.

Troughs should have a drain outlet for easy and regular cleaning. In corrals and paddocks, ensure the trough sides are safe so as to prevent injury to horses while drinking. Troughs raised above the ground are less likely to become contaminated with wind blown dust, dirt and organic matter.

> **HINT**
>
> *Always position water troughs so that they do not project outwards along fence lines as horses may gallop into them when running the fenceline. Also, a number of horses in a paddock may not be able to drink as a social group when access to the trough in a fence line is limited to one side. Ideally, troughs should be located in a shady area out from the fence line. In small yards, locate the drinking trough across the corner to reduce the risk of injury. If troughs are located under trees, ensure leaves are routinely removed as rotting leaves may effect the taste of the water.*

> **HINT**
>
> *Always ensure that the ball-cock, valve or float ball is covered to prevent horses playing with the mechanism, and either wasting water or cutting off the supply. With new concrete troughs, ensure that any sharp edges of cement moulding are rasped off from inside and outside borders of the trough to prevent horses lacerating their tendons and lower limbs as they paw in the water in hot weather. If automatic waterers are placed on a wall in a stable, cover the edges of the waterer with rubber matting, a piece of old bicycle tire, or other padded material to reduce risk of injury.*

Water Taste

Individual horses can distinguish various water tastes when travelling from place-to-place on a racing or show circuit. This may affect their water and feed intake, leading to dehydration. A small amount of honey or molasses, [2 tablespoons per 4 gallons (about 20 liters)] of fresh water may be useful in masking any changes in taste, encouraging adequate water intake.

HINT   *Accustom a horse to drink water containing a commercial rehydration fluid (such as Recharge) on a regular basis after work or travelling. This will help to rapidly replace electrolytes and fluids, and help mask water taste.*

Watering vessels must be cleaned daily to prevent souring and fly attraction if laced with sweetening substances, electrolytes or rehydration fluids.

Some horses on show circuits, yearling sales etc. will not readily accept chlorinated town water when they are accustomed to drinking rain, river or well water. In most cases, horses will accept the water if water buckets are filled and allowed to stand overnight to allow the chlorine odor to evaporate. Alternatively, take a quantity of home water in a steel or hard plastic container (to avoid the plastic taste) and mix it with the chlorinated water.

HINT   *Adding 10ml (2 teaspoons) of an iron supplement (such as Ironcyclen) to 4 gallons (about 20 liters) of chlorinated tap water may also help to speed up the release of chlorine gas, and improve the acceptance of the water.*

HINT   *Some horses, perhaps through habit, do not drink sufficient water to maintain their correct hydration levels, particularly when worked hard or fed on dry feed. The addition of electrolytes and salts to the feed (such as Humidimix, Neutradex etc) will often encourage the animal to drink. However, for the horse that is a poor drinker and doesn't appear to drink adequate water, float a large apple in a well anchored water trough or bucket (to prevent the horse tipping the bucket over to get the apple). Most horses will attempt to grasp the apple in their teeth, and in doing so, sip extra water. With time, a smart horse will drink a 2 gallon (8 liter) bucket of water to obtain the apple.*

FEEDERS, TUBS, BUCKETS

When horses are fed concentrated rations in the paddock, or in a stall or corral, they should be provided with a safe feed tub or bucket. Placing feed into tub rather than on the ground or stall floor reduces wastage and trampling of feed, and minimizes uptake of worm eggs.

Stabled Horses

It is important that an adequate sized feed tub, approximately 4-6 gallons (16-24 liters) capacity, be provided for stabled horses. For safety and comfort, although not natural, most horse owners attach the feeder on a wall at chest height.

This will help prevent the horse from pawing the tub, tipping it over, or fouling the feed with urine and feces.

HINT   *In horses suffering from respiratory tract disease, such as a respiratory virus, it is a good idea to place dampened hay and feed at floor level in a safe feed container so that the airways will drain during feeding. Also ensure that the bedding is not dusty, to reduce the risk of dust inhalation during feeding.*

HINT   *Some impatient horses develop a habit of spilling food by pushing it over the sides during feeding. Provide a deep feeder with a retaining lip around the sides to reduce waste by these horses. (See Problems Relating to Feeding, page 141.)*

The feeder should have rolled or protected edges to prevent injury, and ideally be located near to or across a corner so as not to protrude out along a wall line.

HINT   *Avoid completely closing in the space under a feeder in the corner of a stable. When feeding, many horses stamp their front legs due to habit, impatience or to dislodge flies etc, hitting the front of the feeder. Over a period, bruising and concussion to the knees can cause swelling, enlargement and lameness. Alternatively, this can be avoided by sloping the base into the wall, or hanging a piece of rubber matting on the front of the feeder.*

Feeders should always be placed in an area where horses can observe other horses whilst feeding, such as through a mesh fence or wall. Young, nervy horses tend to eat more happily when they can see other horses. Studies have shown that horses denied visual contact with others will take longer to eat their meals, and waste more food by taking a mouthful and walking about trying to see other horses. (See Problems Relating to Feeding, page 142.)

HINT   *Many nervy horses or picky eaters do better when kept out at grass in a small paddock, rather than being confined to a stall. However, to ensure they consume adequate concentrate feed to meet their energy needs for exercise, it is best to stable them overnight. (See Poor Appetite, page 51.)*

Studies have shown that young horses are more likely to eat their overnight ration in a dimly lit area. Where the stall is dark, horses often prefer to stand and feed outside in a corral. Many experienced horse persons consider that stabled horses tend to eat better on moonlit nights.

HINT   *Many nervy young horses tend to eat better at night if the feeder is placed under a night light. A low wattage bulb placed in the stall above the feeder will encourage them to stay in the stall and spend more time feeding. However, for safety reasons, cover the bulb and locate well above the horse's reach. In a stable, a central night light will provide a dim glow into all boxes. A yellow insect repellent 60W globe may help to attract fewer insects and reduce spider numbers and cobwebs in the barn.*

It is a good idea to locate the watering vessel on the opposite wall to the feed tub in a stall or small corral. This will discourage horses from alternating between feed and water, building up feed sludge in the water source.

HINT *In horses that develop the eat-drink vice, dampen the food, and remove the water bucket for the first 1-2 hours after the feed is given. (See Problems Relating to Feeding, page 143.)*

Corrals or Small Lots

Feeders should be located across the corner or if possible set into the fence line at chest height. Avoid hanging, or locating feed tubs at ground level along fence lines, as horses may accidentally run into them and injure themselves if frightened. Ensure there are no sharp edges on the tubs and water troughs.

HINT *An old bicycle tire, a split open piece of plastic garden hose or wooden rail to cover the edge will reduce the risk of injury from sharp edges around metal tubs or drums. Heavy duty, reasonably durable plastic tubs are safe and easy to clean.*

Regularly clean out, scrape and wash feeders to remove crusty leftovers and molasses residues. Drill a small hole, or cut slots at the lowest spot so that the tubs are able to drain during wet weather. Regularly clean the drainage holes with a sharp stick or piece of wire.

Paddocks

It is best to spread feed tubs out at least 2-3 horse lengths apart to prevent squabbling and peck order competition in horses pastured together. Aggressive behaviour can lead to injury, especially if a new horse is introduced to the group.

HINT *Provide one feed tub or pile of hay more than the number of horses to allow a new horse some chance of feeding. In a large group of horses, place two or more feed tubs away from the other tubs to give newly introduced horses, or horses low in the peck order a chance to feed.*

HINT *When introducing a new horse (particularly young fillies) to a group of horses, worm out and quarantine the new arrival in a yard for 24-48 hours to empty out worm egg burdens. Bring one of the horses from the group to meet and forge a bond with the new horse, if possible, overnight. This will help to settle it down and provide a companion with which to feed and graze.*

Always empty feed tubs that have caught water after rain, or drill a small hole in the bottom to allow the water to seep out. Poke a stick through the hole from time-to-time to clear it of blockage. It is wise to empty feeders after shifting horses out of the paddock. Concentrate feeds left in feeders for a few days will spoil and go moldy and may cause digestive upset if newly introduced hungry horses eat it.

HINT *To prevent horses tipping over their feed tubs use either a wide, flat based tub, or stabilize the tub by placing a brick, stone or thin layer of concrete*

in the bottom. (Unfortunately, concrete in the bottom of a steel feed tub will trap moisture and causes it to rust out more quickly.) A feed tub may also be set inside a discarded rubber tire to reduce the ease of tipping it over.

In most cases, it is preferable to place feed tubs away from a gate area to prevent horses congregating at the gate, trying to escape when the gate is opened at feed time, or bogging the area during wet weather. If possible, feed tubs should be located in a sheltered, shady area to increase comfort whilst feeding. Choose a well drained location, preferably with an all weather surface. Some larger horse farms construct permanent all weather feed areas by compacting an area of road construction material sited in a well drained location.

Many horse owners prefer to regularly change the location of feeders around the paddock to avoid excessive erosion of one area of a flat paddock. Others consider that it is better to have one permanently denuded area rather than a number of eroded, bare spots in a paddock. In undulating country, locate feed tubs in a well-drained area on the leeward side of a hill during cold weather, or behind a windbreak of trees. In this case, feed tubs can be left permanently in one place. It is best to locate watering facilities some distance away from feed tubs and hay racks to prevent horses developing the eat-drink habit during feeding, as well as encourage lazy horses (eg heavily pregnant mares) to exercise.

HINT *It has been common practice in larger horse farms to use metal tubs or cut-down oil barrels or gas drums as paddock feeders. Often weanlings will bump their knees and ankles on the sides of these feeders when feeding. This can cause enlarged, puffy knees and ankles which detract from the animal's appearance. In this case, more shallow tubs (eg plastic tubs or small wooden troughs) should be provided for weanlings, and the larger feed tubs reserved for older horses. Alternatively, set the feed tub into a discarded rubber tire to reduce the risk of young horses bruising their knees and ankles. However if the enlarged joints appear to be hard and bony, then the Degenerative Orthopedic Disease (DOD) should be considered as a possible underlying cause of the abnormalities (see pages 73, 149).*

Hay Racks

A hay rack or net for hay and green feed, should be provided for stabled horses. Hay racks are often located across a corner of a wall above head height so horses can reach up and pull the hay.

However, brittle or dusty hay placed in these racks often increases the risk of leaf loss, as well as dust inhalation and respiratory irritation when feeding, unless the hay is soaked or dampened. (See page 147.)

In most cases, it is probably better to put the hay in a separate tub or trough next to the concentrate feed or place the portion of hay on its side at the back of the tub and pile damp feed in front of it. Hay racks in corrals or paddocks should be located away from fence lines, on a well-drained area and preferably with some type of cover over the top to prevent the hay being spoiled by rain or snow. The hay racks should be constructed so that there are no sharp angles formed by corner bracing that could snare a horse's leg. They should be stabilized by having a reasonably wide base to prevent them being tipped when horses rub against them, or use them as a play toy to occupy time.

Stable and Paddock Hygiene

Areas under and around feed tubs, hay racks, gateways, shelter and shade trees often become heavily contaminated with feed spills and manure. Generally, horses will not pass manure in the feeding area, and often walk away to deposit it in the roughs of the pasture.

Heavily contaminated areas encourage fly build-up and fly worry after rain in the summer months, and bog during wet weather. Worm egg and larval contamination also builds up, and risk of worm uptake is increased in horses nibbling pasture, hay and feed spills in these areas. Foals and young growing horses are at particular risk from worm uptake and bacterial infection from heavily contaminated areas.

Strict hygiene in stalls and small pens or corrals is essential, with at least once daily collection of manure to prevent spread and trampling of manure into the bedding. In larger paddocks, at least twice weekly clean-up of manure will help reduce levels of worm contamination. In fields, regular removal of manure around feeders and shade trees etc will help to reduce worm uptake, reduce fly breeding and improve overall hygiene. For further discussion, see page 46.

FEEDING HABITS OF HORSES

An understanding of the horse's eating patterns, selective and social feeding habits, and digestive function is essential to ensure health and contentment in grazing and confined horses.

As a free range animal, horses grazed mainly grassland species, and therefore became adapted to a relatively low protein and energy diet to meet their maintenance needs. Once domesticated, horses came to rely on their human caretakers to provide their feed in both grazing and stabled situations. Whilst grazing horses still retain some of their natural feed selection instincts, horses confined to stalls are solely reliant on the adequacy, content and balance of the ration provided.

Modern management practices often provide horses with excessively concentrated diets and alter their social feeding patterns. These can result in digestive and metabolic disorders, behavioural problems, and other man-made ailments related to feeding. Most of the feeding disorders and ailments are the result of poor feeding practices, confinement, or disregard for the normal feeding habits of horses.

NORMAL EATING PATTERNS

Grazing Horses

The horse originated in an open plain environment and consumed small and frequent feeds of just a few forages. Therefore eating is a natural pastime for horses, and they spend a great part of their time feeding. They do not expect or thrive on variety.

Wild horses spend up to 75% of the day and half the night grazing. They usually graze for 12 hours or more out of 24 hours, often only fasting for 3-5 hours at a time between grazing. Most grazing horses sleep and relax between 1am and 6am each day. Domesticated horses confined to pasture spend a similar proportion of their time searching for and harvesting their feed, depending on its availability, energy value and palatability.

Stabled Horses

Once horses are confined to stables or yards, and rely mainly on concentrated feeds to meet energy needs, the time spent feeding is reduced. As horses like to eat to occupy time, they can become overweight, even obese, if given a virtually *ad lib* supply of concentrate feed or very rich hay.

A horse may eat for only 8-10 hours per day when fed on *ad lib* pelleted foods in a stall. Because they do not have to walk and select their feed, they eat almost continuously until each feed is consumed. Between meals they spend time standing, walking, drinking, eating bedding and chewing rails etc. Horses seem to prefer to eat from the floor, rather than from a trough or feed tub.

INFLUENCE OF DIET

Generally, as the amount of roughage in the diet decreases, less time (as little as 14%) is spent eating. Concentrate feeds increase leisure time, which in the confines of the stall is often spent on boredom related vices, such as manure eating and wood chewing. Observers report that in stalls horses spend an average of eight minutes a day nibbling on and chewing wood and stall fixtures, usually during the night. Similar horses with access to corrals or small paddocks only spend on average two minutes daily chewing wood.

EFFECTS OF TEMPERATURE

Eating patterns are influenced by seasonal and weather conditions. Horses tend to increase their intake of roughage during colder weather; cold weather increases their appetite. Fermentation of roughage in the hind gut increases heat production and helps to keep the horse warm.

If roughage is not provided in cold weather, there is an increase in wood chewing behaviour in stalled horses, and time spent browsing in grazing horses during the winter months. More time is spent eating during cold weather, and horses tend to select roughage, such as good quality hay, in preference to concentrates. However, access to concentrates should be restricted as hungry horses may consume excessive amounts in cold weather, especially overnight, leading to digestive upset and metabolic problems such as founder.

During hot weather, horses naturally reduce their calorie intake, eating less food overall, depending on their exercise load. Therefore, in hotter weather, more high energy rations should be provided for exercising horses, with a minimal roughage intake of 1.0% bodyweight to limit heat production from fermentation. Provision of energy dense feeds such as corn, barley, and fats may help reduce heat load, sweating and the risk of dehydration in working horses during the hot summer months.

APPETITE LIMITS

The adult horse will generally eat enough to maintain its bodyweight in free-choice feeding. Grazing horses appear to adjust their appetite to maintain a relatively constant energy intake over a period of time. When horses are provided high energy rations or large volumes of feed, they will easily gain weight and put on condition.

Horses confined to stalls consume more feed and are more prone to weight gain and digestive upset than under grazing conditions where palatability of food is variable. Draft horses and ponies (cold blooded horses) and Warmbloods, are more prone to obesity than hot blooded horses, such as Thoroughbreds and Arabians. Under natural conditions, horses have been observed eating to gain weight in times of plenty, and living on stored fat when less food is available.

SELECTION OF FOOD

Horses select food on appearance, smell, taste and texture and an acquired liking for a particular food. When pasture has many different forages with a wide variety of tastes and textures, horses will selectively eat in order of preference, leaving some forages and weeds. Less palatable forages are avoided until after the more accepted species are grazed out. By this time, the left-overs have generally matured, become even less palatable, and have a lower feeding value. Grazing areas often become full of weeds and less palatable grasses.

Under natural conditions horses will eat relatively unpalatable foods simply to keep themselves alive if their preferred food is not available. However, some spoilt horses would rather starve. Grazing horses tend to partition their total grazing area into preferred feeding areas, which they keep closely cropped as "lawns", leaving other less palatable species as rank grass and "roughs" where they pass their droppings. Adult horses spend most of their time grazing on the lawns. Before defecation, they walk to a nearby rough, pass their droppings, and wander back to the lawn area. Most horses will not deposit droppings onto their feeding area, under shelter trees or near feed bins.

Up to 50% of a grazing area can be lost to roughs and areas contaminated by manure, where heavy concentrations of worm eggs and larvae accumulate. This may be an instinctive grazing technique to avoid parasite egg and larval uptake under natural or low stocking rate conditions.

SOCIAL INFLUENCES

Horses have a gregarious nature and a herd grazing behaviour with an established peck order. They mimic each other in feeding patterns and temperament. A relaxed and feeding horse will encourage others to eat; a strange or unsettled horse will make other horses interrupt their feeding. Visual contact between horses is also important during feeding as horses will eat better when they can see other horses doing likewise.

Horses frequently lift their heads when eating to stay aware of their surroundings and the activity of other horses. Visual contact between stabled horses should be maintained by using a mesh screen rather than a solid partition between feeders or individual stalls to encourage better feeding habits.

Nervous horses will eat more when their feed tub is located in a better lighted area of the stall where they can see other horses. Nervy or young horses often fail to consume a full feed overnight in very dark stables. Feed intake can be increased by shifting the feeders outside to a sheltered area in a yard under moon or star light, or providing a dim light in the stable.

THE DIGESTIVE LAYOUT

The anatomy and function of the horse's digestive system must also be considered when deciding how often and how much to feed. The structure and function of the digestive system is outlined on pages 17-19. Observers report that horses display an expression of anticipation when food is seen, chewing their tongue repeatedly. They nicker, paw their feet, and their heart rate increases, but in contrast to many other animals, horses do not salivate until they actually take a mouthful of food and begin to chew.

The horse is classed as a continuous eater, having a small capacity stomach for short-term storage of food without significant digestive action. The absence of a gall bladder completes the adaptation to a continuous feeding pattern which requires small and frequent feeds.

Punctuality of feed time is important for stabled horse, as they become accustomed to routine and set feed times. Any significant variation can cause behaviour problems such as impatience and boredom vices, as well as risking digestive upset by too rapid food intake in a hungry, bored horse.

LEARNING NOT TO EAT

It is impossible for an obese or overweight horse to learn not to eat, as most horse owners know. It is best to supply bulky low energy foods to fill them up, and increase exercise to utilize the energy. Do not purposely starve a fat horse, and especially a pony, to lose weight, as it may lead to severe metabolic problems, such as hyperlipidosis and death. Horses may avoid foods that make them nauseated, provided the nausea occurs within a few minutes of eating the food.

DIGESTIBILITY AND QUALITY OF FEEDS

The digestive efficiency, or the amount of nutritive value obtained from the feed, can be influenced by various factors, including the degree and type of processing of feeds, the fiber content, efficiency of chewing, the exercise level of the horse, the rate of feed intake, and amount of feed consumed.

PROCESSING

Crushing or rolling generally increases the digestibility and palatability of feeds. Digestive juices, enzymes and bacteria can act more efficiently on open kernels and smaller particles. However, processing can decrease the stability, palatability, and feed value during storage.

HINT *Generally, grains need only be rolled, crimped or cracked for foals, and for mature or old horses with poor teeth, or greedy horses that fail to chew whole grains properly.*

Oats

Studies have shown that crushing or crimping oats improves digestibility by 2-5%. However, in horses with sound, properly cared for teeth, processing of oats may not be economically worthwhile because generally they can chew the whole grain efficiently.

HINT *Where performance horses are fed more than 10 pints (5.6 liters) of whole oats or other grain in a feed, more whole grain may be passed in the manure due to the volume the horse has to chew. In this case, feed rolled, crimped or crushed grain to improve digestibility and feeding value.*

Clipping oats by removing fibrous end parts of the grains (traditionally prepared for racehorses), increases the relative energy and protein concentration. However digestibility is not significantly improved, and it is usually cheaper to feed cracked corn for the equivalent energy content.

Wheat, Grain Sorghum, Rye

Digestibility of hard and rough grains such as wheat, grain sorghum or milo and rye, is increased by up to 15% by crushing or steam rolling, which makes processing of these grains economically worthwhile.

HINT *Steam rolling increases overall palatability, and reduces dustiness of the processed grain. Studies indicate that micronizing oats and grain sorghums increases starch digestibility and overall performance in horses.*

Wheat (and corn) should only be coarsely ground, as fine grinding increases dust content, leading to respiratory allergies and heaves, and possible digestive upset.

Corn

Corn can be fed whole or cracked. Horses with sound teeth can efficiently chew and digest whole corn. When whole corn is mixed into a damp evening feed, the majority of the corn is softened by the time the horse eats it. Cracking corn increases its overall digestibility by about 7-9%. Processing and subsequent storage of corn and oil seeds increases the rate of natural deterioration of vitamins. Storage after processing often reduces palatability and acceptance, due to its stale flavor, particularly by young horses. Deterioration is hastened by oxidization or rancidity of the fat (oil) content of the grain. Studies have shown that the feed value of cracked corn can decrease significantly as it becomes rancid within 3 weeks of cracking or crushing.

HINT *It is best to crack corn freshly or for use within 2-3 days. If cracked corn is purchased in a bag, leave it in the bag and fold down the top after use to reduce surface layer oxidation and rancidity. Avoid storing cracked corn in large bins or drums if it is fed only in small amounts over an extended period.*

Barley

Whole dry barley grain is unpalatable to most horses. Barley is generally better accepted if it is steam rolled, as this softens and opens up the grain, but only increases digestibility by up to 5%. Cooking or boiling barley, or wheat bran, does not significantly increase digestibility, feed value or destroy harmful molds. However, cooking tends to attract more flies to the feed in the summer time. Cooking also reduces the fermentation rate of starch, and may reduce the risk of hot or playful behaviour in some horses due to slower energy release.

Roughage

Pelleting or fine grinding of hay causes it to pass more quickly through the digestive tract, and may reduce its overall digestibility. However, studies with alfalfa pellets containing a high percentage of leaf and lower fiber than loose alfalfa hay, indicated an increase of 32% in nutritive value for pellets as compared to long hay. Other studies using alfalfa cubes indicated a better feeding value could be expected from alfalfa cubes than baled alfalfa hay. Chopping hay does not significantly increase its digestibility. However, it does increase the dust content, and rations containing large amounts of chopped hay or chaff should be dampened to minimize dustiness and thus reduce airway irritation.

| HINT | *Chopping hay or feeding alfalfa meal allows it to be easily mixed with pellets or grains to "dilute" and slow down the rate of intake. Bulking the ration in this way minimizes the risk of digestive upsets, and increases eating time and overall digestibility in stabled horses. It reduces the incidence of wood chewing and other boredom related vices that can occur when horses are fed solely on pelleted diets. Feeding chopped hay also prevents selection of more palatable parts of loose hay, such as leaves and seed heads, and thus helps to avoid wastage.* |

Horses tend to waste up to 10-12% of loose grass hay when feeding from hay racks or directly off the floor or ground. However, wastage can be reduced to less than 5% if it is placed in a large tub or trough for stabled horses.

Processing

Large volumes of bulky, fibrous feeds may reduce overall digestibility as the rate of passage through the gut is increased, and the time for bacterial fermentation of fiber is reduced.

However, an adequate level of fiber in the diet, at least 1.0% bodyweight, is important to open up the digestive mass and maintain adequate flow of feed through the digestive tract. (See page 24 for more discussion on fiber.)

EFFICIENCY OF CHEWING

Poor teeth, particularly sharp edges on the molar grinding teeth, will discourage proper chewing action, and not prepare the feed for efficient digestion. In severe cases, horses may be slow eaters, drop or quid food, and pass whole grains or long straws in their manure. Therefore, regular teeth care is an important part of feeding management. (See page 16.) In old horses with poor teeth, dampened pellets, or soaked, cooked or crushed grains and chopped hay, should be fed to improve digestibility, and ensure they obtain maximum benefit from the feed.

EXERCISE INTENSITY

The level of exercise can also affect digestive efficiency. Light exercise improves digestibility of the feed by reducing the rate of passage through the gut, thus allowing increased time for digestion. However, severe hard work slows digestion, and often may result in horses losing their appetite.

| HINT | *Low-grade muscle soreness resulting from fast work too early in training, is a common cause of loss of appetite. A careful cooling down procedure will often help to minimize muscle discomfort and maintain the appetite. (See page 51.)* |

INDIVIDUAL RESPONSES

Individual horses seem to have differences in digestive and perhaps metabolic efficiency. Some horses are easy keepers or good doers and do well on any type of feed, whereas other horses, particularly nervy, highly strung animals, fail to maintain themselves even when fed on high quality feeds. Ponies appear to be able to do well even on relatively poor quality feed. The rate and control of metabolism by glucose/insulin response in some breeds (eg ponies etc.) may be the underlying reason for their apparent differences in digestive and metabolic efficiency. Studies indicate Thoroughbreds have a delayed insulin response following carbohydrate feeds, and this can increase the risk of hot and nervy behaviour within 4 hours of eating a concentrated high fermentable grain based feed. This may affect the temperament of show and racehorses on the day of competition.

RATE OF FEEDING

The rate of ingestion, and amount of feed consumed, may influence digestibility and benefit to the horse. Greedy horses, or those that bolt their feed, generally do not chew it properly. This reduces digestive action on the feed, and makes them more prone to digestive upsets and colic. Whole grains may be passed undigested. However, even a horse that eats at a normal rate will pass some unchewed grain if fed large amounts of whole grain, such as oats. Greedy horses are also liable to choke if they eat chunks of apple, carrot and hay too quickly.

| HINT | *The rate of intake of concentrate feeds in greedy eaters can be slowed by feeding small amounts at a time, or diluting the feed with chopped hay. Alternatively, a large smooth stone can be placed in the feed tub, and only small amounts of feed filled in around it to limit the rate of intake. For helpful hints on correcting Gorgers, see page 142.* |

TASTE PREFERENCES

Each horse has its individual likes and dislikes, and it is helpful to know which feeds and tastes (or flavors) a particular horse will accept. Specially flavored feeds can then be offered to horses that are off their feed, or can encourage a horse to eat more concentrate, or accept supplements. Horses rely heavily on their sense of smell to accept food so that even slight changes in smell of feed may result in a fussy eating habit or total rejection. Indeed some horses will refuse medicated feed without even tasting it because of the difference in aroma, (eg worming granules added to the feed). Cracked corn that has turned rancid on storage may be refused by young horses in particular because of its stale aroma and flavor, although they relish freshly cracked grain.

HINT *Feed containing a small amount of cooked barley, or hot soaked grain or wheat bran, with molasses as a sweetener, may tempt a horse to eat following sickness or injury.*

Supplements and worming compounds are often flavored to increase palatability or acceptance, or associate a pleasant taste with the medicine or treatment. It appears that most horses like aniseed, vanilla, yucca or apple flavoring, (providing they have tasted apples previously). Most horses will acquire a taste for garlic mixed into feeds.

HINT *To condition a horse to accept a flavor (eg vanilla, garlic etc) place a couple of drops of the flavor on your finger and smear inside the horse's nostrils, and touch the tip of the tongue for a couple of days. Once conditioned in this way, most horses will then accept the flavor when it is mixed into feed.*

HINT *Five to ten drops of vanilla essence, or juice squeezed from a clove of garlic, mixed into the top layer of a damp feed will often help increase the feed intake of a picky eater. A tablespoon of salt mixed into a feed may also improve the palatability to some horses.*

Horses also like feeds with a chocolate or peppermint flavor, and most horses relish strong peppermints as a reward.

NOTE: Chocolate flavorings should not be used in performance horses as the metabolites of chocolate (eg theobromine) cannot be distinguished from caffeine metabolites in a swab.

Pasture

Horses are selective foragers and do not graze plants in proportion to the abundance of the plant. Palatability plays an important part with younger, sweeter plants being selected. Studies have shown that horses prefer a clover-grass mixture, in pre-bloom or early bloom stage. Generally, horses find more mature plants less palatable. For example, it has been observed that most horses prefer young, short stands of growing alfalfa up to early flowering stage, leaving the more fibrous matured plants.

Hays

Horses will accept and utilize good quality leafy and sweet hay, in preference to mature fibrous hay. Most will accept a clover or alfalfa mixture, and good quality clover hay is often preferred by stabled horses. However, once accustomed to one particular hay, (eg alfalfa hay) they are less likely to accept other types of hay, particularly mature grass hay. Most horses readily accept chopped hay or chaff. Chopping hay largely prevents horses from selecting the more palatable parts in the hay, such as the leaves and seeds.

In horses confined to stables for long periods over the winter, it is essential that dust in feeds be minimized. Therefore, dampen all feed, including hay, to reduce dust and risk of respiratory allergy and airway problems.

HINT *Dampen dry or dusty concentrate feeds with 2-4 teacups of 50:50 water/molasses, and mix in well. A tablespoon of salt mixed in well may also increase acceptance of the dampened feed. To reduce dust in hay, wrap up the portion in a wet burlap bag for at least 2 hours (8 hours maximum) before feeding. This will help to reduce leaf loss and wastage, eliminate dust, and make the hay softer and more palatable. Feed half the portion at a time to reduce gorging that could lead to digestive upset in hungry or greedy horses. Where hay is very dusty and causing chronic airway disease with wheezing and coughing on exercise, it should be soaked in water for at least one hour and allowed to drain before feeding. (See page 147.)*

Grains

Various studies have shown that horses appear to prefer the common grains in the following descending order: oats, corn, wheat, barley, rye, soybean (crushed). However, once a horse becomes accustomed to one particular grain, (even barley or rye), it will often accept these in preference to newly introduced, or more palatable grains, such as oats or corn. Oats has become a popular grain for horses because of its universal palatability and acceptance. Oats are also less likely to cause digestive upsets than corn, wheat or barley. However, corn is now a cheaper source of energy for hard working or racing horses. Often young racing horses in work will accept crushed corn only if it is introduced gradually to their ration.

HINT *Many trainers introduce young horses (eg 2 year olds) in early work to a variety of feeds such as carrots, apples, all types of grain and hays to accustom them to the tastes so as to minimize likes and dislikes later on in the horse's racing career.*

Sweet Feeds

Most horses seem to like sweet feed mixtures of grains, protein meals, wheat bran, and chopped hay sweetened with molasses, particularly when fed whilst warm and moist. Commercial feeds of grains and concentrates are popular as an evening feed in many racing stables. However, long term storage of pre-mixed feeds in a dampened state may result in deterioration of vitamins, and additional vitamin supplements may be beneficial for performance horses.

Studies have shown that only 80% of horses like sugar or a sweet taste. Sugar cubes are often used as rewards or treats, but some horses may not accept them readily at first. A warm molasses/water mixture is commonly used as a sweetener to increase grain intake, settle dust, and tempt fussy or picky eaters and horses with poor appetites. However, sweeteners should not be used to disguise poor quality feeds to encourage their consumption. Horses with poor appetite can also be tempted to eat by offering them soaked or cooked grain, (eg cooked barley) or sprouted grain (eg oats sprouted on a wet bag for 2-3 days) or turning them out to graze on green pasture for part of the day. (See also Horses with Poor Appetite, page 52.)

Minerals

Contrary to popular belief, horses do not instinctively seek out feeds containing nutrients that are deficient in their diet. Horses will, however, consume salt freely if they are lacking in sodium, and will seek out sources of salt when grazing. Therefore, in most cases the required nutrients and supplements must be provided in balanced proportions. Mineral imbalances can occur if a very palatable feed (eg young grass) or supplement is eaten in excess. Apparently, horses will refuse feed that has previously made them feel sick, provided that the nausea occurs a few minutes after feeding.

PUNCTUALITY OF FEEDING

Horses, particularly those stabled for long periods, are creatures of habit and routine. They prefer to be fed at a regular time, and at set intervals. Research has also shown that feeding horses at regular times can increase digestive efficiency. It has been found that punctual feeding of grain concentrates can increase digestibility of the grain by up to 40%. It is important to feed horses at regular times, week in and week out, to reduce metabolic upsets, and the boredom of confinement.

HINT
An increased incidence of wood chewing vices can occur in horses that are fed at irregular times. Some horse owners deliberately feed their horses at varying times within a two hour space, so that they do not become reliant on a particular feed time, and waiting for food. However, if a horse is hungry, the risk of chewing wood is increased.

When horses have access to pastures, punctuality of feeding is not as important. However, where performance horses are required to eat a concentrate feed to meet their energy demands, it is best to confine them to a stable or yard until they have consumed the majority of their energy feed.

HINT
It is often claimed that stabled horses in full work on concentrate feeds will appear to graze on pasture when turned out for a run each day. In most cases however, pasture is mainly of psychological benefit to these horses with only small amounts of pasture actually being eaten. (Often the difference is highlighted when a hungry horse is turned out to pasture.)

HINT
Where a young horse loses its appetite when confined to a stable, it is often better to allow it to run at pasture or train it from the paddock, to

maintain its appetite. It will generally develop a more willing and happy attitude towards training and exercise.

QUALITY OF FEEDS

The physical and nutritional quality of feedstuffs must be considered when selecting feeds for horses. Only good quality feeds should be offered. The quality of feeds can be influenced by the degree of maturity at harvest, harvesting and curing methods, processing, and conditions and length of storage. Most horse owners have little control over the harvesting, curing and storage carried out prior to purchase of the feed. However, many owners store and process feeds prior to feeding their horses.

The combined effects of light, heat and oxidation, particularly on processed feeds, can severely reduce the nutrient availability. Guidelines for selecting individual feedstuffs are given on pages 174-177 and 182-183.

Proper storage and processing of both hays and grains is essential to ensure that the nutritional quality of the feed is maintained.

STORAGE OF FEEDS

Most horse owners purchase sufficient feed for 2-3 weeks at a time, with larger stables and breeding farms purchasing bulk feed at competitive prices determined by seasonal availability.

Hays

Hays should be stored under cover, preferably raised off ground level on flooring, logs or pallets to prevent moisture damage to the under surface of the bales. Where possible, hay should be stored in vermin-proof sheds. If outside storage is necessary, it is wise to cover stacks with sheeting to prevent rain damage, mold build-up, wastage and leaching of soluble minerals and vitamins.

HINT
As an example of the loss of vitamins during processing and storage, the carotene activity (the form of Vitamin A in feeds) in alfalfa hay is reduced by 80% during three months of storage under hot, summer conditions. Alfalfa loses up to 65% of its Vitamin E content when harvested late in full bloom; 40% when dried by sunlight on the ground when curing; 73% in hay stored for 12 weeks in the summer time; and 50% loss occurs during compression to form cubes. Alfalfa also contains an antagonist (binding substance) that can further inhibit absorption and reduce Vitamin E utilization by up to 33%.

Grains

Grains should be stored in bags or drums with tight fitting lids, or in bulk in silos. This will lessen the risk of excessive drying and reduce the adverse effects of light and air (oxidation) on vitamin stability. Obviously, care should be taken to prevent moisture and vermin damage. Although some natural deterioration occurs, good storage conditions minimize these losses.

The level of dust in stored grains (eg oats), increases over the storage period, presumably due to the slow natural breakdown of the outer seed husks. Once grains are rolled, cracked, crimped or crushed, there is an increased chance of deterioration of nutrient content. The natural vitamin content of feed often falls after processing. Processing opens up the grain kernel, exposing it to the effects of oxidation, light, heat and moisture during subsequent storage in feed room bins. Ideally, processed grains should be used within a few days.

Processing may increase the palatability and acceptance of certain feeds, but overall digestibility is not increased by more than 5-10% in the common grains fed to horses. (See Digestibility of Feeds.) The increased cost of processing may not be justified by the marginal increase in digestive efficiency.

Crimping, crushing, cooking, or soaking grains for foals, sick horses, or old horses with poor teeth or digestive problems may be worthwhile to improve the digestibility, acceptance and general nutritional value. However, cooking barley, for example, destroys some of the heat sensitive B-Complex group of vitamins contained in the grain.

Grains with a higher oil content (eg corn, soybean, sunflower seeds etc) are more prone to deterioration due to rancidity (or oxidation) of fat, resulting in destruction of vitamins, particularly the fat-soluble vitamins A, D, and E.

The nutrient content of corn is reduced by 50% within 3 weeks of crushing the whole seed. Corn loses up to 21% of its vitamin E content when stored in moist containers; 30% on crushing; and 35% when stored cracked for over six months. When feeding only one or two horses, purchase only small amounts, sufficient for 2-3 weeks, or even better, process the grain just before feeding. To prevent oxidation in cracked corn, leave it in the bag in which it is purchased (a burlap or open weave synthetic bag) and carefully fold in the top after each day's supply is removed to restrict contact with air. If necessary, the bag can be put into a drum or feed bin to protect it from mice etc.

When processed grains are purchased in bulk, store them in bags or airtight drums that can be resealed after use. Large wooden bins, which are popular in many stables, increase the surface area exposed to the effects of oxidation, and some of the nutrient value may be lost if processed grain is stored for a long time.

Old chest type freezer units are a convenient method of storing whole grain and processed grain, as they are insulated, well sealed and can be easily cleaned.

NOTE: Care should be taken to ensure that children cannot become trapped -- remove the latching mechanism.

PRACTICAL FEEDING HINTS

There are certain "do's" and "don'ts" that should be observed when feeding horses. A degree of commonsense applies to the art of feeding horses. However, certain rules for feeding should be strictly followed. Proper feeding management ensures that a horse stays in good health and receives maximum benefit from the ration.

THE DO's

Always measure the ration by weight, not volume.

1. The ration should contain a balance between roughages (hay, cubes, pasture) and concentrates (grains, wheat bran, protein meals, fats etc.) relative to the horse's requirements.

Horses grazing on good pasture need little supplementary feed, except when they are growing, pregnant, nursing a foal, or in training. Most commonly, nutritional stress occurs with high stocking rates, or when the pasture has little nutritional value. Short green winter pasture or lush spring pasture often has low nutritional content. Dry summer grass also has lowered feed value, and supplementary feeding may be needed. Supplementary feeding should be commenced at the first sign that horses are losing weight. During droughts, horses may require full supplementary rations. (See Drought Feeding, page 60.)

Once a horse is stabled, the formulation of the ration becomes more important.

HINT

When formulating a ration, always start with the roughage base, and then add grains etc. in direct proportion to exercise needs.

HINT

Horses doing light work or exercise only require a diet consisting of good quality hay and minimal grain. If the horse is required to perform strenuous exercise, then INCREASE the grain portion accordingly. Many horses, particularly show horses and ponies, are overfed relative to their needs.

As a guideline, the following balance between hay and grains (or concentrate feeds) on a weight basis will meet relative demands. (Refer to Tables 4 & 5 on page 172 for further practical guidelines.)

Work/growth needs	Hay %	Grain %
Resting horses	90-100	0-10 maximum
Light work (Pleasure, dressage, show horse) Late pregnancy 8-11 months/Long yearling - 18 months	65-75 (Average 70%)	25-35 (Average 30%) (Nervy types: feed minimum grain, or add extra 5% fat)
Moderate work (Ranch work, roping, cutting, jumping) Late lactation after 3 months/Yearling - 12 months	55-65 (Average 60%)	35-45 (Average 40%)
Intense work (Racing, polo, eventing) Early lactation first 3 months/Weanling - 6 months	45-55 (Average 50%)	45-55 (Average 50%)
Endurance (Endurance riding)	Average 50% (helps store water)	Average 45% grain 5% fat

Excessive amounts of poor-quality roughage may extend the gut capacity or lead to hay belly, due to too much fibrous food. Too much concentrate relative to exercise need can result in hot, playful manners, or digestive upsets, such as colics and founder, and habits such as crib chewing etc.

HINT   *The absolute minimum hay or roughage intake is 1.0% bodyweight (10lb/1000lb or 4.5kg/450kg bodyweight) to maintain efficient digestive function.*

Always ensure the feed store is secure so as to avoid accidental ingestion and overload of high energy grains such as corn, which could result in diarrhea and founder.

2. The ration should be modified to suit individual horses.

Horses should be fed to maintain their body condition and vitality at a desirable level. If available, use weighing scales or a condition scoring system to monitor bodyweight and condition. (See page 163-166.)

Horses differ in appetite and likes and dislikes, so if necessary modify the ration to maintain appetite and acceptance. Some horses are easy keepers, others are fussy or picky eaters, and are hard to keep. Feed each horse as an individual. The feed bucket is a barometer of a horse's stress level and well being.

HINT   *Where a horse is not taking its ration well, the food can be made more attractive by adding cooked or boiled barley, or molasses; or the appetite can be stimulated by supplementing with B Complex vitamins. Check the teeth for sharp edges, and assess general health, as appetite may be reduced due to illness, injury or pain.*

HINT   *If a horse is consistently leaving food and appears to be working well and maintaining bodyweight, then reduce the bulk of the food to a volume it can consume. If a horse is licking clean at every meal -- it is hungry or not getting sufficient volume - increase the bulk of feed.*

HINT   *Condition young horses to accept a variety of feeds (eg oats, corn, barley, soybean, linseed etc.) to make them less likely to develop distinct likes and dislikes or reject unavoidable seasonal changes in feed.*

Some horses are allergic to feedstuffs, and this is usually shown by skin bumps, diarrhea and colics -- change the ingredients if necessary. Blend newly harvested grain with the previous seasons stored grain to avoid feed allergies, introducing in a step-wise manner over 10-14 days if necessary.

3. The effects of a ration should be carefully observed.

Scientific calculation is useful to check the nutritional adequacy of the ration. Recommended feeding amounts on labels of custom mixes, sweet feeds and pelleted feeds are a guideline for average horses. However, the horse's body size, appetite and exercise demand must be assessed when deciding what and how much to feed.

4. The ration should be fed at regular times.

The horse is a creature of habit and comes to expect to be fed at the same time every day. Its digestion patterns will coincide accordingly. Regular feeding at approximately equal intervals is especially important for stabled horses in training. Many stable vices develop as a result of boredom waiting for feed. Punctual, regular feeding can increase the digestibility and feeding value of grain based feeds.

5. The ration should be fed at least twice daily.

Where horses have no access to pasture they should be fed at least twice daily.

The horse has a small stomach, no gall bladder, and chews its food slowly. Therefore, an almost continuous supply of food should be available, especially with hand-fed, stabled horses. Racing horses in training should be fed at least 3-4 times a day. Slow eaters should be fed little and often. Horses should be given adequate undisturbed time to eat.

HINT   *Space the feed times equally throughout the day, with the last feed containing the most bulk including additional roughage to keep the horse occupied overnight.*

6. The ration should always be fed at the same place.

Locate feed tubs in a sheltered place and leave them there. Place them away from a gate area to avoid excapees at feedtime and bogging the area in wet weather. Avoid shifting them around the corral or paddock unless the site becomes excessively boggy in wet weather. It is better to erode only one area rather than several around a small corral or lot.

Pick a well drained area with a hard surface. In cold windy weather, place feeders on the leeward side of a hill or behind a windbreak. (See Feed Tubs page 29.)

7. The feed should be regularly assessed for quality.

Try to feed the best quality available (see page 182-183 for guidelines). If you are measuring feed by volume, then be sure to check the weight to volume of each new batch of feed, as requirements are based on weight of feed. This will avoid changes in energy, as well as unnecessary cost. Regularly weigh new sources of grain to allow for differences in quality due to foreign matter, seasonal and district variations.

HINT   *A small spring balance with the required amount of feed placed in a plastic bag is ideal to check weight for volume on the standard measure (eg scoop or can) you are using, and adjust volume to feed the same weight of feed.*

8. The ration should be well mixed.

Mix ingredients carefully to prevent the horse selecting only the feeds it likes, especially grains which may lead to digestive upset. Make sure there are no lumps of minerals, including salt, because they can cause digestive problems. Dampening feeds, or using liquid supplements, reduces the dust and risk of sifting out additives, less palatable feeds, and medications.

9. The ration should be freshly mixed each feed.

Although dry rations may be mixed in amounts enough for one or two days, do not store dampened mixes for more than 12 hours because they can sour, turn rancid and attract flies in hot weather. These changes may cause digestive upsets, particularly if the ration is dampened with warm water, molasses or oils to reduce dust or increase its palatability. Left-overs must be removed before the next feed is given.

10. The ration should be palatable, economical, practical and supply the horse's requirements.

Rations need not be complicated mixtures, and most rations can be made up from locally available, quality ingredients. (See page 167.) Lonely, underfed and underworked horses are more likely to develop habits such as wood chewing or weaving etc.

All horses should have an opportunity to exercise, or be exercised, each day to gain the most benefit from their ration.

11. The ration should also be complemented by good husbandry.

Careful attention to general health, teeth care, parasite control and provision of regular exercise will ensure efficient utilization of feed and maximum work capacity. Internal parasites and poor teeth are the most common cause of poor condition or unthriftiness, even when an adequate ration is fed.

> **HINT**
> *Monitor the amount, color, smell, consistency and form of the manure passed each day as a practical guide to the overall digestive function, dehydration state, and general health of a working horse on concentrated feed. The volume, color, thickness and smell of the urine, and the ease of passing, is also a valuable guide to the horse's general health and dehydration state. For a practical monitoring guideline of manure and urine, see page 186.*

12. The ration should include adequate clean water at all times.

Horses should have free access to water during hot weather and periods of hard work, or when electrolytes are added to the ration. Care must be taken with horses drinking large volumes of cold water immediately after hard exercise, (see point 12 page 42). Check automatic waterers at each feed time, and clean regularly. (See Water for Horses, page 26.)

THE DON'Ts

There are certain precautions that should be observed when feeding horses, especially horses on supplementary concentrate feeds.

1. Do not make sudden changes in ration proportions or ingredients.

Sudden food changes can lead to digestive upsets or loss of appetite. A slow replacement over seven to ten days or longer is necessary for changes such as old to new season's hay or grain. Ideally, 2-3 weeks is best for radical ingredient changes, for example, oats to barley or pellets, or fat substituted for grains.

> **HINT**
> *Do not change food ingredients within a few days of an important race, event or show.*

2. Avoid sudden increases in grain content, or too rapid introduction to highly concentrated rations.

Always keep the work level ahead of the feed. Increase the grain content of the ration of a horse brought in from pasture, initially adding only about 5 to 10 percent of the planned level and gradually increase it in proportion to work.

> **HINT**
> *Always feed in accordance with work actually done, not work planned to be done. Excess energy intake is a common cause for nervy, hot manners or over playful behaviour in equestrian horses.*

3. Do not feed dusty, moldy or contaminated ingredients.

Dusty foods can cause respiratory problems, particularly in stabled horses over winter. Either sieve the grain, or dampen the ration with warm water or a 50:50 molasses-water mixture. Dusty or brittle hay should be soaked or dampened before feeding. Moldy grains or hays can cause digestive upsets, botulism, or loss of unborn foals. Feed which is contaminated with mice or rat manure, or weevils, must be avoided. Weed infested ingredients spread weeds around yards, and if poisonous, can affect the horse.

> **HINT**
> *Do not use commercial feeds mixed for other animals (eg cattle, poultry) as they may contain ingredients toxic to horses (eg Monensin). Check the ingredients carefully.*

4. Do not feed spoiled "left over" feed.

Clean out any food the horse does not eat each day, particularly feed that has been wet in the tub or feeder, or contaminated by manure or foreign matter. However, good left-over feed may be given to non-working adult horses.

5. Do not feed poor quality feeds.

Poor quality roughage necessitates high intake to satisfy energy needs and leads to hay belly, etc. Unpalatable or poor quality feeds should be avoided, and should not be disguised by a sweetening substance such as molasses.

6. Do not feed full grain ration on idle days.

Reduce grain content to about one-third of the normal amount on idle days to decrease incidence of tying-up or azoturia and digestive upsets when the horse is worked again. Also, besides being costly, excess grain without work may make a horse hot mannered, playful or difficult to handle.

> **HINT**
> *In performance horses, cut the level of grain to one third or less on the night before rest days, and increase grain gradually. Remember, for one day off work - take two days to return to full grain.*

7. Do not allow horses to gorge concentrate feeds.

Greedy horses are likely to choke or consume concentrates too quickly, leading to digestive upsets. Carefully mix the grain, etc, with roughage, such as crumbled cubes or chopped hay, or place a stone or brick (eg a salt brick if you like) in the base of the feeder so the horse cannot take large mouthfuls of the concentrate. Avoid free access to concentrates in cold weather, feed only the amount required by each horse. Feed small feeds often, diluted with roughage to increase the bulk, if necessary.

8. Do not feed lawn cuttings.

Although greenfeed sharpens the appetite, relieves boredom and aids digestion, avoid finely mulched or chopped greenfeed that requires little chewing. Lawn cuttings, besides generating heat and mold when compressed into a heap, can also contain poisonous garden plants, wire, metal, glass, stones and pesticides that can cause colic and other serious complications.

9. Do not feed from dirty feeders or waterers

Regularly clean out feeders to prevent molds and other toxic products. Water troughs should be checked daily and cleaned regularly to prevent build-up of algae and sludges of chewed food. Some horse owners separate the feeding area and watering point to reduce the build-up of grains and food in water troughs where horses have a habit of eating and drinking alternately.

10. Do not feed concentrates or hay on the ground.

Feed on the ground is quickly scattered, pawed and wasted. Parasite and sand intake can be increased when horses are encouraged to search on the ground for feed. Provide an adequate sized container with no sharp edges and enough weight to prevent the horse tipping it over. (See Hints on Feeders page 29.)

11. Do not feed large amounts of hay just prior to working the horse, and avoid working a horse on a full stomach.

To prevent the horse being uncomfortable due to an extended gut, it is best to feed the larger portion of hay overnight. A small feed consisting of 60% grain and 40% hay is less bulky prior to exercise.

12. Do not allow access to large volumes of cold water after work.

It is unwise to allow a hot, sweaty horse to drink large quantities of cold water immediately after exercise. This could cause mild colics, gripes and digestive upsets.

HINT
Many horse owners and trainers will let a horse cool off for a short time, (hosing the animal off if necessary) and provide dampened hay as a feed. Then after 10-15 minutes, they offer a small volume of water [about ½-1 gallon (2-4 liters)] depending on the size of the horse. Then after 30 minutes or so when the horse has cooled down, they allow free access to water. Alternatively, allow the horse to drink a few swallows of water or rehydration drink with the chill taken off every 3-5 minutes during the initial 10 minutes after exercise. (See page 27.)

NOTE: However, in the case of endurance horses, immediate replenishment of water at vet checks is essential to rapidly restore fluid and electrolyte balance. If the water or rehydration drink is very cold, then the chill can be taken off by adding a small amount of warm water before offering it to a hot horse. (See pages 27 and 112 for full details.)

COOKED OR BOILED BARLEY

Cooked barley grain is regarded as an appetizer and easily digested feed after a hard workout, for foals, sick horses, or aged horses with teeth problems. It is also used as a reward after competition, or during cold weather. Cooked grain retards fermentation during digestion, and may be less likely to cause hot or playful behaviour in working horses.

HINT
Cooking or steaming barley, or other feeds, does not generally increase digestibility, but can reduce the natural vitamin content. Cooked barley mixed in the ration is a moist, palatable, soft feed for horses off their feed due to hard work, sickness or age. About 3lb (1.5kg) wet weight of cooked barley, mixed into the normal concentrate feed, will tempt the appetite of most horses.

Method: *Boiling is time consuming and messy. An easy method for preparing cooked barley for one or two horses is to cook it in a ceramic pot roast cooker. Put 4 pints (about 2 liters) of whole barley into the pot. Add water until the level rises above the barley by about 2 inches (5cm). Cook on low setting for 6-8 hours. This makes about 6-7lb (about 3kg) of cooked barley (wet weight).*

WARM BRAN MASH

Warm bran mashes are popular as laxative type feeds about 2-3 days prior to hard or competitive exercise, and on the morning following competition. However, wet bran mashes only increase the moisture content of the manure by 2-3% having little direct laxative effect on the horse. The laxative effect can be slightly improved however, by adding molasses to the wet bran mash.

HINT
Horses find a warm bran mash palatable, and it may be useful to improve the appetite in a horse that is off its feed. Supplements of vitamins and minerals, and some bitter medications may be more readily accepted in a bran mash.

HINT
Do not mix calcium supplements into wet bran mashes as a significant amount of calcium may be bound to the phytic acid content of wet bran, and become unavailable to the horse. It is best to add calcium supplements to feeds other than a 100% warm bran mash. Calcium supplements may be added to normal feeds, containing up to 10% bran, without significantly affecting the calcium uptake.

Method: *Add about 1lb (450g) of bran, or roughly 4 pints (2 liters) to a 2 gallon (8 liter) bucket. Scald by pouring on sufficient boiling water, stirring to achieve a wet but not sloppy mixture. Cover with a bag or towel,* *and allow to cool before feeding. Cooking in this way improves its acceptability.*

DAMPENED HAY

Late cut alfalfa or mixed hay, or hay that has been stored for long periods, is often stemmy, brittle, dry and unpalatable to horses. Dusty and brittle hay can also increase the risk of chronic coughing and respiratory problems, especially in stabled horses. Often, stemmy hay with little leaf is preferred as roughage for horses confined to stables during winter to reduce airborne dust and spores that can aggravate the heaves or chronic obstructive pulmonary disease (COPD). Rehydrating dry alfalfa hay softens it, improves its alfalfa aroma, reduces leaf loss and decreases the dust content.

Method: *Thoroughly wet a porous bag (eg burlap bag) by immersing it in a bucket of water. Shake out excess water. Wrap the flake or portion of hay tightly up in the wet bag for 1-2 hours (no longer than 8 hours). Feed the hay out, half a flake at a time to avoid risk of greedy horses eating too much.*

HINT *Rehydrating alfalfa hay in this way adds extra moisture to the feed which can be of some advantage to working horses in hot weather.*

NOTE: If the hay is very dusty and is causing allergic respiratory disease in stabled horses, it is best to fully immerse the hay in a trough or tub of water. Studies indicate that the duration of soaking is not as important as completeness of wetting. A ten minute soak is sufficient as long as the hay is wetted right through. Overall, it is most convenient to soak hay on a 12 hour basis in clean water -- the evening's hay is immersed in water in the morning. Whilst soaking hay in this way prevents airborne release and inhalation of dust and spores as the horse feeds, harmful mold spores may be still ingested. Do not use hay that has a high mold content as a feed for horses. Consult your veterinarian for advice.

HOT GRAIN SOAK

Hot grain soaks are popular during cold weather, or as appetizing grain bases for a ration in young horses, show horses, stallions at stud, picky eaters, or horses recovering from injury or illness. Grain soaks are time consuming to prepare, but most horses find them palatable.

Method: *Mix total amount of grain, protein meal, wheat bran etc (if included) and molasses to taste into a large tub or half barrel. Add sufficient hot water to cover the total mix. Cover over the tub and allow to stand for two to three hours, stirring occasionally to ensure all the mix is soaked and the grain becomes swollen and soft.*

At feed time, portion out the grain soak for each horse, mixing it in with other grain, or alfalfa cubes or pellets as roughage if necessary.

HINT *Do not add vitamin/mineral mixes (eg Feramo-H) to the ration before hot soaking. Add all supplements at time of feeding and mix into the top layer of cool feed.*

HINTS ON GRAZING MANAGEMENT

Good quality pasture will provide a healthy mature horse that is resting or under minimal stress and performance demands, with a balanced natural diet, providing the pasture is not overstocked. However, once horses are confined to stables or yards and have greater physical demands placed on them, concentrate feeds are necessary to satisfy the nutritional requirement for exercise.

Grazing then becomes more important for its psychological value and as a source of natural free exercise for the horse in training. Whenever a horse has access to pasture, even for a short time, it is important that the pasture be efficiently utilized. Ideally, a lush pasture with plant species palatable to horses, free from poisonous weeds, and with a minimal manure build-up, will help ensure the most efficient use of grazing time.

NOTE: It is beyond the scope of this handbook to include complete recommendations for pasture establishment, care and maintenance.

The following hints are included to highlight some of the more important aspects of practical management to ensure that maximum benefit is obtained from the pasture.

PASTURE SPECIES

The selection and establishment of pasture species is influenced by seasonal rainfall, soil type and general locality. Contact your local USDA Office, County Agent, Farm Advisor or State University for advice on pasture species best adapted to your locality.

Pasture varieties should be compatible with each other, so that less vigorous plants that may provide the nutritional balance will not be crowded out.

HINT
Ideally, a blend of 40% legume and 60% grass species provides the most nutritionally balanced pasture for grazing horses. Horses are selective in their grazing habits, tending to graze out the more palatable species.

It is essential that new pastures are given adequate time for establishment (1-3 years) before subjecting them to heavy grazing and risk of grazing out of the palatable species.

HINT
Assessing the nutritional quality of a particular type of pasture blend is often useful when determining the stocking rate a pasture can carry, or the need for supplementary concentrate feeds. Lush, rapidly growing pastures have lower energy per unit weight than more mature pastures in early mid bloom. Therefore, although the pasture stand may appear to be dense, horses have to eat much more lush pasture to meet their needs.

HINT
Heavy rains or thunderstorms on stands of dry feed may also dramatically reduce the feed available for grazing horses. The feed stand is broken down, seed lost from seed heads, and the remaining pasture surface is contaminated with a scum of manure and other debris. It may take 10-14 days for new grass to sprout, and concentrate feeds and hay should be provided for young growing horses, fat ponies or mares and foals to prevent nutritional set-backs.

Pasture should not be allowed to become too tall or mature

Pasture should not be allowed to become excessively tall, rank, or mature. Tall-grass dominant pastures are generally not well utilized by horses. Horses tend to trample it down, and selectively graze the more palatable parts such as the seed heads or growing tips. Mature pastures, particularly as they dry off, become less attractive and higher in fiber (which dilutes their nutrient value) and are not as well digested by horses.

HINT
On smaller areas, mow regularly to promote fresh regrowth especially after rain or following irrigation. Sweet, growing pastures are better utilized by horses. On larger areas, pasture that is unpalatable to horses may be baled for hay or silage for feeding cattle, sheep or goats. Alternatively, shift horses out, ideally after each worming, and graze off remaining pasture with sheep or cattle. This will also help to improve worm

control on heavily contaminated or horse-sick pastures.

Pastures should not be too short

Pasture should not be grazed too heavily, as short pastures increase the uptake of worms, teeth problems, and risk of sand colic on sandy soils. The incidence of sand colic increases under drought conditions in horses grazing on sandy areas.

HINT *Where possible, shift horses to new pasture on a rotational program, such as after each regular worming, so that adequate regrowth and recovery is allowed. This will help prevent heavily grazed species from dying out, or soil erosion in denuded areas.*

Keep pasture free of weeds and unpalatable species

Horses are selective grazers and will leave unpalatable plants and weeds to thrive and reseed. When pasture is short or limited, such as in a drought or during winter, or when heavily stocked, horses may be forced to eat poisonous plants, particularly when there is little else to eat.

HINT *Regular mowing, renovation, weeding or spot spraying, in smaller pasture areas, or use of selective herbicides, will control unpalatable or potentially toxic plants. Supplementary feed, such as hay or concentrate feed should be provided to decrease grazing pressure on grazed out or short winter pastures that are unable to support heavy grazing. If spot spraying is carried out to control thistles or other weeds, seek advice from the local County Agent on the time required before horses can be safely re-introduced to the pasture.*

Pastures need regular renovation

In uncontrolled grazing conditions, one species of a grass-legume pasture will become dominant due to selective grazing, seasonal conditions or plant competition. Regular renovation to break up compacted soil and re-establish grazed-out species, should be carried out on a programed basis or when required, (usually every 2-3 years), especially around feeding areas, rolling spots, shade trees, gateways and shared fencelines. Annual top-dressing with fertilizers will also help to maintain and promote strong pasture growth.

HINT *Improvement in drainage of soils or boggy areas, and high nitrogen fertilizer applications, can change the availability of minerals, often increasing selenium and zinc uptake, but lowering iron, copper and other trace element availability.*

Soil analysis by the local agricultural extension source, or your local fertilizer distributor, may help determine the need for other top-dressings such as lime, dolomite, phosphates or gypsum etc. to maintain optimum soil pH and environment for pasture growth and safe mineral availability.

PASTURE HYGIENE

Regularly control manure build-up

Measures to control build-up of manure are especially important where the stocking rate is high. As if by instinct, horses avoid grazing close to roughs or clumps of manure in horse sick pastures. Pasture in these areas often becomes patchy and rank, with proliferation of unpalatable plants.

Horses prefer to graze clean areas or lawns, which they will keep closely cropped and relatively free of manure. Up to 50% of grazing area can be lost to roughs in smaller paddocks, and roughs can have up to 15 times the Strongyle worm contamination of lawns. (See page 19.)

Horses are normally only forced to graze close to roughs and manure when the lawns, or preferred grazing areas, are eaten out by overstocking, or pasture is sparse during winter or drought conditions. Heavy contamination with manure obviously increases the risk of parasite infection in grazing horses.

It has been a popular practice to break up and open the manure clumps or fecal balls to the sun by harrowing or dragging chain mesh or welded mesh around the roughs in the pasture. However, this practice is likely to increase the risk of worm uptake in temperate climates as the larvae can still survive for long periods, and may be spread even further over the pasture. It is essential to avoid spreading manure onto the lawns or grazing areas, harrow only the roughs.

Studies have shown that massive increases in Strongyle larval populations (up to 144 fold) can occur in grazing areas after rains in warm weather.

However, exposure of these larvae to weather extremes, such as drought or frost, (which will kill many of them) is an essential part of good pasture hygiene.

HINT *It is now recommended to harrow only during the hottest parts of the season or the evening prior to weather conditions that will most likely result in a frost. Machines are also now available to clean manure from pastures on a regular basis.*

HINT *Grazing with cattle, sheep or goats, or mowing and harrowing on a rotational basis after horses have been shifted to new pasture, will help spread manure, encourage manure decomposition, reduce parasite contamination and stimulate regrowth of pasture.*

HINT *For best exposure of eggs or larvae to the hot sun or frosty weather, pastures that are being rested should be as short as possible. Ideally, for maximum control of Strongyle larvae, rest pastures for a minimum of 4-6 weeks in hot summer, or up to 10-12 weeks in cold frosty winter. Any unseasonal weather (eg a week or so of very hot dry weather or cold frosty mornings) will help to effectively reduce worm populations on grazing pasture. In warm temperate climates, or tropical areas a 6-8 month period is needed to effectively eliminate worm larvae contamination. In these areas, where stocking rates are high, machines to pick up manure from the pasture on a weekly basis are the most effective method of reducing pasture contamination.*

SPECIALIZED DIETS

Specialized rations and individual feeding may be necessary for aged horses, or those suffering from sickness or injury, to ensure they consume an adequate and balanced diet to meet their needs. Manipulation of the diet by substituting alternative low heat waste feeds is also beneficial to reduce risk of dehydration in horses working under hot conditions. Higher roughage rations can keep horses warmer under cold, bleak weather conditions. Horses that are overfed and obese can be put onto a weight reducing diet and exercise program that doesn't deny them the pleasure of eating. Thin horses can be fed to safely increase their body condition without risk of force feeding that could lead to digestive and metabolic problems.

In times of drought, horses can be maintained within the feeding budget on alternative feeds not commonly fed to horses, which can be often purchased locally.

Most of the guidelines outlined in this section relate to adult horses with a bodyweight range of 950 to 1100lb (430-500kg). Adjustments to the ration intake may be necessary in proportion the animal's bodyweight, specific need or appetite.

AGED HORSES

The aging process in horses usually occurs over a period of years; while some horses feel old at 12 years of age, others are fine up to 20 years or older.

Aged horses in retirement at pasture often fall away in condition during winter or summer when pasture is sparse, despite adequate shelter and supplementary hay. Many old horses have lost some of their teeth, reducing the ability to chew grains and hay. Horses that have been kept on sandy areas wear their teeth down more quickly and may start to show the effects of poor teeth at a quite early age. Poor teeth condition can lead to increased risk of colic and digestive problems in older horses.

Pain and discomfort from arthritis and earlier injuries may restrict grazing, and adversely affect the horse's appetite. Heavy worm burdens, and overall reduced digestive efficiency in older horses also may cause ill-thrift and poor condition.

As horses age, their digestive efficiency decreases, and they generally require more energy for everyday life, such as walking, grazing and maintaining themselves. Therefore the energy density of the ration should be increased to maintain a reasonable body condition.

| HINT | *Studies have found that aged horses also require higher levels of good quality protein, calcium and phosphorus in their rations than other adult horses under similar conditions.* |

Many aged horses fall away in condition in the colder weather, and their resistance to worms, respiratory virus and skin diseases may be reduced. Extra feed, warmth and nursing will make their retirement more comfortable and carefree.

Basic Ration

Often aged horses will put on weight and do better when given a completely pelleted ration. Ideally, a pelleted ration with 12-14% protein content will help maintain condition when fed to appetite.

| HINT | *Approximately 1lb pellets per 100lb (1.0kg/100kg) bodyweight should meet needs at rest, with adjustments to maintain condition as required. If the pellets are hard to chew, and are being wasted due to quidding from poor teeth, they may be softened with a 50:50 molasses and water mixture just prior to feeding. Good quality, preferably dampened hay, should be freely provided. In old horses with poor teeth, crushed roughage cubes or chopped hay should be provided as bulk.* |

Alternatively, a home mixed concentrate feed of 50:50 crushed oats and cracked corn (or alternatively rolled barley) mixed with an **equal** volume of chopped hay or crushed alfalfa cubes, all dampened with molasses water, is a suitable basic ration. A good quality commercial working horse mix or sweet feed can be given, provided that the grain is easy to chew.

Generally, a night feed containing damp crushed grain, boiled barley, or whole grain soak (see page 42) mixed with 5% wheat bran, is easier to chew and better utilized in old horses with poor teeth. It is a good idea to have your vet check the teeth every 3-6 months, and correct any problems that may interfere with chewing.

A portion of good quality leafy alfalfa or mixed hay, dampened by wrapping in a wet chaff bag for 2 hours before feeding so that it is easier to chew, should be fed with the concentrate feed when pasture is dry or sparse. If grass hay is given as roughage, provide a supplement of 2oz (60g) per 100lb (45kg) bodyweight of soybean meal as protein uptake is reduced in aged horses.

Supplements

HINT

During cold weather, add an extra 1-1½lb (500-700g) wet weight of boiled barley to the night feed. Ensure the horse is double rugged, or stabled overnight where possible. Additional fat may be added at a rate of 1oz/100lb (60ml/100kg) bodyweight to boost energy density, but larger amounts may not be well utilized and could cause mild diarrhea in old horses.

Many old horses develop a terminal form of low grade diarrhea, perhaps due to loss of gut absorption or reduced digestive action.

HINT

Where aged horses have access to good pasture, but are unable to graze effectively due to poor teeth or arthritis etc, cut about 4½lb (2kg) fresh grass daily as green feed in a small yard. Alternatively, mow small areas every 2-3 days to dry out as soft wilted grass hay on the top of the pasture. However, do not feed grass cut up finely with a lawn mower as digestive upset is likely.

Where pain and discomfort is caused by arthritis, then your vet may be able to prescribe medication to reduce pain and enable the aged horse to lead a happier life.

The night feed may be supplemented with a vitamin/mineral supplement (such as Feramo-H) to provide additional vitamins and minerals to overcome low feed levels and aid general vitality and coat condition. A supplement of 2oz (60g) or 4 tablespoons of dicalcium phosphate (DCP) daily is also recommended in horses over 16 years of age, as the ability to absorb calcium and phosphorus is reduced in aged horses.

HINT

In poor doers, a liquid supplement of B-Complex vitamins, such as 2oz (60ml) of Pulse-8 twice weekly over the tongue may help ensure adequate feed levels and maintain the appetite.

Weekly assessment of condition, pasture value and grazing ability, combined with regular worming and teeth checks will help ensure aged horses maintain themselves in healthy condition. In cold weather ensure the grazing retiree at grass is provided with a warm rug, or is brought into stables overnight.

Weight loss in aged horses is difficult to replace, so it is best to monitor the horse's condition and adjust the ration regularly to ensure health and lifestyle is maintained. Always ensure the feet are well maintained, and the coat is groomed to remove loose hair and caked dirt.

FEEDING HORSES IN HOT WEATHER

Some minor feeding adjustments are useful during the summer months to help horses perform better, and avoid heat stress and fatigue. Horses that are in heavy condition, nervy or excitable, and horses worked over long distances, are more likely to be affected by hot weather. Heavily sweating horses are also prone to electrolyte loss and dehydration which could hamper their performance.

The ration can be modified to reduce the amount of waste heat produced during digestive processes. Hay and fibrous foods, such as oats and wheat bran, produce more wasteful heat during digestion than higher carbohydrate feeds such as corn and barley, and (least of all), fats. The fermentation process in the large bowel that digests roughage and fibrous foods is heat producing, and helps to keep horses warm in the winter. However, extra digestive heat increases the heat load that needs to be lost during hot weather and following exercise. This can cause elevated heart and respiratory rates, due to higher body temperature and panting to lose heat, higher sweat loss, and increased risk of dehydration, body salt depletion and general heat stress in working horses.

As a guide, approximately 15% of energy contained in fat is lost as heat, 20% from corn, 23% from barley, 30% from oats, 40% from alfalfa and protein meals, and 70% from poor quality roughage.

HINT

In exercising horses, the amount of hay or fibrous feeds can be reduced to the minimum safe level of 1% bodyweight of roughage.

HINT

Fiber traps water in the bowel and provides a fluid reservoir for exercising horses. Therefore it is important that adequate roughage is given to horses that are likely to sweat heavily during exercise, such as Endurance horses (see also pages 110 and 112).

Ration Guidelines

Feeding adjustment for hot weather is of benefit for Racing, Polo/ Polocrosse, Eventing, Endurance, and any horse that sweats heavily when worked.

NOTE: The guidelines outlined below are based on oat based rations, if you are already feeding corn, or fat, then heat waste is already minimized.

HINT

Ensure the total amount of roughage is maintained at a minimum of 50% by weight of the ration. Reduce the volume of oats by half, and increase the amount of corn by only half that volume to maintain energy levels. (On a volume basis, corn contains twice as much energy as oats.) This gives a smaller volume, less fibrous mixture of higher energy density and less heat waste. In conditioning type training, fat may also be substituted for grain as an energy source contributing up to 10% by weight of the grain portion of the ration. (See Fats, page 25.)

Feed to work and exercise load, cutting the corn out on rest days or light work days, preferably from the night before. This reduces the risk of tying-up when work resumes. Re-introduce half the corn in the early morning feed, or after the work-out, on the next work day, and return to full corn on the second day.

Feeding Frequency

Every horse has individual feeding habits and the change to the feeding program outlined below may take 2-3 weeks, and may not be practical for every horse.

Divide the total feed volume of grain, protein meal, hay and additives, preferably into 2-3 feeds as follows:

Morning Feed:

Feed one-third of the oats, half the corn, 20% of the hay, and two-thirds of the protein meal. Give half the daily dose of an electrolyte supplement, such as 1 scoop of Humidimix. Provide access to water at all times.

Midday Feed:

Feed half of the remaining oats, half of the remaining corn and one-third of the remaining hay ration.

In other competitive types of horses, which are fed only twice daily, divide these amounts, and add them to each of the morning and evening feeds.

Afternoon Feed:

Provide 2-3lb (approximately 1-1.5kg) of green feed for horses confined to stalls, preferably in the cool of the evening.

This helps maintain the appetite and green forage helps boosts gut fluid content in hard working, heavy sweating horses.

Evening and Overnight Feed:

Feed the remaining concentrate and hay, including vitamin and mineral supplements, as required. Mix in another measure of electrolytes to make up the full daily dose.

Dampen this night feed with molasses and water (50:50) to aid palatability and add useful extra moisture to the dry concentrated feed. It is also helpful to soak or dampen the hay to increase its moisture content for digestion and reduce dust and leaf loss.

General Management Hints

1. Feeding Fats

Fat is a useful alternative energy source in hot weather for horses working for more than 30 minutes daily. Fat is more slowly metabolized, and has low heat accumulation during digestion. (See page 25.)

2. Exercise and Heat Loss

Recent studies have indicated that up to 30% of horses trained under hot climatic conditions blow or pant for up to 30 minutes after exercise. Panting (like a dog) evaporates moisture from the lungs, and supplements sweating as an aid in cooling the blood after hard exercise. Lightly sweating horses are more likely to pant as they cannot lose heat quickly enough from sweating alone.

After LSD or endurance type training, or slow conditioning exercise during hot weather, assist heat loss as follows:

Wash, sponge or hose down with cold water, lightly over the rump to avoid chilling or cramping the muscles. Wait 30 seconds, then scrape water off. Avoid leaving a hot horse with water trapped in its coat. The layer of water acts as an insulator (like a diver's wetsuit) and retains heat. By scraping the water off after it has taken up heat from the skin, the retained body heat will evaporate the residual moisture from the coat quickly, and increase the efficiency of cooling. After 3-5 minutes, if the horse is still panting, repeat the washing or hosing down and scraping off. If possible, walk the horse in between the two washes to promote air flow and aid evaporation during hot, humid weather. Most horses will cease to pant within ten minutes if they are suffering from mild overheating.

HINT
A swim for 2-3 minutes or a hose off in the heat of the afternoon also refreshes stabled horses in hot weather. Scrape off excess water to aid cooling.

3. Exercise in the Cool Part of the Day

Exercise the horse very early in the morning, or in the cool of the evening during hot humid weather. Horses take 2-3 hours to cool down after work, and evening work-outs result in faster cooling down as ambient temperatures normally drop after sunset. Keep stables well ventilated at all times. However, if a horse is hosed and scraped off after exercise in the cool of the evening, allow it to steam off for a couple of minutes and then apply a light cover to prevent a chill.

HINT
Wet your horse down with cool water before a 10-20 minutes training session to help evaporative cooling as the horse heats up during exercise to decrease sweating in tropical weather. Wet horse down every 15-20 minutes during longer works to reduce heat stress under hot conditions.

4. Access to Water

Ensure access to cool, clean water at all times. If a horse is thirsty after exercise, offer a first drink of rehydration fluid, such as half a gallon (about 2 liters) of made-up Recharge to rapidly replenish electrolytes and fluid.

HINT
In very hot weather, a drink of made-up rehydration fluid in a bucket, as well as fresh, clean drinking water can be given.

FEEDING HORSES IN COLD WEATHER

Adult resting horses at pasture are best provided good quality hay during the cool weather and winter months when pastures are short or slow growing.

A greater percentage of waste heat is given off when hay and fibrous grains, such as oats ferment in the large bowel, which provides more of an internal warming effect than that obtained from lower fiber concentrate feeds, such as corn or barley.

| HINT | *Supplement hay at a rate of 1-1½lb per 100lb (approx 1-1.5kg/100kg) bodyweight depending on grazing. Generally, a horse has to eat five times more bulk of green, succulent pasture than hay to obtain similar energy and protein intake. Only good quality, leafy hay should be provided to reduce wastage. Mixed or grass hay is sweet and well accepted by most horses.* |

If the weather is bleak, windy and raining, or the horse is losing condition, then additional grain should be fed daily to boost energy levels. Under still, calm, cold conditions, horses do not lose excessive amounts of body heat until the temperatue drops below 14°F (-10°C)

| HINT | *In non-working horses, feed a fibrous grain such as oats at 4oz per 100lb (about 120g/100kg) bodyweight in addition to hay. This will provide additional energy to maintain warmth during cold, windy and wet weather.* |

| HINT | *In working horses, during cold weather, supplement with a corn based concentrate feed at a general rate of ½lb per 100lb (500g/100kg) bodyweight, depending on work load; or use the ration guidelines outlined for each class of horse. Corn provides higher energy density without increasing bulk of gut contents in hard working or performance horses.* |

Feed tubs should be located on the leeward side of a hill, sheltered from prevailing winds. Horses often stand at feeders for a number of hours whilst eating, and windy exposed sites can significantly increase the chill factor in wet weather. When hand feeding is necessary on short winter pasture, give two feeds daily to provide a more continuous supply of feed; this has a warming effect in cold weather.

| HINT | *Avoid feeding large amounts of concentrates to hungry, cold horses, as they may ingest the ration too quickly and suffer digestive upset and colic. Alternatively, provide them with a portion of hay to eat first to fill them up, then provide the concentrates. Aged horses at pasture, and horses in work, should be double rugged overnight, or preferably stabled and given concentrates and hay depending on their exercise level.* |

HORSES WITH POOR APPETITE

Horses may refuse, or not eat sufficient feed to meet needs due to mouth injuries, sickness, excessively bulk rations, or following hard or fast work. Horses in work, particularly young fillies, often go off their feed, become picky eaters and fail to lick clean when introduced to fast work.

| HINT | *If a horse has a good appetite but consistently leaves a portion of concentrate feeds, reduce the amount, or bulk of the ration by adding higher energy grains such as corn. Conversely, if a horse licks the tub clean at every meal, he is often still hungry. Increase the bulk of the diet by providing good quality hay to appetite.* |

Unpalatable or poor quality feeds, sudden changes in feed, fretting, distracting surroundings, ill-health, pain following injury or surgery, fever and mouth conditions that cause pain on chewing are the most common reasons for loss of appetite in horses. Where the horse is depressed due to ill-health, pain or fever, it is best to seek advice from your veterinarian.

Teeth Problems

Various teeth problems can cause refusal of food, poor appetite or slow feeding in horses.

| HINT | *Signs that teeth may be the primary cause of poor appetite include refusal to eat or picky eating (although the horse appears to be hungry and rushes to the feed), quidding or dropping partly chewed food, and excessively slow feeding. These problems are more likely to develop in young horse 2-5 years of age, or in aged horses.* |

An examination of the teeth and mouth by a veterinarian may be necessary. Regular teeth care should be carried out. (See page 16.)

Unpalatable Foods

Horses have individual likes and dislikes for the different types of feeds. A sudden change in feeds should be avoided, as it may lead to poor appetite, or digestive upsets and colic. All feed changes, including supplements, should be made over 7-10 days in known fussy or picky eaters. If powdered supplements are still refused, they can be mixed with a small amount of water and delivered by syringe over the tongue. Alternatively, paste or liquid supplements can be given over the tongue by oral syringe prior to feeding.

Poor quality feeds, such as very stemmy hay or hay contaminated with weeds or prickly plants, should be avoided. They should not be made more palatable by the addition of sweetening substances such as molasses.

| HINT | *Dampen brittle hay by wrapping it in a wet burlap or other cloth bag for two hours prior to feeding to make it more attractive to a picky eater and reduce leaf loss and wastage.* |

| HINT | *The smell of concentrate feed may be made more interesting by spreading five drops vanilla, aniseed, or strawberry flavoring over the top of the feed, or mixing in garlic juice. (See page 35.)* |

Recovery from Upper Respiratory Conditions

Horses with upper respiratory tract conditions, such as virus colds and strangles, or a nasal discharge, often go off their feed. Horses rely heavily on their sense of smell to accept food, and when they are unable to recognize feed by smell, they may refuse to eat.

HINT *A mucolytic preparation prescribed by your veterinarian will help clear away excessive mucus build-up and hasten recovery from respiratory conditions.*

For horses that have a bad cold, a damp feed of crushed or soaked grains, with added flavors such as molasses or vanilla essence, may help improve their appetite. (See page 35.)

HINT *For any horse with a respiratory condition, it is a good idea to place hay or feed (both dampened) on the stable floor in a smooth edged and safe feed tub. This will encourage drainage of the airways as the horse feeds with its head lower than chest height.*

Dusty feed may aggravate respiratory conditions, and increase the risk of chronic respiratory problems in stabled horses over the winter months. It is best to dampen all feed, including hay, to hasten recovery. (See pages 43 and 147.)

HINT *A horse that develops a snorting habit when feeding is often reacting to dust in the feed. Dampen all feed, including hay, to minimize dust in this case.*

Pain

Mild analgesic agents as prescribed by your veterinarian may reduce pain and help to improve appetite in horses following injury or surgery, or in other conditions, such as founder, chronic navicular disease and slow healing wounds.

Aged horses suffering from low-grade pain of arthritis etc. during cold weather may eat and graze more happily when joint aches and general discomfort are relieved by analgesics. Consult your vet for advice.

Distracting Surroundings/Loneliness

Young or nervy horses can be easily distracted from feeding by noisy stable routine, or being excited or stirred-up by the arrival of new horses into the stable.

Colts in an adjoining paddock to fillies may worry the fence line, run themselves thin and lose their appetite. Grazing horses with lice or itchy skin disease may spend time rubbing, and fall away in condition because they fail to eat sufficient pasture to meet their needs.

Lack of company for horses stabled by themselves may reduce their appetite. Horses often fret when separated from their friends, and consequently lose their appetite. Young insecure horses may develop a habit of walking to the stable door when chewing a mouthful, and waste food. (See Dribblers, page 142.)

HINT *In young, nervy or insecure new horses, a short course of a mild tranquilizer for 3-5 days, as prescribed by your vet, may help settle them down and improve their appetite when confined to a stable. Turning a picky eater out for 2-3 hours a day to graze green pasture and exercise may also improve appetite. In severe cases, a horse may do better if trained from the paddock.*

Most horses like to have a companion in close contact. In some stables a rabbit, chicken, or lamb is stalled with a young horse to keep it company. Night lights are also useful for horses that fail to consume their overnight feed in dark stalls. (See pages 28 and 142.)

Decreasing Bulky Feeds

Where horses on concentrate rations fail to clean up their feed, consider decreasing the volume of the feed by substituting corn and fat to replace half the oats.

HINT *Increasing the level of corn and fat in the diet can significantly reduce the bulk of feed required to provide equivalent energy levels in the rations of performance horses. (See Individual Ration Guidelines.)*

Poor Appetite After Work

Too Fast - Too Early

Fast work, or breezing, particularly in finely built, nervy types of racing fillies, may result in loss of appetite. It is thought to be due to stress, fatigue, or build up of acids (lactic acid) in the back, rump and leg muscles after fast work in the unfit horse, causing soreness, and discomfort. Affected fillies often become sour and bitchy and pick at their feed. This often results from keenness to gallop free or excessive work effort during the first 2-3 weeks of fast work. In severe cases, the back and rump muscles may blow-up or swell up and become sore to touch, causing discomfort and a shortened stride as the horse cools down after fast work.

Recognition

Carefully press the back, rump and hind leg muscles to detect areas of soreness and hardening. If soreness is detected, then adapt the cool down routine outlined below, to improve clearance of lactate from the muscles after fast work.

HINT *Studies indicate that lactic acid can be used as muscle fuel for slow work. During cool down exercise at the trot after fast work, slow twitch muscle fibers utilize muscle lactate for fuel. The heart muscle obtains about 20% of its energy for contraction from oxidation of recycled lactate.*

Do not just walk a horse back to the stalls after fast work and let it stand around until the next feed time. An adequate cool down procedure after fast work will help overcome the soreness in muscles.

Cool Down Procedure

Step 1 - After the "breeze", pace work or fast blow-out, slow down to a walk. Walk for one minute to allow the horse to catch its wind and start to sweat out accumulated heat. This is important to re-oxygenate the blood to metabolize lactate in the muscles and blood after fast work.

Step 2 - Then trot out (no faster or slower) for 4-5 minutes to pump the acids into the blood and encourage their breakdown to energy. Trotting has rapid, short muscle movements which promote the clearance of lactate into the blood stream.

Step 3 - On return to the stables, sponge down or hose off (see page 49), and before the next feed give an oral supplement of alkaline buffer, such as 2oz (60ml) of Neutradex by syringe over the tongue to supplement alkaline salt reserve in the blood. Ensure water is available at all times.

Step 4 - Repeat the cool down procedure after each fast work-out. Cut back on the speed of fast work for 5-7 days, then increase gradually. After a few days, the soreness and sourness should no longer affect the appetite and feeding. However, it is always helpful to make the diet more appetizing. Mix 2 teacups of molasses into an equal volume of hot water, then pour over the feed and mix in. Dosing with a liquid B-Complex vitamin supplement, (such as 2oz (60ml) of Pulse-8 liquid) over the tongue before the night after each fast work day also is widely used to maintain the well-being and appetite in hard working horses. Once the horse regains its appetite, mix the liquid vitamin supplement into the evening feed.

Hard or Strenuous Exercise

It is not uncommon for Racehorses, Polo, Polocrosse, Eventers, and Endurance horses to go off their feed after a hard competition or long ride. (See individual ration guidelines.)

HINT

A pre-ride supplement of liquid B-Complex vitamins over the tongue 4-6 hours before fast, hard or strenuous work, may help to keep the horse on its feed.

A careful cool down procedure after fast work or a day of hard exercise, may also help maintain appetite for the following day of competition. (See page 51.)

If a horse is to be rested on the day after racing or competition, reduce the grain level. (See page 41.)

HINT

Regular access to green feed or green pasture also helps to sharpen and maintain the appetite in hard worked horses, particularly the day after racing, or competition.

Long Term Training

Many trainers find that horses who have been in training for 6 months or more often develop track sourness and a picky appetite.

Recent observations of racing horses indicate a possible relationship between deficiency of B-Complex vitamins and the onset of track sourness as the season progresses. The signs associated with track sourness usually develop in a set pattern. Initially, horses start picking at, or playing with their feed, and become poor doers. Performance then decreases and they fail to do their best.

As the condition advances, the affected horses loses weight, and look thin and bony. As B-Complex deficiency, particularly lack of Vitamin B1, can lead to poor appetite in most animals, observers link Vitamin B deficiency to track sourness. Some believe the condition could be psychological, as many horses get bored with training and stable routines. The condition is less likely to develop in horses that are turned out to green pasture for 1-2 hours a day, but in many larger training stables, access to green feed is limited.

HINT

Supplementation with oral sources of B-Complex vitamins (such as in Feramo-H daily or 2oz (60ml) of Pulse-8 every second day) may help delay the onset of the condition by correcting low levels in grains and concentrate feeds.

If the condition persists, consult your vet for advice.

HORSES WITH DIARRHEA

Diarrhea in horses can be related to feeding, heavy parasite burdens, nervousness, excessive use of antibiotics, and viral, fungal or bacterial infections of the bowel. It is beyond the scope of this handbook to discuss the many causes of diarrhea in horses and foals. Where possible, the underlying cause should be investigated and removed.

Common causes of diarrhea that are related to feeding, include:

*	Lush green pastures	- see page 146
*	High grain intake	- see pages 146 & 150
*	Excessive water intake	- see pages 19 & 143
*	Poisonous plants	- see pages 154-161
*	Sudden feed changes	- see pages 41 & 146
*	Other causes	- see page 150

Diagnosis of acute or persistent diarrhea and its treatment should be carried out by your vet.

HINT

At times, horses under the stress of work develop low-grade or chronic loose droppings or a cow pat form of manure, which appears to be related to food allergy or a reaction to concentrated diets. Dietary management may assist in treating this type of persistent diarrhea, where the horse appears bright and alert, but its performance is hampered.

A bland diet that I have used with success in racing and performance horses consists of:

1 gallon (4 liters) chopped grass hay
6 teacups soybean meal (heat treated)
2 teacups white clay, chalk powder or cornflour
8 teacups cracked corn
1 gallon (4 liters) crushed oats
6 grated apples - left to stand for 1-3 hours after grating before mixing in feed.
5 tablespoons of vanilla flavored yogurt (consult your vet for advice).

Mix well and divide into 3 equal feeds. Avoid feeding alfalfa hay or cubes, because in some horses, the diarrhea may take longer to resolve.

Electrolytes and vitamin additives can be fed in conjunction with this diet for horses in work. Once the consistency of the manure has returned to normal, gradually change back to the standard diet. If the diarrhea persists, seek advice from a veterinary surgeon.

> **HINT**
>
> *In recent years, cultures of yogurt or acidophilus bacteria (eg Lactobacilli spp) (to recolonise the large bowel bacterial flora), have been used with success in treating low grade diarrhea in horses. A supplement of 4oz (114g) or 7 tablespoons of yogurt over the tongue daily by oral syringe, or mixed into the feed, for 4-5 days, often helps to recolonize gut bacteria. These supplements help re-establish fermentation in horses that have mild diarrhea from antibiotic therapy or highly concentrated rations. Tablets containing a wide range of gut digestive bacteria are available for human naturopath therapy and have been used successfully in horses at 5-7 times the normal human dose rate. Consult your vet for advice before treating your horse with those preparations. In severe cases, your vet may tube drench a horse with unresponsive diarrhea with a slurry of fresh manure from a healthy horse in an attempt to recolonize and balance fermentation bacteria in the large bowel.*

TRAVELLING HORSES

Horses that are travelling over long distances, or for more than eight hours to shows, interstate competitions, or sales, and mares being transported to a breeding farm, should be provided with palatable and dampened concentrate feed, or dampened good quality hay.

NOTE: Over recent years, a higher incidence of transport illness or travel sickness, with development of often fatal lung disease (pleuropneumonia) is linked to long distance road and air transport. Diarrhea and laminitis (founder) can also result from travel stress.

> **HINT**
>
> *Horses most at risk include those hauled within a few hours of hard and exhaustive exercise, such as racing, eventing or other strenuous competition. Horses suffering from a low-grade viral respiratory infection are also more at risk.*

The travelling environment can increase air contamination and general stress that can result in serious lung disease. These include dust inhalation from feed or unpaved roads, elevation and short tying of the horse's head above its backline height that prevents drainage of respiratory secretions, high humidity and poorly ventilated trucks or trailers, erratic and fast driving, and inadequate rest stops.

Avoiding Travel Stress

* Avoid hauling exhausted, hot horses over long distances. Allow horses to cool down and recover before travelling, even if it means staying overnight. Offer horses a drink of water or rehydration fluid (such as Recharge) before travelling. Wet down hay, pellets and cubes to reduce dust and increase the moisture content of the feed to help combat dehydration during long distance travel.

* Ensure adequate ventilation, but not cold drafts. Unload horses every 3-4 hours for a green pick. Walk them around for 20 minutes, and offer a drink.

> **HINT**
>
> *Offer a drink of water or made-up rehydration fluid at each rest stop on long distance hauls.*

* Keep the top tailgate doors closed or back flap down on the trailer to minimize dust from unsealed roads entering the trailer.

* Don't tie horses too short. Leave enough rope and room for them to put their heads down - hang the hay net and feed trough below chest height.

* Drive carefully to reduce stress on yourself and the horses. Leave plenty of time to reach your destination. If you are hauling a known nervy traveller, take another quiet horse for company to help settle it.

> **HINT**
>
> *If you are hauling a stallion with female horses, smear a small amount of Vicks Vaporub™ or other menthol gel onto the skin around each of the stallions nostrils before loading to mask the smell of the other horses.*

HORSES WITH SHELLY, "CHALKY" HOOVES

A significant number of horses develop hoof cracks or sand cracks during dry weather due to excessive drying out of the hoof wall.

In some cases, removal of the protective waxy periople on the hoof during farriery increases the risk of the hooves dehydrating and developing cracks. It is beyond the scope of this handbook to discuss hoof care and maintenance. However, regular daily applications of a good quality hoof dressing will help prevent excessive drying out in hot weather, and limit moisture uptake in wet weather.

Cracked, Shelly or Broken-away Hooves

Studies have reported that supplementation with good quality protein, calcium and 15mg biotin (Vitamin H) daily, promotes hoof growth, improved bonding and resilience of the hoof wall in horses with large sand cracks, badly broken-away and shelly or brittle hoof walls.

Reports have indicated that calcium is also required for the bonding of the internal hoof laminae, and when combined with biotin and protein (containing methionine and lysine), the rate of growth and the quality of the horn produced is improved.

> **HINT**
>
> *For a 1000-1100lb (450-500kg) horse, supplement with 4 teacups of protein meal (eg soybean), 1oz (30g) or 3 tablespoons of calcium carbonate, and 15mg Biotin daily. This nutritional combination is reported as being helpful in promoting the growth and strength of the hoof wall and preventing separation at the white line. Supplementation may be required daily for 4-6 months to allow the hooves to grow out and*

strengthen. A general supplement of vitamins and minerals containing vitamin A, zinc and copper (such as Feramo-H) may also be beneficial, to supplement inadequate feed levels of these nutrients in performance and racing horses.

HORSES IN POOR CONDITION (ILL-THRIFT)

The common signs of lack of thrift or poor condition in horses include general ribby appearance; a dull, rough coat; failure to thrive, perform, or look their best; and a poor growth rate in young horses. In some cases, affected horses fail to improve even when given extra feed. The three common underlying causes of ill-thrift, in the absence of other obvious signs of ill-health, are:

* Heavy parasite burdens (worms/lice),

* Teeth problems (sharp edges on molar teeth, worn out teeth in aged horses),

* Inadequate feed (insufficient quality and/or quantity to match work, reproduction or growth).

Therefore, to help improve the health and general condition of horses that are in poor condition, due attention should be paid to:

* Control of parasites (worming/external treatments),
* Condition of teeth (rasping and dental check),
* Quality of feed (see specific ration examples).

If a horse still fails to show improvement within 2-3 weeks, seek advice from a veterinary surgeon.

HORSES WITH A POOR COAT

Show and performance standards require that the coat be glossy and well conditioned. A well balanced ration is essential to ensure health and general condition. Many owners believe that skin and coat condition is a reflection of good feeding, and internal health of the animal.

It is beyond the scope of this handbook to discuss every type of skin or coat problem and recommend a nutritional remedy. Care should be taken to ensure the horse is regularly de-wormed to get full benefit from the ration. Rugging and hooding to prevent bleaching; daily grooming to stimulate production of natural oils in the skin; and exercise, are important to maintain a short, healthy hair coat.

Hints to Improve Coat Condition

To improve bloom and condition

Provide a daily supplement of corn oil or polyunsaturated cooking oil at the rate of 5-10ml (1-2 teaspoons) per 100lb (45kg) bodyweight. A daily supplement of vitamins and trace minerals, such as in 1 teaspoon Feramo-H per 100lb (45kg) bodyweight) is also useful. A product such as Feramo-H contains high levels of Vitamin A, iron, copper and zinc to supplement low feed levels that may be the underlying cause for poor coat condition.

 HINT *To keep the coat manageable, shampoo and add conditioner regularly, and on show day apply a coat gloss preparation if necessary.*

To darken the coat

Generally, an increase in protein and trace mineral content of a ration seems to directly influence depth and intensity of coat color. Try adding 4-6 teacups of sunflower seeds, or 2-4 teacups of boiled whole linseed to the ration. Some owners feed 1/2 - 1 tablespoon of meat meal daily in the night feed, but others have found this to cause uneven color.

A daily supplement of vitamins and trace minerals, including Vitamin A, iron copper and zinc to correct low feed levels, may also help to deepen the color of the coat and give a dappled appearance.

To lighten the coat

Where horses develop an unacceptable dark coat, reducing the protein and fat content of the ration will often lighten the coat within 2-3 weeks. In this case, feed only low protein feeds, based on good quality grass hay. DO NOT feed legume or alfalfa hay, sunflower seeds, soybean meal, corn oil or cooking oil, or a trace-mineral supplement containing iron, copper and zinc as these tend to improve condition and depth of color. If possible, provide access to grazing on cereal-type pasture (not clover blends). The bulk of the concentrate feed can be increased by mixing in chopped grass hay and molasses.

NOTE: It is important to provide a calcium supplement if a grass hay based ration is fed to working horses. Supplement a grass hay based diet with 1oz (30g) or 2 tablespoons of calcium carbonate daily to avoid a dull, lifeless and brittle coat and hooves, that can result from a deficiency of calcium in the diet.

Long, Shabby or Winter Coats

Long daylight hours stimulate hormones in the pituitary gland which trigger the shedding of a long, dull winter coat. However, some horses still retain their winter coats if stabled in cold, dark stables for most of the day, even in spring and summer.

HINT *Allow affected horses to graze green pasture during the day and carefully groom daily with brush or comb in the natural direction of the hair coat, to remove long or yellowed hair. Provide higher protein and trace-mineral levels in the diet by feeding 1 teacup of protein meal, and a supplement of vitamins and trace minerals each day.*

HINT *When measuring small amounts of powdered supplements (such as Feramo-H) on a bodyweight basis, place the number of teaspoons in the product measure and mark the level on the side with a felt tipped pen. This will be an easy way to measure the daily dose thereafter for ponies and small horses.*

SLIMMING THE FAT HORSE

Just as for humans, dieting and controlled exercise can be used to slim down an overweight horse. The relative condition of the horse should be assessed on its type and skeletal structure, breed, and its use. (See Condition Score, page 164.) Obviously, certain show standards require a horse to be in good or show condition. However, obesity can be a problem in good doers, greedy horses, or horses on high energy rations without regular or adequate exercise. This is a particular problem in horses that are used for weekend pleasure riding where they are confined to stables or small yards for most of the week. To keep the horse occupied and contented there is a temptation to provide more than adequate feed relative to the horses needs.

> **HINT** *Do not put overweight mares that are to be bred within the next few weeks on a reducing diet. It is best to feed to maintain them at a steady bodyweight, otherwise fertility may be affected. (See page 128.)*

Some authorities suggest to simply confine an overweight horse to a yard or stable (bare floor, no straw bedding to eat) and starve for 14 days with 3 tablespoons of salt in each 6 gallons (25 liters) of water to drink. This practice is effective, but considered inhumane by many horse lovers. Total starvation can cause serious health problems in some horses, particularly in ponies.

Although it is suggested that feed intake be limited in fat ponies as part of the therapy for obesity, or to avoid or correct laminitis (founder), ponies must not be starved by sudden withdrawal of feed. Ponies are particularly prone to developing *hyperlipidosis* syndrome when their nutritional intake is reduced suddenly. (See page 149.)

The program of weight reduction should be gradual, combining both a decrease in dietary energy levels and controlled, but not excessive, slow aerobic type exercise at the trot and light canter.

> **HINT** *Reduce the energy level in a step wise manner over 10 days, but retain essential protein, fiber, and vitamin levels to meet maintenance requirements. Ideally the smaller bulk of ration should be fed over 3-4 feeds, with access to water at all times.*

Pastured Horses

In pastured horses, simply restricting grazing to one hour morning and night is reasonably effective, combined with a gradual increase in exercise under saddle or at the longe.

> **HINT** *A wire mesh muzzle admits just enough grass to keep horses trying to graze, and walking steadily to try to find better grazing. Muzzling for up to eight hours a day (or more in multiple sessions for obese ponies) is the easist way to reduce obesity and risk of founder in pony breeds.*

Stabled Horses

Concentrate Feed

A suggested concentrate dieting ration is as follows:

Each feed, per 100lb (45kg) bodyweight, provided in the morning, at midday and in the evening:

4oz (114g) dampened grass hay, oat hulls, sunflower hulls
3/4oz (21g) soybean meal
½ teaspoon calcium carbonate
¼ teaspoon salt
(ie for a 1200lb (550kg) horse, multiply the above weight of ingredients by 12.)

In hot weather, add an extra ¼ teaspoon of electrolyte mix and provide a mineral and vitamin mix in the evening feed to supplement low feed levels.

NOTE: If dampened alfalfa cubes or hay are used in place of grass hay, reduce soybean meal to half the above measure.

Roughage:

Dampened grass hay, ½lb (275g) per 100lb (45kg) bodyweight overnight. If available, 1-2lb (0.5-1kg) greenfeed provided overnight will help reduce boredom and risk of crib biting.

> **HINT** *A supplement of liquid B complex vitamins, every second day, will help supplement low feed levels of these vitamins to maintain energy utilization and reasonable vitality.*

> **HINT** *Horses should be confined to a bare yard (not sandy) or a stable with minimal bedding.*

Exercise

Controlled exercise, such as long walks for 30-60 minutes twice daily, or light exercise under saddle for 10-15 minutes, helps to break boredom and assists weight loss. It is best to give two or three short periods of medium exercise, rather than hard or extended work. A plastic bucket or other stable "toy" hung from the rafters may help occupy the extra leisure time between meals.

Water

Ensure that adequate clean water is available at all times to horses on a reducing diet.

HORSES RESTING AT GRASS

Mature horses that have retired, or horses that are not being worked on a regular basis, can maintain themselves on good quality pasture for most of the year. Supplementary feed, as good quality hay, is usually only required when pasture is sparse, short, or of poor feed value. Aged horses at grass may require supplementary concentrates during cold, windy and wet winter weather. (See Feeding the Aged Horse, page 47.)

Many horse owners like to provide a small concentrate feed once a day as a routine to give the horse an affectionate pat, and check on injuries etc.

HINT *A small concentrate feed each evening in cold weather provides additional energy to keep the horse warm, as well as a chance to add a rug if necessary.*

In summer, dried off feed may be spoilt by heavy rains (see page 124). When pasture is sparse, horses may walk off condition in search of food. Therefore, regular assessment of pasture value, and the horse's condition, will help decide the need for supplementary hay or concentrate feed.

Nutritional Management

There is no real need for routine supplementation with vitamins or minerals in mature horses at rest that have no extra requirements for growth, pregnancy, lactation or

exercise. However, if pasture and/or feed is of poor quality, then daily supplementation will provide all essential vitamins and minerals, including selenium.

HINT *It is best to feed easy keepers, cresty or fat ponies at rest with good quality grass or mixed hay, rather than alfalfa, to reduce the risk of laminitis or founder. Remember to worm horses and have their feet attended to on a regular basis, usually every 6-8 weeks.*

HORSES RESTING FROM TRAINING

Racing and other performance horses are turned out periodically to freshen-up or recuperate at grass at the end of each competitive season. The length of the rest period is influenced by the age of the horse, its mental attitude, type of injury or health problems, the stress and duration of the training program and the seasonal conditions.

Short-Term Freshen-up: 2-6 weeks

Short-term rest periods help to rejuvenate a horse's mental attitude to training, particularly after extended training or competitive campaigns, and to enable recovery from minor injuries, such as stone bruises, early shin soreness, splints or low-grade joint conditions.

The horse's general condition will influence the type of ration for the rest period. If a horse is thin and appears to be stressed, then a concentrate ration should be provided at about 20% energy level above maintenance to help the horse regain weight. If the resting area is large enough to allow daily self-exercise, then this extra energy above maintenance, plus that obtained from grazing, will improve condition without risk of metabolic problems.

1000-1100lb (450-500kg) bodyweight. Full access to pasture in large paddock or small lot. One concentrate feed per day. This ration is only a guide, and must be adjusted according to age of the horse, the length of the rest period, size of the rest paddock and grazing, and history of injury or other stress problem.

INGREDIENT	FORM/MIX	DAILY AMOUNT AM	DAILY AMOUNT PM	PROVIDES
OATS or alternatively BARLEY or MILO	Whole, heavy. Dust free. Rolled or crushed, dust free.	Hay in morning and midday	4½lb (2kg) 4lb (1.8kg)	ENERGY, PROTEIN, FIBER - traditional grain - may be replaced by a mix of rolled barley and corn, substituted on a rate of 4½lb oats replaced by 4lb of corn/barley mix.
or alternatively COMMERCIAL MIXED SWEET FEED (Optional)			4lb (1.8kg)	Convenient to feed. Normally requires additional supplement of calcium and minerals to meet repair needs. (See text.)
SOYBEAN MEAL (Optional)	Heat treated. Free flowing, Non rancid.		8oz (230g)	Optional - should be given on grass hay roughage based diets to meet protein needs.
DEHYDRATED ALFALFA PELLETS, CHOPPED HAY, CRUMBLED CUBES (Optional)	Dust free. Sweet smelling, no mold. Mix into grain mix.		1½lb (700g)	Optional - ENERGY, PROTEIN, CALCIUM - bulks out feed for horses that eat grain quickly. Substitute weight by reducing hay intake accordingly.
POLYUNSATURATED OIL or alternatively	Non rancid, keep sealed between uses.		2oz (57ml) (3 tblsp)	Provides essential fatty acids for coat condition.
SUNFLOWER SEEDS (Optional)	Black variety clean and plump.		8oz (230g)	Alternative protein and oil source - provides essential fatty acids for coat condition, - may replace soybean meal as protein boost on grass hay diets.
MOLASSES	Mix 50:50 with warm water, mix well into feed.		4oz (115g) (3/4 teacup) (Not required if sweet feed given.)	Improves palatability, reduces dust and sifting of supplements.
COMMERCIAL VITAMIN/TRACE MINERAL SUPPLEMENT	Mix well into feed.		(eg Feramo-H) 2oz (57g) (½ scoop)	Supplements low feed levels of all essential vitamins to correct feed deficiencies. Vitamin A, iron, zinc, copper for coat condition even if sweet feed used.
VITAMIN E SUPPLEMENT (Optional)	Mix well into feed.		(eg White-E) 1000iu (1 scoop)	Supplements low feed levels with Vitamin E to meet needs on grass or cereal based rations. Mix into top of damp feed.
DICALCIUM PHOSPHATE (Optional)	DCP. Free flowing dry. Mix well into ration.		1oz (30g) (2 tblsp)	Optional - provides CALCIUM and PHOSPHORUS to meet bone repair needs. (See text for full details.)
SALT	Fine grade, mix well into feed.		2/3oz (20g) (1½ tblsp)	Aids palatability and meets sodium need.
ALFALFA HAY or alternatively	Leafy, no dust or mold, dampen if necessary.	5lb (2.3kg)	6lb (2.7kg)	Provides ENERGY, PROTEIN, FIBER and CALCIUM. Contributes excess protein to diet if fed as roughage to horse at rest.
MIXED HAY or alternatively	Leafy, no weeds, no mold, dampen if necessary.	5lb (2.3kg)	7lb (3.2kg)	Well accepted - adequate protein to meet needs. Alternatively, feed alfalfa in morning and grass hay in evening.
GRASS HAY	Leafy, no weeds, mold or dust. Sweet smelling. Dampen if necessary.	5lb (2.3kg)	6lb (2.7kg)	More bulky and lower protein than alfalfa; intake limited by appetite of horse.

NUTRITIONAL INFORMATION: This ration has been formulated to NRC (1989) recommendations to provide 100% of maintenance requirements. The grain mix may be eliminated, and only hay provided if good pasture grazing is available. However a small portion of sweet feed may be given to provide supplements (see text). Each 15lb (7kg) ration provides approximately 17Mcals (71MJ) digestible energy, 700g (grass hay) to 1000g (alfalfa hay) (ave 12%) crude protein, and a minimum of 35g calcium, and 22.5g phosphorus on the grass hay alternative ration.

If the horse is lame and unable to graze effectively when turned out, then only 10% additional energy above resting levels may be required, with the bulk of the ration made up of good quality alfalfa or mixed hay.

In all performance horses, for each 100lb (45kg) bodyweight add 2oz (60g) of soybean meal or equivalent protein meal, as well as 2 teaspoons (10g) of dicalcium phosphate (DCP) and an appropriate dose of a general vitamin and trace mineral supplement each day to the concentrate ration. This should be maintained during the rest period to provide calcium, Vitamin A and D and trace-minerals for musculo-skeletal repair.

Conversely, if a horse is in good condition, then total withdrawal of concentrate rations can cause loss of condition within 7-10 days. Weight loss should be avoided in short-term lay-offs of 2-3 weeks, otherwise the condition will need to be put on again once the horse returns to training. Feed the concentrate in proportion to the available pasture and the amount of exercise the horse is given each day.

Long-Term Lay-offs: 6 weeks - 6 months

The ration should be tailored to suit the horse's general condition, ability to forage, and any underlying injury problems. Generally, it is best to reduce the amount fed each day in a step-wise manner over 10-14 days. A maintenance diet consisting of ½-1lb (230-450g) of good quality alfalfa or mixed grass hay per 100lb (45kg) bodyweight can be provided to supplement grazing as required, so as to maintain reasonable body condition.

On a good pasture in dry weather, most horses will prefer to graze, leaving hay uneaten. However, if a hay rack stocked with good quality hay is provided, the resting horse will normally eat to appetite to maintain reasonable condition.

For racing and performance horses with a tendon or ligament injury, a small concentrate feed containing 50,000iu Vitamin A (Retinol) daily such as contained in a 2oz (57g) dose of Feramo-H will provide adequate feed intake of this vitamin for tendon repair, particularly if green pasture is not available over the summer months. (See Ration Guidelines.)

FATTENING UP A THIN HORSE

Occasionally a horse is purchased or arrives for training or boarding in poor condition and requires building up for work or breeding. Horses that have over-wintered on poor pasture may also lose weight due to inadequate feed intake to meet their needs. Other horses lose condition or are hard keepers despite seemingly adequate rations. Nervy, hyperactive horses or those that fret when confined to stalls require more energy to maintain their condition and performance than their quieter counterparts.

The bodyweight of any horse should be assessed relative to its build, breed, type of condition required for work load or use, seasonal influences and general health. A horse may be best kept in a slim, trim or fit condition for the type of work it is performing (eg for Endurance riding), or a well padded form (eg for showing). (See Condition Scoring, page 164.)

As horses grow older, a combination of poor teeth, reduced digestive efficiency and chronic health problems can cause a gradual loss of condition. (See Feeding Aged Horses, page 47.) A horse with an itchy skin condition may spend a lot of time and energy rubbing; reduce its feeding time, and thus fall away in condition.

Initially, steps to correct the three most common causes of poor condition or failure to thrive - heavy worm burdens or external parasites, teeth problems and poor quality feed -should be considered before increasing the energy content by giving a supplement of concentrates in addition to good quality hay.

A thorough health check by a vet may be necessary to determine any underlying medical cause such as sickness, chronic illness or poor appetite for the failure to thrive. Weight loss is relatively common in the aged horse despite a palatable, good quality ration. (See page 47.) Horses with certain vices, such as weaving, stall walking and particularly the windsucking habit, often fail to thrive because of time spent on the vice relative to eating.

Loss of condition often occurs in 7-10 days after sudden withdrawal of high energy rations when horses are turned out to grass for a rest without a step wise decrease in concentrate feed. (See Resting rations, page 57.) A similar weight loss, and reduced fertility, can occur in newly introduced mares that are turned out into a group of mares that boss them away from feeders. (See page 128.)

Once the underlying cause of the weight loss is investigated and remedied, then the horse can be gradually introduced to a higher energy ration to regain condition. If possible, the horse should be turned out to grazing during the day, particularly if it is not accustomed to a stall and frets when confined.

A gradual, step wise increase in energy and protein levels is recommended so as to avoid digestive upset and metabolic problems. The increase in ration should be complemented by light exercise to help build up the animal, whilst allowing a safe level of excess energy and protein to be laid down as condition.

Preferably walk a newly acquired horse in poor condition for 15-20 minutes, or if time is restricted lightly longe for 3-5 minutes daily for a week or so to help it to settle in. This will avoid added stress caused by riding that may lead to unsettled behavior, mouth injury or fretting with loss of appetite.

The building up process should be carried out over a six to eight week period, with care to avoid over supply of energy which can result in metabolic upsets such as founder, tying-up and diarrhea. In young growing horses, care should be taken to avoid sudden spurts of growth due to high energy rations.

In practice, palatable feeds such as boiled barley or a mixed grain soak, at the approximate rate (when wet) of ½lb per 100lb bodyweight (500g/100kg) added to the normal maintenance ration for an adult horse, will achieve a reasonable weight gain. (See page 42.)

Ensure some type of exercise, such as a daily run in the paddock or longeing at a slow trot for 5 minutes each day, to help maintain the appetite, reduce playful and hyperactive behavior, and avoid metabolic upset.

A supplement of vitamins and trace minerals mixed into the feed daily will provide additional vitamins and minerals to correct feed inadequacies, help ensure vitality and health, and promote coat condition and weight gain.

LETTING DOWN A NEW HORSE

Horses previously in work on high energy feeds, may fail to do as well, and fall away in condition when turned out to pasture for rest, re-schooling or retirement. It may take up to six months or longer to expand the gut capacity and digestive efficiency of hay based diets in horses raised and fed on low roughage racing diets. These horse will then drop down in the belly and assume the proportions suited to the show arena. When Thoroughbred or Quarter Horse racehorses are retired to equestrian sports, the sudden change to low energy rations may lead to excessive sluggishness, with loss of condition and bloom. Some horses find low grain rations less palatable, and pick at their feeds, becoming hard keepers and poor doers.

Obviously, when a horse is used to concentrate feeds in work, then without a stepwise decrease in supplementary feed, the animal will lose condition, particularly under cool conditions on short winter pastures.

Avoid sudden reduction in feed intake in ponies in particular, as it can lead to serious metabolic problems which can be fatal within 7-10 days. (See Hints on Slimming a Fat Horse, page 55.)

In years gone by, racehorse geldings in training were given regular doses of anabolic steroids. Many horse owners believe that when these drugs were withdrawn on retirement, horses appeared to suffer progressive weight loss over 3-6 months despite reasonable quality feeds. In many cases, however, pasture grazing alone may not be sufficient to maintain their energy intake and condition, and their unstretched gut capacity could not efficiently store or digest the larger volumes of roughage required to meet energy needs.

Stabled horses maintained in a relatively parasite free environment may pick up heavy burdens when turned out onto pasture heavily contaminated with Small Strongyle larvae (small red worms or Cyathostomes). Uptake of these larvae can cause heavy burdens within 4-6 weeks, with diarrhea in severe cases, and weight loss within 6-10 weeks.

Worm out new horses on arrival, and if possible quarantine them in a yard for 48 hours to empty out worm eggs and avoid increased pasture contamination. Re-worm again in 3-5 weeks, and then at regular 6-8 week intervals, depending on stocking rate, seasonal conditions, result of fecal egg counts, or veterinary advice.

It is also a good idea to have the horse's teeth checked at turning out, as sharp edges on the molar teeth may interfere with efficiency of chewing. (See page 15.)

If possible, obtain details of the ration the horse has been accustomed to before retirement, and try to use similar ingredients. Slowly reduce the amount, and change the composition of the ration over a 2-3 week period if required. However, the exercise level will need to be maintained in proportion to the grain content of the ration until the desired level is obtained to avoid hot behavior, or metabolic problems such as tying up when the horse is exercised.

Longeing exercise in an enclosed corral for 5-10 minutes daily will help to utilize higher energy feeds, and help the horse become used to the new environment before re-schooling and riding are commenced. Slowly decrease the grain content over 3 weeks in a stepwise manner, and reduce the work intensity accordingly to enable the horse to adjust.

Many fillies and mares retired to stud from racing or equestrian sport competition, may fail to cycle and conceive in the first season often as a result of the sudden decrease in energy level in the ration. This is often due to lack of adequate grazing to maintain condition or being bossed away from feeders by dominant mares in the peck order. In this case it is best to maintain the new mare on the high energy ration and exercise program, mate her when she comes into season, and then slowly decrease the ration and exercise once pregnancy is confirmed. (See page 129 for further details.)

FEEDING A SICK HORSE

The recovery of horses suffering from severe injury or infection, or aged horses with liver, kidney or other internal diseases can be assisted by specially formulated rations. The diet formulated for sick horses must be palatable, meet the specific needs of the animal, and avoid nutrient excesses that could exacerbate a chronic disease, or delay recovery. Dampened, processed grains, pellets and cubes are convenient and easily digested foods for sick horses.It is beyond the scope of this handbook to outline specific diets for all types of injury or disease. Your veterinarian will provide the specialized advice and feeding program most suited to the individual horse.

Most diets are meant for short term nutrition only, and once a horse recovers, then normal diets should be resumed. In horses with chronic organ diseases, the special diet should be maintained and regular health monitoring carried out by your vet to assess the progress of the disease.

As a guideline, horses suffering from one of the following injury or disease problems will require adjustment to their diets.

HINT
A daily supplement of products such as Feramo-H and White-E will help overcome low feed levels of the nutrients required for healing of tendons, wounds and burns.

Injury/Disease	Diet adjustment
Infections, wounds, burns	Increase protein, energy, minerals such as zinc, B-Complex vitamins, Vitamin E, Vitamin C.
Tendon injuries	Vitamin A, zinc and copper.
Bone injuries/fractures	Extra protein, vitamin A, Vitamin D with calcium and phosphorus to specific need.
Persistent, long term diarrhea (See also page 150.)	Increase protein, electrolytes, B-Complex vitamins, adequate water, extra energy if losing weight.
Kidney Disease	Decrease protein, calcium and phosphorus, increase salt, and supply adequate water.
Liver Disease	Increase simple carbohydrates, no protein supplements or fats. Extra B-Complex vitamins, Vitamin E, Vitamin C.

DROUGHT FEEDING

Prolonged dry weather without adequate rainfall to sustain pasture development or regrowth for grazing horses will result in the pasture being grazed out. Although droughts are not common, horses must be provided with supplementary feed to meet their needs for maintenance, exercise, growth and breeding. There is usually more risk of plant poisoning under drought conditions as horses may eat plants normally avoided. It also increases the likelihood of sand colic as horses graze closer to the ground on sandy soils.

In most cases, provision of hay or cubes in quantities to maintain resting horses, or with small amounts of concentrate rations with a hay base, will meet the needs of exercising horses. The amount provided is relative to the age, activity and use of the horse.

HINT
Aim to at least maintain a trim bodyweight in most horses, but Show horses may need sufficient feed to maintain a fleshy condition even under drought conditions. A condition score between 3 and 4 would be suitable for lightly worked adult horses.

The feeds provided in a drought depend on the availability and cost including freight within the limitations of the horse feeding budget. Hay is usually the least expensive in terms of energy units. Horses can be sent away for boarding or turnout to a non-drought area, others may need to be supplemented to keep them productive and in work.

HINT
In most cases, under severe drought conditions, it is best to bring horses into corrals or dry lots to feed them. Horses in larger paddocks or range areas will walk off their condition in search of food even when adequate supplementary food is provided to maintain the average animal. Feed long or baled hay in hay racks or troughs to reduce wastage, as up to 10% is lost when fed on the ground.

If the country is denuded, there is an increased risk of soil erosion when horses are obliged to graze virtually bare paddocks.

HINT
Worm the horses regularly as normal, and check teeth, so as to ensure maximum feeding efficiency from feed provided. Large burdens of resting or encysted larvae of Small Strongyles (Small Redworms) in the large bowel wall can increase the risk of sand colic in horses grazing short pastures during drought conditions.

Horses grazing around fence lines, or on green areas around dams, creeks or water courses are likely to ingest large numbers of larvae in contaminated areas. Where hay, grain or mixed commercial feeds are available and can be purchased at reasonable cost, then diets using the ration guidelines for stabled horses can be provided as most horses are best confined to a dry lot to conserve energy, with light exercise daily to maintain efficient digestive function. (See Individual Ration Guidelines.)

Commercial concentrate feeds formulated for cattle, pigs and poultry should not be fed to horses in case they contain growth promotants, such as Monensin, that are highly toxic to horses. Seek advice from the manufacturer, local County Adviser or your veterinarian.

Alternative Feeds

Under drought conditions, alternative feeds that are not normally fed to horses are often available. The substitution values provided below are approximate values only, compared to the feeding value of oats for energy and grass hay for roughage. Energy and protein comparisons for common roughages, grains, and protein meals are given on pages 173-177.

Most alternative feeds are low in protein or deficient in essential amino acids, and a source of protein meal, such as 3/4 - 1lb (350-450g) of soybean should be added to rations for growing, pregnant, lactating and working horses. However, in most cases, it is best to feed growing horses, pregnant and lactating mares on commercially prepared sweet feed or custom mixes so as to ensure the best nutritional balance to match their specific needs.

ALTERNATIVE ENERGY FEEDS
Approximate Energy Equivalent to 1lb (450g) Oats

Substitutions per 1lb (450g)as Approximate Energy	Energy		Protein Equivalent
Bread (Limit to 3lb daily)	1lb 4oz	(560g)	Similar
Rolled Barley or Cracked Sorghum (milo)	14oz	(400g)	Similar
Crushed Rye (dampened)	13½oz	(385g)	Similar
Molasses* (mix 50:50 with warm water - max 16oz daily)	17oz	(480g)	None
Tallow* (warm and liquid - max 16oz daily)	6oz	(170g)	None
Polyunsaturated oil* (eg Corn oil - max 16oz daily)	5oz	(145g)	None
Sunflower seeds (limit to 1-1½lb - 450-700g daily)	11½oz	(330g)	Double

HINT: For replacing corn, multiply the above substitution weight by a factor of **1.2**, as corn is higher in energy than oats.

* 4-8oz (1-2 teacups) can be sprayed onto grass hay or mixed into seed hulls to boost energy levels in horses in poor condition - introduce in a step-wise manner over 10-14 days to ensure acceptance, particularly if the maximum amount is being supplemented.

ALTERNATIVE ROUGHAGE FEEDS
Approximate Energy Equivalent to 1lb (450g) Grass Hay

Substitutions per 1lb (450g)as Approximate Energy	Energy		Protein Equivalent
Sunflower hulls	1lb	(450g)	One-third
Cotton seed hulls	15oz	(430g)	Half
Oat hulls	1lb	(450g)	Half
Clean non printed cardboard	1lb 5oz	(600g)	None
Clean, dust free, good quality cereal straw	1lb 2oz	(510g)	Half
Grass silage (Non moldy) (Estimate 70% moisture content) (Do not exceed 30% of total roughage)	2lb	(900g)	Half

HINT: For replacement of alfalfa hay, multiply the above substitution weight by a factor of 1.4

* Molasses, warm tallow or corn oil can be sprayed onto hay or mixed into seed hull roughage base to increase energy value. Introduce in a step-wise manner over 10-14 days to ensure acceptance. (See the above table for recommended amounts.)

Feeding Management

Substitution Rates

The best quality alternative feeds should be purchased, ensuring freedom from mold or spoilage, and if dusty, they should be dampened prior to use. Do not disguise large bulks of poor quality feeds with sweetening substances such as molasses. However molasses, warm tallow and corn oil can be sprayed onto grass hay to boost energy levels (see tables above).

Alternative feeds should be introduced in a stepwise manner over 10-14 days. In most cases it is unwise to phase out normal feeds completely, but at least 50% can be replaced by cheaper feed sources. This is particularly important in growing, pregnant or lactating horses to avoid feed imbalances or deficiencies. It is best to provide these horses with good quality commercial feeds, and add cheaper sources of roughage, supplemented with vitamins and trace minerals to correct low roughage levels.

HINT
If silage is being fed to horses, it should not constitute more than 30% of the roughage intake, and must be of high quality to avoid clostridial poisoning. Where bread is used as an alternative feed, avoid providing more than 50% bread in a concentrate feed by diluting with roughages such as oat hulls or chopped hay.

Regular Observation

Where the horse feeding budget is limited and cheaper alternative feeds are used for longer periods, the effects of the ration should be regularly monitored. Keep a close watch for digestive upsets such as diarrhea or constipation, and loss of condition.

HINT
In very cold, wet and windy weather, extra grain or fat may need to be added to boost energy intake, or small amounts of quality hay fed to maintain condition.

Supplements

As alternative feeds may be low in protein, minerals and vitamins, supplementary levels should be added to meet daily needs.

HINT
A general vitamin/mineral supplement, such as Feramo-H, will help make up any shortfall of vitamins and trace minerals in the diet of resting and lightly worked horses. A daily supplement of 1 teaspoon (5g) of salt, and 2 teaspoons (10g) of dicalcium phosphate per 100lb (45kg) bodyweight is also recommended.

HINT
Fibrous roughage and oil boosted diets will often be lower in protein than normal grain or hay based diets. As a guideline, add 1½ teacups of soybean, cottonseed or sunflower meal (or 3 teacups of linseed meal) per 330lb (150kg) bodyweight to rations containing a roughage base of less than 6% average crude protein, such as oat straw and hulls, cardboard and cottonseed hulls.

Water

Always ensure horses are provided with good quality, clean water to drink, even if it has to be rationed.

Break of Drought

When the drought is broken by rain, then care should be taken to ensure that pasture is able to re-establish before horses are allowed to graze it full time. Do not cease supplementary feeding too early when the new pasture is succulent and has a low dry matter and energy content. Ensure adequate roughage is provided during wet, cold, windy weather as the drought is broken, otherwise horses may lose more condition and weaken. If horses are in poor condition and weak, then bring them into a sheltered dry lot, corral or stall during wet, cold weather and provide additional hay, and small amounts of concentrates if required.

After fires and droughts, there is often an increase in germination of poisonous plants, or rapid regrowth of potentially toxic pastures such as sorghums, phalaris and fall fescues. Horses hungry for green feed may overeat, leading to diarrhea and colic. Regular observation and limiting grazing to a maximum of two hours daily may help to avoid these problems.

HINT
The first green flush after rain often triggers the release of massive numbers of resting Small Strongyle worms (Small Redworms) from the large bowel wall reservoirs, into the gut. Diarrhea, with loss of condition and vitality, can occur within 2-3 weeks of return of green pasture. Check with your veterinarian for advice on worming horses affected in this way, particularly if they are in general poor condition or weakened by wormy diarrhea.

Special Case Horses

Young growing horses, lactating mares, and aged horses are normally more affected by drought conditions. Foals should be weaned and fed separate commercial rations to maintain rate of growth and development. It is important to avoid fasting ponies for longer than 12 hours under drought conditions, as it may result in metabolic problems related to mobilization of fat reserves, and death within 7-10 days (see page 149).

SECTION THREE

GROWING HORSES

The nutritional requirements and management of growing horses has probably been subjected to the closest scrutiny and specific research of any class of horse over recent years. The standards required in growth and development of nursing foals, weanlings and yearlings have been fully revised over the last decade. In an attempt to produce well grown and developed young horses, breeders often become overzealous in trying to achieve maximum growth potential in the early formative years. However, with time, trace back of unsoundness problems in young racing and older horses highlighted overfeeding, vitamin and mineral imbalances and interrelationships and lack of adequate exercise as being the predisposing factors of developmental orthopedic problems. In recent years, much more knowledge has been gained, and a more conservative approach to feeding and management adopted.

More emphasis is now placed on an adequate or optimum rate of growth, which is controlled by a careful combination of balanced nutrition, feeding management and adequate exercise. A few ribs showing are once again accepted as fashionable in young horses.

NEWLY BORN FOALS

At birth, the foal leaves the womb which has provided nutrition and protection against disease and injury. The newly born foal comes in contact with a relatively contaminated and hostile environment. Foals are born with a reserve of energy in the form of brown fat, which is stored in the gut tissues prior to birth. It has a higher calorific value, water content and digestible value than ordinary fat stores. It provides sufficient energy to sustain a foal for up to 36 hours under temperate conditions, enabling it to stand, move around, suckle and maintain body temperature. Under adverse, chilly conditions this reserve may sustain a foal for as little as eight hours.

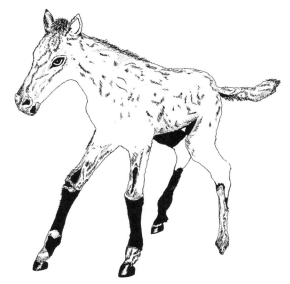

> **HINT**
>
> *Foals should be considered abnormal if they do not stand within 60 minutes of birth, fail to exhibit shelter and care-seeking behaviour within 2 hours of birth, or have not attempted to nurse within 3 hours of birth.*

The Importance of Colostrum

It is most important that all newborn foals receive adequate colostrum (first milk) within 8-12 hours after birth. A healthy active newborn light breed foal will suckle from 5½-9 pints (3-5 liters) of colostrum within 12 hours of birth.

Colostrum provides immune antibodies that are concentrated into the pregnant mare's milk during the last 10-14 days before foaling. The transfer of circulating antibodies from the mare's blood is prevented by the numerous layers of placental barrier.

Only low levels of antibodies are present in the foal's blood at birth and intake of colostrum is the natural way to boost immunity against local diseases. These antibodies are vital to provide immunity against common diseases during the first few weeks of life. Failure to either obtain or absorb adequate levels within 18 hours after birth will predispose the young foal to a higher risk of bacterial infection. Foals that do not receive adequate colostrum or antibody cover by this time usually fail to thrive and are likely to succumb to infectious disease.

Colostrum also contains proteins that help the absorption of antibodies. It is highly digestible and promotes a natural laxative effect to stimulate the bowels to expel accumulated wastes (meconium) within the first day of life. Most foals pass meconium within 3 hours of suckling colostrum.

Secretion of Colostrum

A mare only produces colostrum for the first 2-3 days of lactation, but the level of antibodies is highest in milk secreted in the first 6-12 hours. Studies have shown that up to 23% of foals tested within the first few weeks of life, have low blood levels of antibodies. This failure of passive transfer of antibodies via the first milk can result from low levels secreted by the mother, or failure of the foal to suckle or to absorb sufficient amounts. Expert management and care of new born foals on breeding farms is essential to ensure that foals receive adequate immunity.

Studies show that up to 12.4% of mares run their milk, or prelactate with milk splashed down their legs before foaling. If a mare runs her milk for more than 3 days before foaling, she can deplete her colostrum reserves at foaling. There is no way to prevent prelactation in mares about to foal.

If a mare bags up and starts to drip colostrum, then it is best to milk her out two or three times a day each time she accumulates enough colostrum to drip. Wash the teats and glands thoroughly and collect hygienically into sterilized plastic containers. The colostrum can be frozen to prevent it souring in case she does not foal for 2-3 days. Begin to slowly thaw the frozen bottle of colostrum in lukewarm water as soon as she foals, and give ½-1 pint to the newborn foal at hourly intervals by bottle or tube, beginning 1-2 hours after birth. Consult your vet for advice.

Old mares over 18-20 years of age generally have lower levels of antibodies in their colostrum. Serious illness in a mare in the first month of pregnancy may reduce the level of antibodies. Mares that foal earlier than 320 days of pregnancy may not accumulate adequate colostrum reserves to feed her foal. However foals born early are still able to absorb colostrum antibodies.

Shy maiden mares may resent initial attempts to nurse and deprive their foals of essential colostrum. Foals that are poor suckers, dummy foals, or foals that are weak or become separated from their mothers at birth may also be denied adequate colostrum intake. If you are unsure as to whether a foal has suckled sufficient colostrum, consult your vet for advice.

Absorption of Colostrum

Foals that are born prematurely and survive, should be able to absorb antibodies because special transport cells are formed early in fetal development. Although a foal's immune system can produce antibodies from 2-3 weeks of age, full scale response is not developed until 10-12 weeks of age. Therefore, colostrum must provide a temporary cover against common diseases over this period. The low point of immune protection in foals that do not receive adequate colostrum occurs at about 5-6 weeks of age. Newly foaled mares produce colostrum for only 2-3 days, but the level of antibodies rapidly falls after 12-14 hours, once the foal has suckled the initial colostrum reserve.

A sample of the foals' blood taken after suckling (12 hours after birth) can be checked with a Foal Antibody Test Kit to see if adequate antibody levels have been established. Following supplementary colostrum, the foal's blood can be tested in 2-3 hours to ensure adequate protective levels of antibodies taken in colostrum have been absorbed. Consult your vet for advice.

Orphan Foals

Orphaned foals require careful feeding and management, particularly if they are orphaned at, or soon after birth. For orphaned foals, colostrum can be collected from the foal's dead mother, provided the mare was otherwise healthy. Consult your vet for advice. Alternatively, extra colostrum can be collected within 12 hours of foaling preferably from mares that have a stillborn foal, or have lost their foal soon after birth, or are over productive milkers. Always wash and dry the udder and teats and practice good hygiene when stripping colostrum.

In many areas, colostrum is available from a commercial colostrum "bank" for use on large breeding farms. Local horse breeders may freeze excess colostrum for community use in case of orphan or colostrum-deficient foals. Consult your vet for advice.

Supplementary Colostrum

Once a mare's own foal has suckled and removed the first colostrum, the quality of subsequent colostrum secreted after 12 hours declines as antibodies are drained. Your vet can assess the antibody level remaining in the mare's colostrum by a specific gravity test.

A foal that has failed to nurse effectively, or one orphaned at birth, should receive approximately 3½ - 5½ pints (2-3 liters) of good quality colostrum by bottle if they will suck, or alternatively over the tongue by syringe or by stomach tube. Feeding or drenching about 1 pint (550ml) at hourly intervals is recommended, preferably within 6 hours of birth.

The special type of antibody transport cells in the foal's gut lining are shed and replaced by more mature cells that cannot absorb antibody proteins after 18 hours of life. After this time, the absorption of antibodies is significantly reduced. However, antibodies given in colostrum will still provide protection to the gut lining itself against bacterial germs taken in when suckling.

NOTE: In foals less than 6-12 hours of age, DO NOT feed milk or water until colostrum is given, as the transport cells will cease uptake of antibodies. Consult your vet for advice.

If fresh or frozen colostrum has a lower level of antibodies, then larger volumes need to be given. Colostrum can be stored frozen for 12 months. If colostrum is not available, your vet can harvest serum antibodies from an environmentally adapted donor horse (eg a mare or gelding), or purchase a commercial concentrated source. These antibodies can be given either by stomach tube, or dripped into the vein, depending on the age of the orphan.

A booster of plasma antibodies from an environmentally adapted horse that has been on the breeding farm for some time may be worthwhile to boost immunity levels in young foals transported interstate with their mothers for breeding, to give them more specific protection against local diseases. Consult your vet for advice.

Where a mare's milk has previously caused neonatal jaundice, or hemolytic anemia in one of her foals, her colostrum can be tested for anti-red-cell antibodies by your vet before her new foal is allowed to suckle. If fresh or frozen colostrum is to be given to these foals, it should be tested for hemolytic antibodies before administration. Consult your vet for advice.

NURSING FOALS - FIRST 8 WEEKS

Once the newborn has suckled sufficient colostrum to give it an adequate blood reserve of antibodies, then it should begin regular nursing to obtain nutrition for early growth and development.

Nursing Behavior

Healthy normal foals nurse on average about four times per hour (or about 100-105 times per 24 hours), during the first week or so of life, often only suckling for one minute at a time. The high sucking frequency is thought to protect the gut lining against bacterial germ invasion during the first 2-3 days of life, provide security, and enable the foal to identify and learn to follow its mother.

If a foal nurses very often, for longer periods, or aggressively as if hungry, then the mare may not have sufficient milk. A nurse mare or hand rearing may be necessary. Consult your vet for advice.

Flat shiny teats indicate that a foal is suckling. Enlarged, dirty teats mean a foal has not suckled, perhaps the mare will not allow the foal to drink. The foal may be sick, or the mare may have mastitis. Consult your vet for advice.

After the first week of life foals drink 2-3 times per hour, or 60-65 times daily.

Eating Solid Food

Most foals will start to nibble grass by 5-7 days of age, but it contributes little to their nutrition. It is normal for foals to eat horse droppings from 7-10 days of age, most commonly fresh feces passed by the mare. This behaviour is thought to help establish fiber digesting bacteria in the developing bowel. There is little danger of foals taking in worms (except Strongyloides westeri infections - see your vet) from fresh droppings. Infective larvae of Strongyle worms take a week to develop after the feces are passed. Nevertheless, mares should be wormed at foaling and then every 6-8 weeks, depending on the type of worms and recontamination rates. Consult your vet for advice.

After 2-3 weeks of age, foals will begin to graze if succulent grass is available. Foals graze closely to their mother's muzzles, as if to mimic and learn grazing technique and food selection. Foals graze only when their mothers are grazing.

Regular Observation

It is important that young foals be observed at least once daily for signs of ill-health, failure to nurse, or injury. Consult your vet for advice if necessary.

THE ORPHAN FOAL

Once the foal has received adequate colostrum (where possible confirmed by a blood test at 12 and 24 hours after birth), then the foal can either be reared using a foster mother, or hand reared on a bottle and bucket.

Commercial nurse mare services will rent a suitable mare to foster mother an orphan. A milking goat, standing on a raised platform, can be used to foster feed a very young foal. Where a foster mother is not available, or the foal will not take to a foster mare, then hand rearing is recommended.

Dietary Guidelines: First Week of Age

Bottle feeds can be given for the first 5-7 days with a commercial milk replacer formulated for foals. There are a number of good quality milk replacers available. These should be used in preference to mixing the milk formula yourself. Milk replacers must be mixed and fed as directed. Most foals can be taught to drink from a bucket from 2-3 days of age without too much trouble.

In an emergency, whole fresh milk, full cream powdered milk, or commercial calf milk replacers can be used. Cow's milk contains more fat and less sugar than mare's milk so it should be fortified with 6-7% additional sugar to give the approximate composition of mare's milk. It is best to house orphan foals in a stable for the first 1-2 weeks, particularly during cold or wet weather. A milk preparation and feeding regimen which I have found successful for rearing orphan foals is outlined in the following guidelines.

Preparation of Milk

As mentioned above, specialised foal milk replacers should ideally be used. These save time in preparation, are generally less expensive, and minimize risk of digestive upset than if you mix the milk formula yourself. However, if you need to make up a formula, then use the following recipe that was used before commercial replacers become available.

Dissolve approximately 1oz (30g) of lactose (1½ tablespoons), or alternatively dextrose (table sugar) or brown sugar, in each one pint (550ml) of cow's milk, or accurately reconstituted cows milk powder mixture.

In each quart (1100ml), mix in one level teaspoon (5g) of clean calcium carbonate powder, as cow's milk is lower in calcium, an essential bone building nutrient, than mare's milk.

Feeding Method

Make up milk freshly at each feed as required. Use either a commercial baby's bottle or a soda drink bottle fitted with a small lamb's teat. The hole in the teat should be made large enough so that a drip of milk collects and hangs when the full bottle is held teat downwards. Feed at blood temperature 98°F (37°C). Test by dripping some milk on your inside wrist, it should feel just warm. Shake occasionally during feeding. Milk temperature can be gradually lowered to ambient stable temperature of about 60-75°F (20-23°C) by two weeks of age, as bucket feeding is introduced.

HINT *For weaker foals, or poor drinkers, an oral vitamin supplement at a foal dose rate (such as one teaspoon of Pulse-8 liquid vitamins) may be given to enhance their appetite and general health.*

Feeding Volumes: First 5-7 Days

Follow the directions on the foal milk replacer you are using. However, for home mixed milk formula the volumes of milk are based on Thoroughbred sized foals of about 100lb (45kg) birth weight. The volumes of milk offered are guidelines only, and should be adjusted to the foal's demands.

Age	Volume/day	Suggested Feeding Times
0-7 days bottle feeding	5 pints (3 liters) [10oz (300ml) per feed or about 2-3 cups at each of 10 feeds]	Every 2 hours from 6am to 10pm; once at 2am (10 feeds).

HINT *If the foal is hungry and seeks more milk, give an extra half volume in between the two-hourly feeds. Do not overfeed as excess milk intake can cause gastric overload and result in diarrhea. If the foal develops a white paste-like form of diarrhea, dilute the milk by 30%, and feed smaller volumes more often until it clears up. If the diarrhea persists or changes to a darker color, consult your vet for advice.*

Dietary Guidelines - 7 days and older

Most foals at 2-3 days of age can be taught to drink from a bucket. If possible, bucket feeding should be phased in during the first week. Always take the bucket to the foal, rather than man-handle the foal to the bucket.

Bottle to Bucket Change

Studies have shown that foals of most breeds are intelligent enough to accept bucket feeding at 2-3 days of age.

HINT *It is best to start with a dish containing 2-3 inches (5-7.5cm) of milk. In foals less than one week of age, or those that refuse to drink, stimulate the drinking by letting the foal initially suck on a finger (dip the finger in warm milk and then move it against the palate and tongue to initiate the sucking reflex). Once the foal starts to suck, lift the dish of milk up so the foal's mouth is in the milk. Do not immerse its nostrils in the milk. Once the foal starts to take in milk, then remove the finger. Forcing the foal's head down into the milk is counter-productive. Repeat the process until the foal learns to drink.*

Most young foals will nurse on a finger, and once the milk has been tasted after one or two attempts, they will learn to drink directly from the shallow dish.

Foals that have been bottle fed during the first week, usually need less coaxing to drink from the dish. Put milk in a wide shallow container in a small enclosure with the foal. Show the foal where the milk is, and if necessary splash warm milk on its nose. Leave the foal alone with the dish of milk. Most foals will start to drink once they become hungry.

HINT *Once the foal learns to drink from the dish, a shallow plastic bucket 12 inches (300mm) diameter, 8-10 inches (200-250mm) deep, secured about 24 inches (600mm) above the ground is ideal to prevent the foal standing in it, tipping it over, or fouling it. Some larger stud farms have automatic nipple delivery and bucket feeding systems designed for orphan foals.*

Although the milk mixture for young foals (see above) can be used for bucket feeds, recent research has shown that powdered milk replacers diluted 1 to 10 with water, and supplemented with good quality concentrate or sweet feed will ensure adequate growth and development in foals over 2 weeks of age. The volume of diluted milk is provided as self-take drink between feed times. Discard any left-overs, but check that the foal is drinking at least 75% of milk allocation between feeds. If a lot of diluted milk is being left, but the damp sweet feed is being consumed, then only provide the solid feed at alternate meal times.

Concentrate Feeds

Most young foals will nibble supplementary concentrate feeds and milk-based pellets from 7-10 days of age.

HINT *Many commercial "starter" feeds, in pellet, meal or sweet feed form are available for young foals. These save time , are generally well balanced in nutrients (eg energy, protein, calcium, copper etc) for young foals, and are palatable and well accepted. Over recent years, many commercial companies in conjunction with University researchers, have carried out extensive studies to formulate suitable "starter" feeds for young and growing foals. Consult your vet for advice on choice of a suitable feed if necessary.*

HINT *The dry feed, without molasses added, can be made up and stored for a few days. Prepare the molasses and water, and mix in each day as required. If a commercial feed is used, additional Vitamin E (such as White-E) at a daily supplement of 250iu per foal, and molasses sweetener, may be mixed into the feed.*

After 2-3 weeks, most orphans (and nursing foals), will begin to graze to supplement their milk intake if fresh pasture is available. Alternatively, leafy good quality alfalfa hay (dampened by wrapping in a wet burlap bag for 1-2 hours) can be offered. Dampening the hay will soften it, and make it smell attractive and easier to chew. Dampening the hay also helps avoid excessive intake of dry roughage, which may lead to constipation in younger foals.

Feeding Volumes - Older foals

NOTE: The volumes of milk are based on growing Thoroughbred sized foals with a birthweight of 100lb (45kg). These are guidelines only - adjust to foal's demands.

Age and other feed	Milk requirement/day	Suggested feed times
7-14 days (bucket feeding). Provide 2lb (1kg) concentrate sweet feed for nibbling between feeds (see formulation below).	Increase to 9-11 pints (5-6 liters) daily, [2-2.5 pints (1000-1250ml) per feed].	**4 hourly:** 6am - 10pm (5 feeds)
14-21 days. Provide 3½lb (1.5kg) sweet feed (12% protein) daily between milk feeds.	Increase to 11-14 pints (6-8 liters) daily, [3-4 pints (1.5-2 liters) per feed].	**6 hourly:** 6am - 10pm (4 feeds)
21 days to 8 weeks Provide sweet feed to suit appetite.	Start on 15 pints (8 liters) daily. Increase by 3.5 pints (2 liters) weekly, up to 7 pints (4 liters) per feed.	**8 hourly:** 6am, 2pm, and 10pm (3 feeds)
After 8 weeks Feed ad-lib to appetite. Start to wean off milk onto concentrate feed and good pasture.	Provide 11 pints (6 liters) twice daily. Reduce by 1½ pints (1 liter) per feed each week until milk is no longer taken.	Morning and evening. (2 feeds)

Foals 2-16 weeks:

For horse owners who prefer to mix feeds themselves, a high quality protein, low fiber, palatable sweet feed for young foals can be mixed as follows, and offered *ad-lib* in a shallow trough.

Feed	Quantities
Crimped or crushed oats	4½lb (2kg)
Cracked corn	2lb (900g)
Milk powder	10oz (285g)
Soybean meal	7oz (200g)
Alfalfa cubes crushed/chopped hay	1lb (450g)
Vitamin/mineral supplement	(eg Feramo-H) 1oz (30g) (¼ scoop)
Vitamin E	(eg White-E) 250iu (¼ scoop)
Dicalcium phosphate (DCP)	1oz (30g) (1½ tablespoons)
Salt	15g (3 teaspoons)
Molasses	2 teacups (mixed with two teacups warm water)

Foals 6-16 weeks:

When foals are more than 6 weeks of age, reduce milk powder by 3oz (90g) per week, and substitute with 3oz (90g) soybean meal.

Although milk powder in the ration may give slightly higher growth rates than comparable amounts of soybean meal (due to its better digestibility in young foals), soybean meal is generally less expensive and is a well balanced protein source for older foals.

Where molasses is used as an appetizer, feeds should be made fresh each day.

As a rule of thumb, foals over 16 weeks of age can be supplemented with concentrate feed at the rate of 2.0% of bodyweight [2lb/100lb bodyweight (1kg/50kg)] daily, with access to good quality pasture, leafy alfalfa or mixed hay.

Hints on Hand Rearing

Utensils

Cleanliness of utensils is vital, especially when feeding foals during the first three weeks of life to avoid gastric upsets, bowel infection and diarrhea. Handy hints include:

- Wash bottles, teats and buckets with clean cold water after use to remove milk residues. Rinse with boiled water, and drain.

- Wash utensils in a warm detergent solution once daily to remove fat and other deposits. Rinse repeatedly with boiled water, and drain.

- Sanitize utensils in boiling water or suitable cold hypochlorite sanitizer before feeding. Soaking utensils in solutions used for baby's bottles, or dairy iodophor is good practice between feeds. It is inexpensive, easy, less time-consuming and at times more efficient than boiling bottles and mixing jugs. Always follow the directions on the bottle when making the sanitizer solution. Rinse bottles etc with warm boiled water and allow to drain.

Shelter

Weak foals need special nursing in a warm box, or roomy stable. Warmth is most important. Consult your vet for advice.

- Clean straw or hay bedding is soft and easy to turn and clean.

- Shelter from wind, rain and snow is important for the first two to three weeks, and foals are best stabled at night when weather is wet and cold.

- Outside paddocks should be well drained, sheltered from prevailing winds, rested or rotated and contain good green pasture if possible. Keep paddocks clean. About 1-1½ acres (half a hectare) per foal is ideal. Fences must be injury proof, preferably post and rails, chain mesh or covered plain wire.

- Provide clean water at all times, preferably in a soft plastic bucket placed in a corner area so as to avoid injury.

Companionship

An orphan should have a companion animal to prevent it fretting, or becoming a nuisance by demanding too much human attention.

- Another foal is best. A quiet old pony, a small calf, an old ewe, or a couple of pet lambs are also suitable.

- Provide separate feeding utensils for the companion animal(s).

Feeding Rules

Certain rules of feeding should be strictly followed to reduce risk of gastric upsets, diarrhea or food refusal.

- All changes in diet must be made gradually over 5-7 days.

- The earliest feeds should be offered at blood heat 98°F (37°C). After a week, gradually lower the milk temperature to ambient stable levels.

- Do not over-feed. It is best to give small feeds more frequently on demand, rather than large milk feeds in young foals less than two weeks of age.

Observe Bowel Action

Newly born foals should pass their first dung or meconium within 2-3 hours of their first feed of colostrum. It may be wise to give an enema to day old orphans, particularly to colt foals. If a foal strains with its tail up for a time or is exhibiting colic-like discomfort without passing meconium, seek veterinary advice.

Prevent Diarrhea

Increased intake of fibrous feeds, such as green grass, can cause mild diarrhea from seven days of age. However, if a foal develops severe diarrhea, it may die of dehydration or infection. Milk overload can cause light colored pasty diarrhea in foals during the first week. In this case, reduce the milk volume or dilute it by 30% and increase frequency of feeding under your vet's supervision. Treatment for Intestinal Threadworms (Strongyloides westeri) may be necessary if the foal develops a persistent brown bubbly type of diarrhea without a rise in temperature from 5-10 days of age. Seek veterinary advice.

Exercise and Sunlight

Ensure the foal has sufficient area to exercise and receives at least two hours of sunlight a day, preferably more. The foal should be taught to lead as soon as possible.

Parasite Control

The foal can be treated for worms at 4-6 weeks of age with a paste formulation. Repeat worming every 4-6 weeks, shifting to a new pasture after each worming if possible. Seek advice from your vet.

General Observation

Watch for signs of ill-health, diarrhea, colic and poor appetite, and seek prompt veterinary advice if you are concerned. Attend to the umbilical cord of the orphan foal the same way as for a normal foal.

It is good practice to give the new born foal a tetanus antitoxin booster injection. In weaker foals, consider an additional immune boost during the first week, and at one month of age with preparations containing serum antibodies. Consult your vet for specific advice.

Discipline

Ideally, orphans should be weaned into a group of other weanlings as soon as they are eating pasture and growing well, to encourage normal psychological development. An orphan foal can become rather difficult to manage because it does not get its mother's discipline and has no herd position. Care and strictness in handling the foal orphan are therefore important. Do not allow it to play games with you.

NURSING FOALS 8 WEEKS TO WEANING

Adequate nutrition of the nursing foal is important to lay the foundations for proper and steady development. The peak of lactation in mares occurs about two months after foaling, which corresponds to the foal's most active growth period. For the first two months, most foals will obtain sufficient nutrition to meet their needs from suckling, supplemented with green grazing and nibbling at their mother's concentrate feed from 2-3 weeks of age.

> **HINT**
>
> *Where a mare's milk dries up in the first 2-3 weeks after foaling due to mastitis, sickness or injury, and she is unable to provide at least 50% of the young foal's daily needs, then it is better to wean the foal and rear it as an orphan. Providing extra milk to supplement poor milk supply in a mare is not practical, as most suckling foals will not take milk offered in a bucket. (See Guidelines for Feeding Orphan Foals.)*

During dry summer conditions, or under heavy stocking rates, the contribution from available pasture may fall short of requirements, and young foals will need supplementary milk pellets or concentrate feed to maintain an even and steady rate of growth and development. However overfeeding to boost growth rate or catch up on set-backs must be avoided.

Supplementary Feeds

After the third month of lactation, the nutritional contribution from mare's milk alone decreases significantly. Any shortfall must be made up by grazing, or a supplement of good quality concentrate feed prepared for young foals.

However, growth rate and development must be monitored, and the feed intake adjusted accordingly, to maintain an adequate, but not excessive, rate of growth. Some larger breeding farms weigh foals regularly to monitor their rate of growth.

> **HINT**
>
> *Studies indicate that an average foal bred for racing or equestrian use will gain about 3lb daily (about 1.3kg) from birth to 3½ months of age. Young foals will eat up to 1½lb of creep feed daily, plus pasture and milk from nursing to achieve their rates of growth. After this age, the rate of growth and bodyweight gain begins to slow down, with an average gain of about 2¼lb (about 1kg) up to six months of age. Rapid rates of growth, resulting from high energy concentrate creep feeds, are discouraged, and must be avoided. Many horse breeders consider that an optimal rate of gain about ¼lb (4oz or 114g) less than these rates is safe. The simple recommendation - aim at 80% of maximum growth rate.*

Good quality commercial concentrate feeds formulated especially as creep feeds for foals are available. Controlled feeding of these, to maintain an optimum rather than maximal rate of growth, will help to maintain even and steady growth rates prior to, and after weaning. Supplementary concentrate feeds can be provided either in a separate creep feed area, or as a co-feed shared with the mare. Sheltered creep feed areas (eg situated in a corner of a field near the mare's feed tubs) are designed to allow access only to foals.

However, bolder foals will often boss the more timid foals away from the creep area. This can result in injury, and defeats the purpose of providing extra feed for less developed foals. Over-eating of concentrated energy feed on a free choice basis will increase the risk of digestive upset and diarrhea. It can also lead to excessive bodyweight and over-development which can predispose young horses to Developmental Orthopedic Disease (DOD) and to future limb unsoundness problems.

Most foals are more content to share feed from their mother's feed tub, or eat from a separate adjacent tub. Feeding with their mothers provides younger foals with a sense of security. It also encourages them to mimic and develop eating behaviour, and accept concentrate feed more readily once they are weaned.

> **HINT**
>
> *A long trough to allow the mare and foal to stand together to share feed is more suitable than the traditional high sided feed tub that only allows one animal to eat at a time. A foal will be encouraged to eat if the mare is provided with a suitable co-feed ration that she finds palatable.*

The "co-feed" trough can be constructed by sectioning off the end of the feed trough with slats spaced closer than the width of the mare's muzzle, usually 3 or 3½ inch (75-85mm) gaps for Thoroughbred sized mares). For safety, the slats should be spaced wider than the width of the foal's hooves. Ideally, the foal feeding area in the trough should have a false bottom raised higher than the mare's section, so that the foal can feed comfortably. To facilitate cleaning, the slats can be hinged like a lid, so that unspoiled left-overs (NOT wet, moldy or sour), can be removed, and recycled into the mare's ration.

Rate of Feeding

It is best not to allow free access or ad-lib feeding of creep feed in young nursing foals. Provide only sufficient creep feed for half to one day's consumption by a group of foals. If mares are feed twice daily, then feed half the creep allocation twice daily. This will encourage foals to eat by themselves, and avoid overeating of ad-lib feed.

HINT

Studies have show that an adequate intake of copper is essential to ensure proper cartilage development in the joints. Although earlier studies suggested high levels of copper should be provided, recent recommendations suggest that an addition of 20-30ppm of copper to the diet of growing foals is adequate.

Young foals can be supplemented with concentrate rations at a rate of 2-2.5% bodyweight: 2-2½lb/100lb (2-2.5kg/100kg) without risk of overfeeding and development of bone deformities, providing adequate exercise, pasture and good quality hay is available.

NOTE: A suitable creep feed ration is outlined on page 67. Guidelines for a shared feed for a lactating mare and foal appear on pages 134-135.

Avoiding Overgrowth

It is essential that overgrowth stimulated by excessive amounts of high energy rations, combined with restricted or inadequate exercise, be avoided in foals and older growing horses. The incidence of Developmental Orthopedic Disease (DOD) is greater in young foals with rapid rates of development or spurts of rapid growth. This results in enlarged growth plates or epiphysitis, contracted tendons, and internal abnormalities in knee, hock, and ankle joints and bone malformation of the spinal canal in the mid to lower neck vertebrae. A more detailed discussion on feeding to avoid DOD is included under guidelines for weanlings on pages 73 & 148.

HINT

Recent research on the East Coast in young horses raised on small lots with "wobbler" like symptoms of incoordination of the hind limbs, has discovered a link between low feed levels of Vitamin E and EDM in growing horses. Preliminary work suggests a nerve degenerative disease related to low levels of Vitamin E, inadequate exercise and lack of access to green pasture. This research suggests that nursing foals and weanlings confined to small lots should be supplemented with 1000iu Vitamin E (such as White-e) daily to overcome low feed levels. Research is continuing. Consult your vet for up to date advice.

In young foals, growth rate can be restricted quite safely for 3-4 weeks. This can be done by reducing the amount, or energy content, of the concentrate feed, and providing extra space for exercise. Consult your vet for advice.

HINT

Newly born foals that have symptoms of enlarged knees or ankles, or bent legs, should be confined to a stable for 7-10 days, and their feet trimmed accordingly. Consult your vet for advice.

HINT

Recent reports on the treatment of foals with contracted tendons, or upright pasterns, indicate that foals should be confined to a stall or small corral for 2-3 weeks. Pain caused by excessive or forced exercise can result in contracture of the tendons of the forearm flexor muscles, causing foals to raise up on their toes. Confinement to restrict exercise, combined with carefully monitored doses of pain killers so as to avoid toxicity, will promote a more rapid recovery. Consult your vet for further advice.

DIETARY GUIDELINES - YOUNG FOAL

8 Weeks to Weaning. Creep Feed Concentrate. Feed at a rate of 2lb/100lb (1kg/50kg) bodyweight daily, providing only sufficient for one day at a time to a group of foals. Do not feed on a free choice basis. Do not overfeed - cut back if growth rate is too rapid.

INGREDIENT	FORM/MIX	CONCENTRATE MIX		PROVIDES
		per 10lb of mix (4.5 kg)	per 100lb or mix (45kg)	
CORN	Cracked. Freshly processed. If purchased cracked, store in bag, fold down after use. Not rancid/sticky.	4lb (1.8kg)	40lb (18kg)	ENERGY, PROTEIN. Adds energy without excessive bulking out of ration. Palatable when freshly processed.
OATS (Can be substituted with rolled barley or crushed milo)	Crimped or rolled. Dust free.	3lb (1.4kg)	30lb (14kg)	ENERGY, PROTEIN, FIBER. Palatable and adds fiber to establish digestive bacteria and reduce risk of digestive upset if gorged in cold weather.
SOYBEAN MEAL	Heat treated. Free flowing. Non rancid.	1½lb (700g)	15lb (6.8kg)	ENERGY, PROTEIN, with essential amino acids. Not always well accepted in young foals - introduce slowly over 7-10 days.
MILK POWDER	Spray dried. Free flowing, dry, non rancid.	8oz (230g)	5lb (2.3kg)	ENERGY and good quality PROTEIN, CALCIUM. Taste often preferred by foals - can replace with SOYBEAN after 2-3 weeks - substitute slowly.
MOLASSES	Mix 50:50 with warm water, mix well into feed. Store mixed sweet feed 2-3 days only.	8oz (230g) (1½ teacups)	5lb (2.3kg)	ENERGY and some CALCIUM. Damp sweet feed improves palatability, prevents separation and sifting of ingredients. Clean feeders regularly.
COMMERCIAL VITAMIN/TRACE MINERAL SUPPLEMENT	Mix well into feed. Feed to directions on label	eg Feramo-H 2oz (57g) (½ scoop)	eg Feramo-H 20oz (570g) (5 scoops)	Supplements low feed levels with essential vitamins, particularly vitamin A & D, and trace minerals including iron, copper and zinc for optimum bone and muscle development.
COPPER SULFATE MIX	1 part Bluestone (21% copper) in 9 parts granulated or confectioner's sugar. Mix well.	5g (1 teaspoon)	1 3/4oz (50g) (2½ tablespoons)	Supplements low feed levels with an additional 20ppm copper for cartilage formation.
VITAMIN E	Vitamin E powder. Mix well into feed.	eg White-E 1000iu (1 scoop)	eg White-E 10000iu (10 scoops)	Supplements low feed levels with of Vitamin E - recommended for race or competition bred foals - aids in optimum muscle development and avoids EDM related Wobbler Syndrome
DICALCIUM PHOSPHATE	DCP. Free flowing, dry. Mix well into feed.	2oz (57g) (3 tablespoons)	20oz (570g) (4 teacups)	CALCIUM and PHOSPHORUS to balance Ca:P ratio to meet growth needs.
CALCIUM CARBONATE	Ground limestone. Select good quality only. Mix well into feed.	1oz (30g) (1½ tablespoons)	10oz (300g) (2 teacups)	CALCIUM to meet calcium needs, particularly where foals are grazing grass pastures.
SALT	Fine grade. Mix well into feed.	½oz (15g) (3 teaspoons)	5oz (150g) (1 teacup)	Increases palatability and prompts water intake when grazing dry pastures.

NUTRITIONAL INFORMATION: The above ration can be consumed at a rate of ½-3/4lb (250-350g) per 100lb (45kg) bodyweight daily. Each 1lb (0.45kg) concentrate mix provides approximately 1.3Mcals (2.9Mcals or 12.1MJ/kg) digestible energy, 70.6g (157g/kg) crude protein (15.7% CP), 3.4g (7.5g/kg) elemental calcium, 2.7g (5.9g/kg) elemental phosphorus [Ca:P ratio 1.26] and 3.8g (8.4g/kg) lysine and 25ppm (25mg/kg) of additional copper. Ad-lib good quality alfalfa or mixed grass hay should be provided for mare and foal, depending on available pasture.

WEANLINGS

Adequate, rather than excessive, nutrition is one of the cornerstones of breeding and rearing horses, and at weaning, it assumes even greater importance to avoid any set backs in growth or long-term skeletal problems caused by overfeeding. A well managed weaning process minimizes psychological, nutritional and health stresses on the young foal. The initial mental stress of separation from the mare and competitive stress associated with establishing friendships and pecking order in groups often results in a loss of appetite, condition and lower resistance to parasites and viral respiratory diseases.

The developmental stage between weaning and yearling age is one of the most critical periods in a young horse's life. A steady growth rate fueled by balanced nutrition sets the foundation for the eventual physical stature and soundness of the adult horse. It is much safer to raise foals by underfeeding to give a slower rate of growth and slightly prolong their growing time than to maximize growth rates by overfeeding of concentrate feeds and restricted exercise. A low body condition score of 4-5, with the ribs showing, is acceptable, provided growth and development is encouraged by exercise and an adequate and balanced diet. It is better to err on the side of caution, rather than feed to demand and appetite.

Time of Weaning

Most foals are weaned between 4 and 6 months of age. Weaning may be carried out earlier or later depending on the relative development and size of the foal, available pasture, seasonal conditions and physical state of the mare.

Studies have shown there is <u>no</u> advantage weaning after 7 months of age. Generally, by 5 months of age, most foals have almost weaned themselves, with little reliance on nursing, although some may still suffer from the emotional stress of separation. Early weaning at less than 4 months of age is also considered of little advantage, except where a mare has inadequate milk to feed her foal. Some larger breeding farms successfully wean foals at 3½-4 months, but for hobby breeders, 5 months is a practical weaning age.

HINT

If a foal has been supplemented with concentrate feed, either as a creep feed or by sharing the mare's ration, it is less likely to suffer nutritional setback at weaning as it will be accustomed to eating concentrated feeds. Younger foals in a group may be encouraged to eat concentrates by the example set by older, more independent weaners. The more timid weaners may also be bossed away from feeders. Spread feed tubs out to ensure there is room for squabbling until a peck order is established.

There are numerous systems for weaning foals, but whatever method is used, it should aim at minimizing stress and fretting on the weanling. The most popular system is to wean foals by observing and selectively removing the dams of the oldest, best socialized foals once or twice a week. The weaned foals are left with the herd until all the mares have been removed over a four week period. An aged gelding or barren mare is often introduced as a "nanny" and steadying influence to the group of weaners. On some farms, it is customary to early wean foals in pairs (decided by sex, relative age, size and temperament) into stalls for 5-7 days to help forge friendships, before turning them out into weanling paddocks. An individual weanling should be provided with the company of a quiet, mature gelding, or even a goat or sheep, to avoid fretting, encourage it to eat and help it settle down.

Nutritional Requirements

If the weaning process is carefully carried out to reduce stress and fretting, then appetite will be maintained. It is important that a palatable diet and good, clean, quality pasture be available.

As a general guideline, weanlings should be fed approximately 1-1¼lb per 100lb (1-1.25kg per 100kg) bodyweight of 14-16% protein concentrate ration, supplemented by about an equal amount of quality hay and grazing. It is not wise to provide free choice access to concentrate feed. Only measure out sufficient feed for one day at a time. In cold weather, feed half the feed morning and evening to avoid gorging and digestive upset. This should be adjusted seasonally as fall and winter pastures have reduced nutritional value for young growing horses.

> **HINT**
>
> *Heavy rains on dried summer feed may dramatically reduce available feed for young horses, as the feed stand is broken down and contaminated with manure and other debris. Ensure that supplementary hay or additional concentrate feed is provided for all horses for 10-14 days or until new grass is available for grazing.*

As the weanling increases in bodyweight, the daily ration must be increased accordingly, taking care to avoid overfeeding but ensuring adequate opportunity for paddock exercise.

> **HINT**
>
> *As a guideline, for light-horse breeds, weaners should have a minimum daily bodyweight gain of 1-1¼lb (450-600g) at 5-6 months. Early weaned foals should gain about 2lb (900g) daily until 6 months to ensure adequate development. Do not overfeed to maximize growth and development.*

Dangers of Overfeeding

Any set-backs in growth rate due to sickness and injury, or stunted growth caused by poor nutrition in weaners, must be compensated slowly over a 3-6 month period. Studies indicate that change from a low protein to a higher protein diet will help young horses to catch up in size and general development. (See page 24.) Feeding higher amounts of carbohydrates or energy in concentrates will boost growth rate, but excessive energy intake will increase the risk of bone, joint and tendon developmental problems. (See DOD below.)

Various earlier surveys concluded that excessive weight bearing stress placed on the developing musculo-skeletal structure can result in leg problems as the animal matures, particularly in young racing and performance horses. Generally, the faster the growth rate the greater the risk of developmental problems. However, other research suggests that orthopedic problems are not always related to rapid growth, and are influenced by genetic predisposition, undefined environmental factors, and certain vitamin/mineral imbalances. However, the bossy good doers in the group of weanlings are more prone to leg developmental problems.

Counteracting Overgrowth and Limb Deformities

It is virtually impossible to recognise the signs of Developmental Orthopedic Disease (DOD) before the skeletal damage is done. It is better to ensure preventative measures are adopted in the feeding program of all growing horses. If not checked, DOD will result in enlarged joints, and structural damage and deformities to knees, hocks, ankles and neck vertebrae in growing horses. More research is needed to establish definite links and inter-relationships with diet, exercise and hereditary factors in the development of DOD. (See also page 148.)

Studies have concluded that excessive energy intakes (more than 128% of NRC (1989) recommended levels), and possible imbalances in the calcium to phosphorus ratio, combined with inadequate exercise, are likely predisposing causes for DOD in growing horses.

Recent observations suggest that the incidence of DOD is increasing in Thoroughbreds and European raised Warmblood breeds. Controlled studies have shown that high energy diets, containing high proportions of carbohydrate and even fat (as corn oil) fed to weanling foals, produced abnormal bone development and internal joint cartilage changes.

> **HINT**
>
> *Weanlings on high energy diets and intense exercise regimens are less likely to develop DOD than young horses on high energy diets confined to small yards without adequate exercise. Young horses on high exercise/low energy diets also have a higher incidence of DOD related problems. Although high protein diets have often been blamed as a cause of DOD, there is little evidence to link long-term intake of protein rich rations with DOD, except perhaps when it provides extra energy in diets already well above requirements.*

Current measures to reduce DOD and subsequent wastage in growing foals of performance horse breeds include:

1) Provide balanced nutrition - avoid excessively high growth rates by overfeeding.

2) Aim for steady growth patterns, and avoid sudden spurts and over-development.

3) Avoid excess energy intake in any form - high protein, carbohydrates and fats in grains and oil.

4) Ensure the level of copper in the feed is above 10ppm, aim at 25-50 ppm (25-50mg/kg) of total feed consumed.

5) Ensure foals and weanlings have access to free paddock exercise for at least 2-3 hours a day, preferably 12-24 hours.

6) Avoid breeding from horses with a family history of DOD.

> **HINT**
>
> *As an example of a specific problem related to DOD, it is considered that the Wobbler Syndrome in young Thoroughbreds is influenced by bloodlines of horses that are good doers and gross over developers. One type of this condition is caused by developmental abnormalities in the vertebrae in the mid to lower neck area. This results in misalignment and narrowing of the spinal canal, which eventually damages the spinal cord.*

Recent observations suggest that Thoroughbred yearlings that have developed Wobbler Syndrome, often show signs as early as 2-3 weeks of age. Potential Wobbler foals tend to eat with their legs wide apart, and continue to pace with head held forward rather than learning to trot or canter when exercising. They often appear uncoordinated when learning to lead, or lack normal hind leg co-ordination when the tail is pulled sideways at the walk.

In these horses, slowing the growth rate by managing the diet as outlined above is recommended. Consult your own vet for further advice.

HINT
Recent research suggests that a low level of Vitamin E in the diet of growing horses confirmed to bare lots on the East Coast without access to green grass can cause EDM. This is a nerve degenerative disease with similar symptoms to bony or DOD type Wobbler Syndrome. Supplementation with 1000-1500iu of Vitamin E (such as in White-E) daily is recommended to correct low feed levels. It is possible that another cause of Wobbler Syndrome is related to Salmonella bacterial infection in young horses in mid-west states. More research is needed on all forms of Wobbler Syndrome.

Exercise

Exercise is important to promote steady and well proportioned muscle and bone development and ultimate soundness. Studies have shown that young horses will grow well on relatively low protein diets (6-8%) when adequate, but not excessive, energy and exercise is provided.

HINT
Most weanlings will exercise sufficiently when grazing, particularly if the country is undulating. Placement of feeders well apart from water troughs will also encourage exercise.

HINT
Special attention should be given to feeder location and safety of feed tub and hay rack design to prevent injury in weanlings. (See page 29.)

Dietary Guidelines

Commercial rations such as sweet feed mixtures, pellets and growing horse mixes for weanlings are popular because of their convenience, uniformity of energy, protein and calcium/phosphorus levels, and savings of time in mixing and distribution. Manufacturers provide recommendations for feeding that generally provide optimum growth without over-development.

Home mixed rations must be palatable to tempt the youngster to eat the feed, and contain adequate <u>energy</u> to fuel growth rate; <u>protein</u> to provide the building blocks for body development; <u>fiber</u> to maintain efficient digestion, (excess will cause a hay belly); and <u>minerals.</u> A balanced level of calcium and phosphorus is essential to build strong bone; complemented by an adequate intake of copper, zinc, and trace-elements to meet the need for growth and skeletal development.

Molasses can be added to make the ration more palatable and reduce dust.

HINT
A 440lb (200kg) weanling requires approximately 27g calcium, 16g phosphorus, and adequate Vitamin A and D each day, all of which may not be provided by grain based feeds or short winter grass pastures. These rations are likely to be relatively deficient in copper and other essential bone forming trace-minerals.

Nutritional Contribution from Pasture

Growing horses should be provided with access to good quality pasture as the basis for their ration and to encourage exercise necessary for development.

However, the grass/legume blend in the pasture can influence the important calcium/phosphorus balance in growing horses. The ideal is a mixed pasture stand containing grasses and legumes, but content may be influenced by locality, seasonal conditions and stocking rate. Once a pasture becomes dominant in either grass or legume, supplementary concentrate feed may need additional sources of calcium (Ca) or phosphorus (P) to provide the best Ca:P ratio for growth and development. The following points should be considered:

1. Grass based pastures (Cereal grasses in general)

Spring and winter pastures, or irrigated grass based pastures will provide higher levels of phosphorus relative to calcium. The feed should contain additional calcium (see ration guidelines) to counteract excessive phosphorus intake from grazing. Alfalfa or mixed hay may also be provided to add calcium.

2. Legume based pastures (Clovers, alfalfa)

Under suitable conditions, particularly under dry summer conditions, alfalfa will dominate the pasture stand. In these pastures, excessive calcium intake may lead to a relative deficiency of phosphorus, particularly if alfalfa hay is provided as a roughage supplement.

The feed ration should contain an additional source of phosphorus. Calcium carbonate powder may need to be omitted from the concentrate feed in high alfalfa diets.

3. Tropical Grasses

In warmer, tropical areas, weanlings grazing pastures containing subtropical and tropical pasture grass species which contain high levels of oxalate salts, may develop symptoms of early DOD over a 3-6 month period, and limb deformities. Other tropical pastures, such as Setaria, Pangola and Buffel grasses contain higher levels of oxalates. Oxalate salts bind up calcium in the bowel, and interfere with its absorption and blood levels. Although alfalfa contains oxalate compounds, they are below the level considered to have an effect on calcium uptake in horses.

In severe cases, this can lead to resorption or mining of calcium from bones to maintain blood calcium levels, resulting in bone deformities in the nasal area and limbs. Tropical grasses are particularly dangerous when growing rapidly following irrigation or top dressing with fertilizers, such as phosphate or poultry manure. As cereal grasses dry-off in the summer, tropical grasses may remain green and succulent, particularly along water courses, banks of dams, or in hollows etc. Young horses tend to graze these in preference to other dry paddock feed, including supplementary alfalfa hay. The high oxalate intake can interfere with calcium uptake which can result in joint and limb growth abnormalities. Consult your Extension Service about your pastures.

If big knees or apple joints (external signs of epiphysitis or enlarged growth plates) or other limb deformities become apparent in weanlings grazing topical grass based pastures, then the diet must be supplemented with additional calcium. Affected weanlings are best brought into a corral once a day, and each given a 10-12% protein concentrate feed at the rate of 1½lb/100lb (1.5kg/100kg) bodyweight containing 2% calcium carbonate powder. Consult your vet for advice.

Nutritional Management

NOTE: Adjustments to the ration guideline may be necessary to suit individual weanlings according to age, growth rate and development, particular breeds of horses, and pasture availability. The supplements of calcium, minerals and vitamins should be maintained in proportion at all times. Increase the amount of feed provided as the young horse develops.

- Some weanlings may find soybean meal unpalatable initially. Therefore, commence with a protein mix of 50% soybean meal and 50% of either linseed meal, or milk powder. Increase the amount of soybean meal in a step wise manner over 2-3 weeks and reduce the other meals accordingly.

- Pelleted or specialised protein supplements, or commercial weanling rations, may be added to replace all or part of the ration. Seek advice from manufacturer on amounts to provide each day.

- During very cold weather, a concentrated feed containing 20% cooked or hot soaked barley is helpful to encourage the appetite in younger weanlings. It is also useful as a tempting feed for weanlings that are off their feed due to injury or respiratory disease. Add 2lb (1kg) of hot, wet barley and mix well into ration whilst it is still warm.

If you are taking the feed out to grazing weanlings during cold weather, portion ration into individual bags, and pack closely to maintain warmth during transport. Molasses may be left out of the mix if boiled barley is used.

Remember, be cautious - don't aim for maximum growth. Maintain a steady growth rate and provide space for exercise. Deworm on a regular program. A few visible ribs are far safer than a fat, heavily conditioned young horse.

450-500lb (200-230kg). 6-12 months of age, eventually maturing to 1000-1100lb (450-500kg) adult horse at 3 years of age. Access to pasture. Divide ration into two feeds daily in cold weather, or when pasture is poor. If grazing, provide one feed daily. Avoid overfeeding.

INGREDIENT	FORM/MIX	CONCENTRATE MIX				PROVIDES
		Legume Hay/Pasture		Grass Hay/Pasture		
		per 10lb of mix (4.5 kg)	per 100lb of mix (45kg)	per 10lb of mix (4.5 kg)	per 100lb of mix (45kg)	
CORN	Cracked. Freshly processed. If purchased cracked, store in bag, fold down after use. Not rancid/sticky.	4½lb (2kg)	45lb (20kg)	4½lb (2kg)	45lb (20kg)	ENERGY, PROTEIN adds energy without bulking out ration. Palatable when freshly processed.
OATS	Crimped or rolled initially then may be fed whole, dust free.	3½lb (1.6kg)	35lb (16kg)	3¼lb (1.5kg)	33lb (15kg)	ENERGY, PROTEIN, FIBER. Palatable and adds fiber to help avoid digestive upset if gorged in cold weather.
SOYBEAN MEAL	Heat treated. Free flowing. Non rancid.	1lb (450g)	10lb (4.5kg)	1 3/4lb (800g)	17½lb (8kg)	ENERGY, PROTEIN, with essential amino acids, particularly lysine for grass based roughage. Commence on half amount initially, increasing to full amount over 5-7 days.
MOLASSES	Mix 50:50 with warm water, mix well into feed. Store mixed sweet feed 2-3 days only.	8oz (230g) (1½ teacups)	5lb (2.3kg)	8oz (230kg) (1½ teacups)	5lb (2.3kg)	ENERGY and some CALCIUM. Damp sweet feed improves palatability, prevents separation and sifting of ingredients. Wash residues from feeders regularly especially in warm weather.
COMMERCIAL VITAMIN/ TRACE MINERAL SUPPLEMENT	Mix powder well into feed.	eg Feramo-H 2oz (57g) (½ scoop)	eg Feramo-H 20oz (570g) (5 scoops)	eg Feramo-H 2oz (57g) (½ scoop)	eg Feramo-H 20oz (570g) (5 scoops)	Supplements low feed levels with essential vitamins, particularly vitamin A & D, and trace minerals including iron, copper, zinc and selenium.
COPPER SULFATE MIX	1 part Bluestone (21% copper) in 9 parts granulated sugar. Mix well.	5g (1 tspn)	1 3/4oz (3½ tspn)	5g (1 tspn)	1 3/4oz (3½ tblsp)	Supplements low feed levels with additional 20ppm copper for cartilage formation.
VITAMIN E	Vitamin E powder. Mix well into feed.	eg White-E 1000iu (1 scoop)	eg White-E 10000iu (10 scoops)	eg White-E 1000iu (1 scoop)	eg White-E 10000iu (10 scoops)	Supplements inadequate feed levels of Vitamin E - recommended for racing or competition bred weanlings - aids in optimum muscle development and avoids EDM related Wobbler Syndrome.
DICALCIUM PHOSPHATE	DCP. Free flowing, dry. Mix well into feed.	1oz (30g) (2 tbsp)	10oz (285g)	1oz (30g) (2 tbsp)	10oz (285g)	CALCIUM and PHOSPHORUS to balance Ca:P ratio - more phosphorus required on legume based roughage.
CALCIUM CARBONATE	Ground limestone. Select good quality only. Mix well into feed.	not required	not required	1oz (30g) (2 tbsp)	10oz (285g)	CALCIUM to meet calcium needs, on mixed hay and grass based roughage.
SALT	Fine grade. Mix well into feed.	½oz (15g) (3 tspn)	5oz (150g)	½oz (15g) (3 tspn)	5oz (150g)	Increases palatability and prompts water intake when grazing dry pastures.
ALFALFA HAY or alternatively MIXED HAY or alternatively GRASS HAY	Good quality leafy. No dust or mold.	Initially provide 3lb (1.4kg) alfalfa or mixed hay, or 4lb (1.8kg) grass hay daily; amount dependent on pasture. Increase to 50% of ration by 12 months for <u>each</u> weanling.				Provides essential roughage for digestive function. Increase to 1lb (450g) per 100lb (45kg) bodyweight by 12 months of age.

NUTRITIONAL INFORMATION: The concentrate mix is recommended at a rate of 1-1½lb (450-700g) per 100lb (45kg) bodyweight daily. This ration is formulated for a six month old weanling growing at a moderate rate to provide 100% of daily needs based on NRC (1989) guidelines. Each 10lb (4.5kg) of concentrate, plus 3lb (1.4kg) hay provides approximately 16.7 Mcals (70MJ) digestible energy, 810g (13½%) crude protein, and a minimum of 31g calcium, 19g phosphorus and 34g lysine.

YEARLINGS

Most well grown young horses should have achieved 90% of their mature height, 95% of their mature bone length, and 70% of their adult bodyweight by 12-15 months of age. The yearling age is therefore ideal to assess the growth and development of young horses so that nutritional management can be modified to achieve a well grown horse without the risks associated with overfeeding.

Surveys have shown that foals, regardless of breed and final mature height, have similar growth patterns, with maximum increase in height at the withers in the first 3 months of age. A combination of adequate and balanced nutrition to control the growth rate, combined with exercise in a large paddock, is the basis for achieving these goals. Aim at an average daily gain of 1-1¼lb (about 450-600g).

Grazing Yearlings

During winter or periods of poor pasture growth, young grazing yearlings can be supplemented with 1¼-1½lb per 100lb bodyweight (1.25-1.5kg/100kg) of a 12-14% protein concentrate with adequate calcium, phosphorus and trace-minerals, and a minimum of 1-1¼lb per 100lb bodyweight (1-1.25kg/100kg) of good quality alfalfa or mixed hay. Generally, yearlings grazing mixed grass and legume pasture require no supplementation with concentrated feeds in a normal spring season. However, provision of good quality alfalfa or mixed hay in a hay rack will help ensure an adequate growth rate and provide roughage. Roughage ferments on digestion to maintain body warmth and helps keep the animals occupied in eating to avoid over consumption of concentrates during the cold winter months.

HINT

Nutrition during the weanling to yearling age should aim at producing slabby, gangly and lean bodied yearlings, particularly in young fillies. Strict attention to the diet at this age will help the

young horse fill-out to balanced proportions by 18-21 months of age.

Where predominantly cereal based pastures are available, which usually contain lower protein levels, and phosphorus in excess of calcium, provision of good quality alfalfa or mixed hay, as well as a balanced concentrate feed is useful to help improve protein quality and maintain a positive calcium to phosphorus ratio. However, where pastures are legume based, or oversewn with alfalfa, then total phosphorus intake may not meet the requirements for the developing yearling. In this case, the concentrate feed should contain less added calcium, with a source of phosphorus such as dicalcium phosphate (DCP). (See ration guidelines.)

HINT

Small amounts of bran can be used as a source of phosphorus, one pound (450g) provides the same amount of phosphorus as 1oz (30g or 2 tablespoons) of DCP.

HINT

In cold or wet weather, groups of weanlings and yearlings often start to chew each other's tails and manes, possibly because of boredom, or a inadequate roughage intake from short or sparse pasture. This practice can sometimes be averted by providing good quality hay in a hay rack situated in a sheltered area. (See also Tail Chewing - Young horses page 144.)

HINT

Many breeding farms bring yearlings into a dry lot or a stall at 12 months of age for a week or so to provide extra basic handling education before they become too strong and difficult to manage and lead safely.

Yearlings for Sale

Preparation of a young horse for sale, from yearling (12 months) to long yearling (18 months), requires careful attention to nutrition, exercise and general presentation, particularly during the 3-4 months prior to the sale. Unfortunately, the trend over recent years has been to produce an overdeveloped young horse, with the appearance of being boosted or pumped up for sale. Breeding yearlings for sale is a business, and the product (the horse) offered must be of high standard and well constructed. However, a well grown and strong yearling does not have to be fat and over conditioned to command attention or a higher price. It is also important to educate the youngster to lead, parade and exhibit itself to show off its attributes in the sale ring.

| HINT | *It is best to plan for a 4-6 week period to educate, improve the coat and attractiveness of the yearling prior to the actual auction sale.* |

| HINT | *A carefully programed preparation will help avoid the risk of musculo-skeletal injury, and digestive and metabolic problems associated with forced feeding and little exercise that may increase the risk of breakdown later in the horse's life.* |

Initial Appraisal

Appraise the yearling for growth, development and condition in the lead up to sale. Each yearling must be treated as an individual, in feeding, the amount of exercise, coat and feet preparation, and minimizing blemishes. Shaping of the hoofs, in particular, needs to start early because it takes up to two months to grow out chips and broken away areas, and even longer for wall cracks.

| HINT | *Carefully assess each horse and prepare an individual timetable for sale preparation. Be prepared to modify the program to avoid excessive condition. Plan for a regular light work or rest day once a week, as young horses often go sour if exercised every day. Reduce grain intake to half on rest days, commencing the night before.* |

| HINT | *Even if the yearling is not being offered for sale, a thorough assessment of body size, proportion and overall general condition at yearling age is important to ensure the young horse is within breed standards.* |

Final conditioning to produce a well proportioned and athletic physique, without excessive fat, is achieved by a combination of careful feeding and regular exercise. Where possible, it is best to bring the young horse into a corral twice daily, or overnight into a stall in colder weather. This will allow a basic education, opportunity to groom and control the ration and daily exercise.

| HINT | *Where poor seasonal conditions, injury, or sickness have resulted in poor development or stunted growth, a longer preparation may be necessary. The yearling can be stabled overnight for the preceding couple of months to ensure that it receives an adequate and rising plane of nutrition, without being overfed and under exercised.* |

Ideally, yearlings should be given access to pasture and exercise during the day time, with confinement to a sheltered corral or dry lot overnight during inclement weather. During the last 3-4 weeks, stabling indoors overnight with paddock exercise or longeing in a dry lot or corral during the day will minimize risk of injury and help coat preparation.

Feeding Management

If the yearling is stabled with access to a corral or dry lot, then it should be fed at least three times daily. Provision of good quality hay during the middle of the day and overnight will help keep the horse occupied. Roughages and green feed will reduce the risk of boredom and development of stable vices such as crib biting, stall walking or pawing the floor. Introduce the feed over 1-2 weeks, in proportion to exercise and general body condition.

| HINT | *Deworm the young horse about six weeks prior to the sale, repeat worming about for 2-3 weeks prior to sale. It is also a good idea to have the teeth checked for sharp edges once the horse settles down and can be handled safely. A yearling that is a slow eater may have sharp-edged teeth. Consult your vet for advice.* |

| HINT | *Reduce the concentrate feed to half on any rest days to avoid metabolic problems such as tying-up and colic when exercise is resumed. Even on rest days, the yearling should be put into a safe, outside exercise area to encourage free exercise. This will provide psychological relief from overnight stall confinement, and help maintain appetite. To avoid injury, it is best to turn young horses out alone, or in view of a friend from an adjacent stall.* |

Practical Ration Guidelines

Only an adequate and balanced ration will achieve the accepted condition for the sale ring. Many of the larger breeding farms compound their own rations, whilst others prefer to provide part or all of the ration using commercially prepared feeds to help ensure uniformity of the content, and for the convenience of ready made feeds. A dietary guideline for a home mixed feed is outlined on pages 82 and 83.

General Considerations

Feed each horse on an individual basis. Aim at a weight gain of about 1-1¼lb (480-600g) daily. Poorly conditioned yearlings may benefit from extra feed, such as 3lb (1.5kg) (wet weight) of cooked or hot soaked barley or grain mix in the evening feed. However, as energy is increased, the amount of exercise must also be increased to avoid swelling in the legs from grain in excess of exercise needs, and a spurt in growth that could lead to over conditioning and future limb unsoundness. Addition of polyunsaturated oil, even in volumes of 4oz (about 100ml) daily will help improve coat condition and eliminate any dust in the grain feed.

| HINT | *Overly fat yearlings should be placed on a maintenance diet of good quality hay and only half concentrates, and the exercise intensity and duration gradually increased to slim the bodyweight, without imposing excessive stress on* |

the limbs that could lead to joint and leg problems. Longeing at the trot for an extra five minutes twice daily will often help to achieve a steady weight loss, without causing musculo-skeletal injury.

Assess feed intake and appetite each day by noting the time taken for the horse to consume its feed, and the amount of leftovers. Clean feeders regularly, and ensure an ample supply of fresh, clean water at all times. Modify unpalatable rations to ensure acceptance and to cater for individual horse's preferences.

Picky Eaters

If a yearling is a slow eater and slobbers when feeding, have its teeth checked and rasped if necessary. For picky eaters, reduce the bulk of ration by increasing the weight of higher energy feeds, (such as rolled barley or corn) by up to 10% over 7-10 days, and reduce lower energy feeds such as oats by 15%. On rest days, the barley and corn should be cut out, and oats reduced to half to avoid risk of hot manners and handling problems, as well as tying-up, when exercise is resumed.

> HINT
>
> *For fussy or picky eaters, or generally poor doers, particularly those that go off their feed after a few days of exercise, an oral feed supplement of B-complex vitamins, (such as in Pulse-8) may be helpful. Administer over the tongue for 2-3 days until they regain their appetite, then mix a dose into the feed every second day as a maintenance supplement. It is also a good idea to ensure that yearlings confined to stalls can see other horses whilst feeding; and at night, a dim light in an otherwise dark stall may help encourage feeding.*

Alternatively, the bulk of the feed can be reduced by adding extra polyunsaturated fat. On an <u>energy</u> basis, one teacup (125ml) of polyunsaturated oil is equivalent to 12oz (350g) of whole oats, or alternatively 10oz (285g) of cracked corn. Fats are digested and utilized more slowly to release energy, and may reduce hot or nervy behaviour and handling difficulties in some young horses. Introduce the oil slowly to the ration, starting with 2oz (60ml) morning and evening and increasing over 10-14 days to the required level - usually two teacups (about half a pint or 250ml) morning and evening (total of about 1 pint or 550ml). Reduce the grain accordingly. Most horses are able to consume all their feed once the volume of ration is reduced.

Lethargic Yearlings

Occasionally an individual yearling will lack vitality and stamina despite adequate feed. They should be checked for worms, and general health by a vet. Daily supplementation with B-complex vitamins, (such as in Pulse-8 liquid) may help improve general vitality. Ensure the yearling is exercised to the energy level in the ration at all times.

Vaccinations

It is good management to administer a tetanus booster when a young horse is stalled in case it sustains bruises or minor lacerations when rolling in the stall or exercising. Other vaccinations, such as Flu, Rhino Rabies etc, may be advised by your vet.

Exercise

A carefully planned aerobic exercise routine is essential for a yearling to fully utilize feed and aid in conditioning to produce an athletic, fit looking horse. Exercise programs will vary, depending on the time and facilities available.

Paddock Exercise

Ideally, access to pasture and paddock exercise during daylight hours will counteract the confinement and concentrate ration when a young horse is brought into a corral or stalls overnight.

However, due to the risk of injury and the need to avoid bleaching and damage to the coat, many farms restrict paddock exercise to a few minutes each morning and evening.

Walking

For yearlings confined to stalls or a corral due to weather conditions, walking for 30-40 minutes daily is the safest form of exercise for the young, inexperienced horse. Daily walking helps to utilize the higher energy ration and accustoms the yearling to being paraded. During the daily walk, the yearling can be allowed to pick at green feed, and be taught to stand square for inspection. However, walking individual horses is labor intensive and unpleasant in wet weather.

> HINT
>
> *The yearlings should be walked in a small group in a safe area such as along laneways, large lots, small paddocks or other enclosed areas where the risk of injury is minimal. If possible, a young nervous horse should initially be lead with an older quiet horse and ideally have another person to follow behind to make it keep up.*

Exercise at the longe

This can be beneficial if regulated carefully to suit the individual horse's condition and temperament. Longeing exercise should be carried out on a firm, but not compacted surface (such as a 75:25 sand/wood shavings mix) to reduce concussion and avoid lower leg strain which can be caused by a surface that is too heavy. Longeing can be done at the slow trot once daily for 10 minutes each way, depending on the animal's general condition. The radius of the longe circle should be at least 20-25ft (6-8 meters) so as to reduce turning strain on the lower limbs during exercise. Be careful not to allow the horse to exercise too enthusiastically, particularly on compacted surfaces or in deep heavy sand. Ensure the surface is raked and levelled after use and keep the horse away from outside walls or rails when longeing.

> HINT
>
> *Ensure that you keep the sand mix around the outer edges levelled off, as build up of banks around the outside can place additional stress on the lower legs as the horse circles.*

> HINT
>
> *Horses that are exercised should be taken for 5-10 minutes walk on the lead to cool out after longeing.*

> HINT
>
> *For best control, most owners prefer to exercise yearlings using light control produced by a round yearling bit. It is a good idea to have the teeth checked prior to commencing work, as sharp edges on the molar teeth can lead to a sore mouth, loss of appetite, and handling problems. Longeing should be done in a cavesson, depending on the animal's behaviour and need for control.*

Handling

Young horses straight from the pasture often need a basic re-education to settle them down, and allow them to be lead safely. It is wise to treat each young horse as an individual, and spend time to educate it, particularly to stand-up squarely, lead from the shoulder, and respect command. It is important that the horse is taught to exhibit or show itself off well "on the line", or in the sale ring.

> **HINT**
>
> *Ensure the horse is accustomed to examination of the head and legs, and to lifting all feet for inspection.*

Make sure that stalls are safe and that there is nothing lying around in corrals, paddocks, or walking areas that could cause injury. Always keep the tack in good condition.

Common Problems Related to Feeding

Swelling in the legs

Excessively high amounts of grain may result in soft cold swellings or filling (edema) of the lower legs, often accumulating overnight in the hind legs. In this case, replace half the grain in the ration with additional hay. Give up to 10 minutes light exercise twice daily at the trot, and hose swollen legs with cold water for 10 minutes twice daily to help remove the fluid build-up. Re-introduce half of the grain in a step wise manner over 7-10 days, and maintain adequate exercise. Consult your vet for advice.

> **HINT**
>
> *Once the youngster is accumstomed to handling of its legs, application of a cold dressing (such as EquiLint^{TM*}) under a light pressure bandage of Vetrap Bandaging Tape^{TM*} for 5-10 minutes as required, is an easy and convenient way of reducing swellings from bumps, kicks and lacerations, and minor joint filling. An*

EquiLint^{TM*} dressing is a useful first aid item to have on hand at all times.

Contracted Tendons

The symptoms of contracted tendons, with the appearance of a straightening of the pastern angle (up on the pasterns or standing on the toes) are more likely in less well developed yearlings put onto excessively high energy rations in an effort to build them up prior to sale.

In early cases, reducing the concentrate to one quarter and replacing with good quality hay and confining the horse to a stall to restrict exercise, with a low dose of pain killers, will promote recovery. Consult your vet for advice.

Joint Problems/Thoroughpin, etc.

Sprain of the joints, and strain of tendons and leg structures can occur if young horses are worked hard when overweight, or on heavy working surfaces.

These conditions can be avoided by feeding a weight reducing diet with minimal concentrate and good quality grass hay with access to a large dry lot for exercise. The yearling may be lightly exercised at the slow trot by longeing morning and evening for 10 minutes, to help reduce excess weight and increase its fitness and overall strength.

Udder Swelling

Occasionally, yearling fillies on energy rations will swell in the udder and start to drip milk. It results from a thyroid stimulant reflex to an excessively high energy ration and is sign that the filly is being boosted too quickly, which could also lead to limb problems over a 2-3 month period. Reduce grain to half and increase the amount of mixed hay to appetite. Allow paddock exercise if available, or increase longeing to 10 minutes at the trot, and light canter for 2-3 days. Consult your vet for advice, particularly if the fillies' glands become hot and swollen.

715lb (325kg) at 12 months, 880lb (400kg) at 18 months, maturing to an adult bodyweight of 1000-1100lb (450-500kg). Access to average quality pasture and exercise. Divide ration into two feeds daily in cold weather, or when pasture is poor. If grazing, provide one feed daily. Growth rate approximately 1-1¼lb (450g-600g) daily to 18 months of age.

INGREDIENT	FORM/MIX	CONCENTRATE MIX		PROVIDES
		Legume Hay/Pasture	Grass Hay/Pasture	
CORN	Cracked. Freshly processed. If purchased cracked, store in bag, fold down after use. Not rancid/sticky.	4lb (1.8kg)	4lb (1.8kg)	ENERGY, PROTEIN adds energy without bulking out ration.
OATS or alternatively BARLEY or MILO	Whole or crimped.	3½lb (1.6kg)	3½lb (1.6kg)	ENERGY, PROTEIN, FIBER. Essential fiber to offset lower fiber in corn. Palatable.
	Rolled or crushed. Dust free.	3lb (1.4kg)	3lb (1.4kg)	Higher in energy than oats, and can be substituted depending on availability and cost. Introduce slowly if changing from oats.
SOYBEAN MEAL	Heat treated. Free flowing. Non rancid.	1lb (450g)	2lb (900g)	ENERGY, PROTEIN, with essential amino acids, particularly lysine for grass based roughage. Introduce in a step wise manner over 10-14 days to ensure acceptance.
MOLASSES	Mix 50:50 with warm water, mix well into feed.	8oz (230g) (1½ teacups)	8oz (230g) (1½ teacups)	ENERGY and some CALCIUM. Damp sweet feed improves acceptance, prevents separation and sifting of ingredients. Wash residues from feeders regularly especially in warm weather.
COMMERCIAL VITAMIN/ TRACE MINERAL SUPPLEMENT	Mix well into feed.	eg Feramo-H 2oz (57g) (½ scoop)	3oz (72g) (3/4 scoop)	Supplements low feed levels of vitamins, particularly vitamin A & D, and trace minerals including iron, copper, zinc and selenium for optimum bone and muscle development.
COPPER SULFATE SUPPLEMENT	1 part Bluestone (21% copper) in 9 parts granulated sugar. Mix well.	1/3oz (10g) (2 teaspoons)	1/3oz (10g) (2 teaspoons)	Supplements low feed levels with an additional 20ppm copper for cartilage formation.
VITAMIN E SUPPLEMENT	Mix well into feed.	eg White-E 12-15 months 1250iu (1¼ scoops) 15-18 months 1500iu (1½ scoops)		Supplements low feed levels of Vitamin E - recommended for racing or competition bred yearlings - aids optimum muscle development and avoids EDM Wobbler Syndrome.
DICALCIUM PHOSPHATE	DCP. Free flowing, dry. Mix well into feed.	3/4oz (22g) (1½ tblsp)	Not required	CALCIUM and PHOSPHORUS to provide extra phosphorus on legume pastures.
CALCIUM CARBONATE	Ground limestone, select good quality only. Mix well into feed.	-	2oz (57g) (4 tblsp)	CALCIUM to meet calcium needs, particularly on grass based roughage.
SALT	Fine grade. Mix well into feed.	½oz (15g) (3 teaspoons)		Increases palatability of ration.
HAY	Good quality, leafy. No dust or mould.	Legume (Alfalfa) Hay or Grass (Timothy) Hay 6½lb (3kg) Initially provide 6½lb (3kg) daily for each horse, amount dependent on pasture. Increase to 50% of ration by 18 months of age.		Provides essential roughage for digestive function. Increase to 1lb (450g) per 100lb (45kg) bodyweight by 18 months of age. Hint: In rapidly growing yearlings provide 50:50 legume and grass hay to boost energy, protein, mineral and lysine intake, or if available, good quality mixed hay.

NUTRITIONAL INFORMATION: The ration is formulated for a young horse between 12 and 18 months of age, growing at a moderate rate to provide 100% of daily needs based on NRC (1989) guidelines. The average 19lb (8.6kg) concentrate mix with hay given daily provides approximately 19.5Mcals (81.6MJ) digestible energy, 1000g (11.6%) crude protein, a minimum of 32g calcium and 22.5g phosphorus and 38g lysine. Provide a blend of 50:50 legume and cereal hay will provide energy, protein, calcium and lysine content to meet growth needs on grass pastures. Do not overfeed young growing horses.

Bodyweight 715lb (325kg) at 12 months, 770lb (350kg) at 14 months, 880lb (400kg) at 18 months, 1000lb (450kg) at two years of age. Grazing and paddock exercise during day, stabled overnight, depending on weather and coat condition. Stabled full-time with 10 minutes longeing at slow trot twice daily, 45 minutes walking daily. Adjust ration to appetite, condition and exercise. Avoid excess bodyweight gain - aim at 1-1¼lb (450-600g) daily.

INGREDIENT	FORM/MIX	DAILY AMOUNT			PROVIDES
		AM	NOON	PM	
CORN	Cracked. Freshly processed. If purchased cracked store in bag, fold down after use. Non rancid/stick.	1½lb (700g)	1½lb (700g)	2lb (900g)	ENERGY, PROTEIN - adds energy without increasing bulk of ration. If yearling is not exercised, cut out the midday meal to avoid risk of tying up. Feed fresh greenfeed instead.
OATS or alternatively BARLEY or MILO	Heavy oats. Whole or crimped. Dust free.	1lb (450g)	1½lb (700g)	1½lb (700g)	ENERGY, PROTEIN, FIBER. Essential fiber to offset low fiber in corn. Palatable.
	Rolled or crushed. Dust free.	1lb (450g)	1lb (450g)	1½lb (700g)	Higher in energy than oats, and can be substituted depending on availability and cost. Introduce in a step-wise manner over 7-10 days, reducing oats according.
SOYBEAN MEAL	Heat treated. Free flowing. Non rancid.	8oz (230g)	-	8oz (230g) (1½lb (700g) if grass hay used exclusively as roughage)	ENERGY, PROTEIN with essential amino acids for growth, especially lysine. If yearling is not accustomed to taste, introduce slowly in a step-wise manner over 10-14 days to aid acceptance.
POLY-UNSATURATED OIL eg CORN OIL or alternatively SUNFLOWER SEEDS	Non rancid. Keep sealed between uses.	3oz (85ml) (4 tbspn)	-	-	Provides essential fatty acids for coat condition.
	Black variety. Clean, and plump.	4oz (115g)	-	4oz (115g)	Provides essential fatty acids for coat condition - also some protein.
DEHYDRATED ALFALFA MEAL/ CRUMBLED CUBES (OPTIONAL)	Dust free, sweet smelling, no mold. Mix into grain mix.	1lb (450g)	8oz (230g) (dampen with water if necessary)	1½lb (700g)	Optional - provides ENERGY, PROTEIN and CALCIUM. Aids in bulking up ration to keep young stabled horses occupied eating and reduces rate of grain consumption and risk of digestive upset.
MOLASSES	Mix 50:50 with warm water. Mix well into feed.	4oz (115g) (3/4 teacup)	-	4oz (115g) (3/4 teacup) (Not required if commercial sweet feed replaces evening concentrate meal.)	Sweet feed - aids palatability, prevents dust and sifting of feeds.
GREEN FEED or GREEN PICK or CHOPPED CARROTS	Fresh cut grass or legume forage, green pick on lead. Fresh carrots - chopped.	-	3lb (1.4kg) Early afternoon (avoid wet alfalfa greenfeed).	-	Provides variety to ration. Alternate between greenfeed, green pick and carrots depending on weather and availability - helps maintain appetite and well-being.
COMMERCIAL VITAMIN/MINERAL/ TRACE MINERAL SUPPLEMENT	Mix well into feed.	-	-	eg Feramo-H 2oz (57g) (½ scoop)	Supplements low feed levels of all essential vitamins, particularly vitamin A & D and trace minerals iron, copper and zinc for bone and body development, and Vitamin A, iron, zinc and copper for optimum coat bloom and condition.
COPPER SULFATE SUPPLEMENT	1 part Bluestone (21% copper) in 9 parts granulated sugar. Mix well.			1/3oz (9g) (2 tspn)	Supplements low feed levels with an additional 20 ppm copper for cartilage development.
VITAMIN E SUPPLEMENT	Mix well into feed.	eg White-E 1250-1500iu	-	-	Supplements low feed levels with vitamin E - aids muscle development and avoids EDM Wobbler Syndrome.
ELECTROLYTE SUPPLEMENT (Optional)	Mix well into feed.	eg Humidimix 3/4oz (22½g) (1 scoop)	-	eg Humidimix 3/4oz (22½g) (1 scoop)	Supplements diet in addition to salt in hot weather to replace salts lost in sweat, and maintain springy coat condition. Helps combat dehydration when travelling or at sales in hot weather.

INGREDIENT	FORM/MIX	DAILY AMOUNT			PROVIDES
		AM	NOON	PM	
DICALCIUM PHOSPHATE	DCP. Free flowing, dry. Mix well into feed.	-	-	All hay alternatives add 1oz (30g) 2 tblsp	CALCIUM and PHOSPHORUS to balance Ca:P ratio. Vitamin A & D and trace minerals provided by a mineral supplement.
CALCIUM CARBONATE	Ground limestone. Select good quality only. Mix well into feed.			Mixed hay - add ½oz (15g) 1 tblsp Grass hay - add 1oz (30g) 2 tblsp	Provides extra calcium to meet needs on mixed and grass hay based diets.
SALT	Fine grade. Mix well into feed			½oz (15g) (3 tspn)	Aids palatability and maintains water intake.
ALFALFA HAY or alternatively	Good quality, leafy. No dust or mold	1lb (450g)	-	3lb (1.4kg) overnight	Provides ENERGY, PROTEIN, FIBER and CALCIUM. Palatable and provides essential roughage.
MIXED HAY or alternatively	Leafy, no weeds, no mold, dampen if necessary.	1lb (450g)		4lb (1.8kg)	Adequate protein to meet needs. Alternatively give alfalfa in morning and grass hay in evening.
GRASS HAY	Leafy, no weeds, mold or dust. Sweet smelling. Dampen if necessary.	1lb (450g)		4½-5lb (2-2.3kg) (Appetite may limit bulk.)	More bulky and less protein than alfalfa, needs extra calcium and protein boost (see calcium above).

NUTRITIONAL INFORMATION: The ration is formulated to promote controlled development, condition and bloom in response to exercise and coat care. The average 18lb (8.2kg) ration, including alfalfa meal and hay alternatives, (excluding greenfeed/carrots) provides 100% of the daily needs for a yearling given light exercise for 20 minutes daily, based on NRC (1989) guidelines. Each 18lb (8.2kg) provides approximately 21 Mcals (88MJ) digestible energy, 1050g (12.8%) crude protein, and a minimum of 32g calcium, 23g phosphorus, and 48g lysine.

After Purchase - Useful Hints

Buying a yearling can be one of the most thrilling and rewarding experiences of a lifetime. However, a few simple hints will help ensure that your new yearling settles into its new home.

• Immediately after purchase - arrange suitable insurance.

• Make arrangements for the yearling to be properly cared for prior to the trip home. Arrange with the vendor to look after the horse. Obtain details of the basic ration, if possible.

• Plan to haul the horse so as to arrive at your stalls before evening to ensure that the horse has time to settle in before night fall.

• Ensure all fences are safe and strong.

• Avoid turning a young horse out by itself in the paddock. If possible, confine it to a stall or small corral for a couple of days on reduced rations to help it settle down. An older mature gelding is ideal to form a friendship and have a steadying influence on the young horse when they are eventually turned out together. Be sure to cut back the grain ration to half if the young horse is not being exercised on a regular basis.

• Worm the horse before turning out. Give a booster vaccination against tetanus.

• Many owners arrange for the yearling to be educated and broken in after the sale. Ensure the young horse has time to settle in, and check its teeth prior to mouthing.

• Provision of a balanced and adequate ration, combined with exercise, is essential to ensure the youngster grows into a strong, sound two year old horse.

• Basic feeding should be carefully managed to ensure the continued development of a strong musculo-skeletal system in preparation for racing as a two year old, without risk of developing Developmental Orthopedic Disease (DOD) - do not overfeed.

RACING HORSES

Feeding to match the complex nutritional requirement of the racing horse in training is a combination of scientific and practical feeding skills. With increased "best to best" breeding, and the adoption of scientific training techniques, it is essential that nutrition is not the limiting factor to maximum performance.

The majority of young racing horses in training are not physically or mentally mature enough to withstand the stress of training and racing on a repeated basis. Thus, adequate nutrients for growth and development in response to exercise, work and high speed performance must be contained in the horse's diet to maximize potential success on the track.

The feeding routine must be designed to create a natural feeding pattern, providing a nutritionally balanced and palatable diet. This will help horses do their best in training when stabled full-time. The feeding program must cater to the horse's individual needs at each stage of training, with punctual and frequent feeds.

Regular assessment of each horse's body weight and condition, general vitality and appetite will enable adjustments to the ration to ensure the horse "does well" in training. For smaller framed horses, such as Standardbreds and Arabians, the bulk of the ration may need to be reduced in proportion to appetite, exercise program and the individual horse's metabolic efficiency. Some horses may perform well on smaller amounts of grain and sweet feed.

GALLOPERS/SPRINT RACERS

(Thoroughbreds/Quarter Horses, Paints, Appaloosas, Arabians - flat sprint and jump racing)

Nutritional Requirements

Energy

Flat and jump racehorses, and sprint horses, require large amounts of energy to fuel rapid muscle activity during exercise. In young, growing 2-3 year old horses, additional energy has to be provided for growth and performance, as well as muscle, bone and blood repair processes. Lack of energy for growth can lead to poor condition and development, which can reduce the horse's performance potential in its racing career. Many younger, nervy horses also expend a large amount of energy when confined to stalls, with up to two-thirds of the total energy supplied lost due to fretting.

HINT

Nervous picky eaters or fretful types of horses often do better on smaller amounts of concentrate feed when given access to day time pasture for grazing, or in bad cases, full training from the paddock.

Further energy reserves are depleted during transport and trackside raceday nerves, with nervy horses often running their race before the start. Under raceday conditions, it has been estimated that a nervy, unsettled horse that trembles and sweats during transport and in the stalls, can waste up to 25% of its energy reserves on pre-race anticipation and fear.

All racehorses, including older, more settled horses require energy (and protein) to repair damaged muscles, and for continuous remodelling and strengthening of tendons and bones, particularly when racing frequently.

> **HINT** *Whilst the energy level in the ration must be adequate to maintain bodyweight and match requirements for exercise, excess energy can make a horse more playful and hard to handle, and increase the risk of problems such as tying-up. (See Energy, page 24.)*

Over recent years there has been controversy as to the value and utilization of fat as an energy source for galloping horses. Recent studies on racing Thoroughbreds suggested that race time over 1600 meters was improved by 2.5 seconds on a diet containing 12% of the energy as corn oil. The use of fat in warmer weather in racing horses may also reduce heat waste and the effects of dehydration. (See page 48.)

Protein

Protein provides the building blocks (amino acids) for growth and development of muscles and blood, as well as continuous repair of bone and muscle tissue during long-term training and repeated racing. The proportion of protein in the total ration need not be increased significantly with exercise. Generally, as the energy content of the ration is increased by adding grain, and the appetite and feed consumption increases with exercise, the increase in protein supplied by that grain will meet normal needs in racing horses.

Adequate levels of protein are essential for the efficient utilization of high energy rations. Excess protein can be utilized as an energy source during exercise, although not as efficiently as carbohydrates. Excess protein intake, besides being more expensive than grains as an energy source, may cause higher heart and respiratory rates, heavier sweat loss and dehydration, and decreased performance in young racehorses. (See Protein, page 24.)

> **HINT** *Surveys of feeding practices indicate that most trainers feed rations with moderate to high levels of protein (12-14%) early in training to help build muscle, bone and blood. Once a horse starts racing on a regular basis, protein levels can be decreased to 10-12% without affecting overall performance.*

Fiber

Although higher grain content in the ration is required to provide energy to meet exercise needs, adequate fiber must also be provided to ensure efficient digestion and minimize digestive upsets. A diet containing 50% concentrates and 50% hay by weight is the maximum level of concentrates that should be fed. Reports from Hong Kong indicate that there is a 50% incidence of gastroduodenal ulceration in stabled racehorses fed on highly concentrated diets of up to 75% grain to 25% roughage.

Minerals

The traditional high energy, grain based diet is relatively deficient in calcium, iron and copper, and certain other trace-minerals. It is estimated that racehorses require at least 1-1¼oz (30-35g) of elemental calcium daily, for growth and continuous remodelling of bone to maintain maximum strength under strenuous exercise. Grains contain from 3 to 20 times more phosphorus than calcium. A deficiency or imbalance of calcium in the diet may result in lameness problems and unsoundness, particularly in young, growing horses in their first preparation.

Although alfalfa and mixed hays help to counteract this imbalance, horses cannot eat sufficient amounts of bulk as hay to balance the ration when consuming up to 17lb (7.5kg) of grain to meet energy needs.

> **HINT** *Studies in Hong Kong suggest that supplementation of high grain rations with about 2oz (60g) calcium carbonate (limestone) reduced the incidence of bone and joint problems by 35% in racehorses on high grain rations.*

As calcium is also lost in sweat, extra calcium should be added to the diet of heavily sweating horses, particularly under hot, humid conditions.

> **HINT** *Most of the hay purchased for racing horses is not locally grown, and often grown on long established irrigated fields, where leaching can distort trace-mineral content. Many soluble salts of iron, copper, magnesium and manganese, may be leached out and result in low feed levels. In areas where selenium deficiency is known, supplementation with selenium to correct low feed levels is widely considered to improve performance. A daily supplement of a general vitamin and mineral supplement is recommended to correct inadequate or low feed levels of a range of minerals. Consult your local Agricultural Adviser, or equine nutritionist.*

Vitamins

Cereal grain based diets contain low levels of Vitamin A (as carotene), Vitamin D, E and many B-Complex vitamins. The natural content of these vitamins can be depleted during harvest and storage of grain. Horses under stress of training and repeated racing are less able to efficiently convert carotene to Vitamin A (Retinol). It is also considered that horses in work on high grain, low fiber diets, may not be able to synthesize and absorb adequate amounts of their own B-Complex vitamins (produced by bacterial fermentation in the large bowel) to meet elevated needs for energy utilization during fast exercise.

Vitamins A & D

Storage of grains and hay results in destruction of up to 80% of the potential vitamin A activity in 3-6 months. Observations suggest that a supplement of 50,000iu Retinol (Vitamin A) given daily to racehorses on deficient cereal based diets, may reduce the incidence of tendon weakness and breakdown. Adequate Vitamin A is also required to maintain the blood count and overall performance. The stable environment and early morning training also limits the opportunity for natural synthesis of Vitamin D from sunlight on the skin. Although adequate Vitamin D is provided by quality sun-cured hay, cubes and dehydrated hays may not provide sufficient Vitamin D to meet requirements of a high phosphorus, low calcium diet.

Vitamin E

Vitamin E is relatively deficient in grains, and losses of up to 50% or more occur during harvesting, storage and processing of grains and hays. Recent studies indicate that supplementary Vitamin E (600-1800iu daily) is required to maintain normal blood, liver and muscle levels in horses in training on cereal grain and hay based diets.

HINT

The NRC (1989) suggests that all working horses be routinely provided with 1,000iu Vitamin E (such as in White-E) daily.

B-Complex Vitamins

Many of the B-Complex vitamins are required for efficient energy metabolism and blood formation. Horses in work on grain based rations that contain relatively low levels of natural B-Complex vitamins will often benefit from B-Complex supplementation.

HINT

Recent observations indicate that supplementary B-Complex vitamins help maintain appetite, particularly following hard exercise or racing, and

prevent the onset of work or track sourness, and weight loss in racing horses in long-term training. (See page 52.)

Electrolytes

Studies have indicated that provision of adequate water and a daily intake of electrolytes helps to prevent dehydration and maintain appetite and performance in racehorses.

HINT

During early conditioning work under cool conditions, a supplement of 1½-2oz (45-60g or 3-4 tablespoons) of salt (sodium chloride) will normally meet electrolyte needs in horses on a standard grain and hay diet. Horses that are nervy, or sweat heavily due to conditioning work or hot weather, will benefit from additional potassium and chloride salts. A supplement of these electrolytes will help boost feed levels to meet elevated needs. When horses are racing regularly, a supplement of alkaline buffer salt after each fast work or breeze, in addition to routine supplementation with daily electrolytes is widely recommended. (See page 90.)

TROTTERS/PACERS

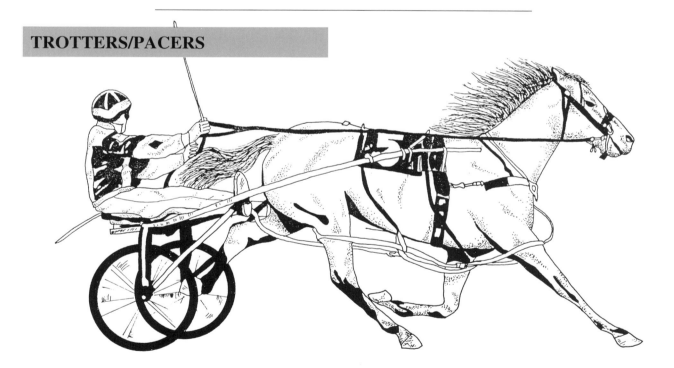

Standardbreds

Racing Standardbreds have different nutritional needs to gallopers and sprint horses.

Generally, younger standardbreds require even more energy for growth, development and exercise because the total amount of work effort expended is more than for galloping horses. Pacers and trotters work a lot harder in training than gallopers.

Studies have shown that Standardbreds exert about 12 times more effort than a Thoroughbred in the preparation period to racing fitness, and on average Standardbreds race about three times as often. Standardbreds also maintain their all out speed for much longer than gallopers.

Most Standardbreds are smaller framed, and have a quieter temperament than Thoroughbreds, Quarter horses and other breeds of flat racehorses.

Nutritional Requirements

The major difference in requirements for Standardbreds compared to galloping and sprint horses are summarized below.

Energy

Because Standardbreds expend more work effort than galloping racers, their requirements for growth, development and exercise are also relatively greater. However, Standardbreds are usually smaller framed horses that cannot eat as much as racehorses. Therefore, the energy density of the ration should be increased, usually by adding extra energy-rich grains, [eg corn or barley, or a source of fat (eg corn oil)] to replace some of the bulk, particularly in nervy young fillies.

Although older Standardbred horses under heavy training may have finished growing, they still require extra energy to repair damaged tissues and remodel their bones when subjected to frequent hard racing. Failure to provide sufficient energy for these processes may result in increased risk of musculo-skeletal breakdown, with symptoms of over-training such as loss of vitality, stamina and performance.

Protein

Although the requirement for protein, as a percentage of total ration, does not increase significantly with extra exercise, many trainers consider Standardbreds perform more consistently over a longer period with a ration containing about 12-14% of high quality protein. Usually a higher amount of protein is given in early training, reducing to a maintenance level once a horse is fit and racing regularly.

Calcium

The comments relating to Thoroughbreds are also applicable to Standardbreds, particularly those jogging in hot weather with heavy sweat loss, or horses that are naturally heavy sweaters.

HINT

Analysis of sweat indicates that iron, and other trace minerals, including selenium are lost in sweat. Supplementation with selenium may be worthwhile to maintain muscle strength and performance, particularly if the feed is known to contain low levels of selenium. Consult your local Agricultural Advisor for advice if necessary.

Iron

It is an interesting observation that many trainers of Standardbreds consider their horses need extra iron in their feed to maintain the blood count, stamina and performance when subjected to hard work and regular racing. This could be explained by considering the relatively poor uptake of iron from feed (15-18%) and the higher loss of iron in sweat (24ppm or 24mg/liter) by Standardbreds subjected to slow, long distance conditioning work. This may result in a deficiency of iron relative to needs, and supplements in the feed will help to make-up this shortfall.

Vitamins

Standardbreds in hard work have similar requirements of Vitamins A and D, E and B-Complex to those of gallopers. Vitamin E and B-Complex are helpful to maintain stamina and appetite when horses are in full training and racing once or twice a week on average. (See page 52.)

Electrolytes

Conditioning work, such as jogging for extended periods of 30-40 minutes daily, will result in heavy sweat output particularly during hot weather. Over a 3-4 week period this can lead to development of higher bicarbonate levels or *alkalosis* of the blood. Studies indicate that elevated blood bicarbonate may lead to increased respiratory rates and symptoms of fat inside, such as thick in the wind and blowing after exercise. Some affected horses become spooky and shadow jump, are more likely to break at the start, and develop bad barrier manners.

Dehydration resulting from electrolyte and fluid loss by heavy sweat output is more common in Standardbreds. The incidence of muscle related problems, and loss of performance is increased if horses that are tucked up and dried out in the coat are raced hard.

Nutritional Management Hints for Racing Horses (Gallopers, Sprint Racers/Pacers,Trotters)

The dietary guidelines may require adjustments to allow for an individual horse's appetite, body condition, temperament and day-to-day exercise needs, likes and dislikes and seasonal climatic conditions.

Feed Substitution

The widely available cereal grains - oats, corn and barley, are the traditional energy feeds for racing horses. The mix of grains is usually based on a horse's individual size and its appetite, stage of training and overall energy demand for exercise. It is worthwhile outlining the practical use and merits of the different grains more fully as a guideline for substitution.

Oats

Oats is still widely used in many areas as the grain base for racing rations. It is a safe grain that is unlikely to cause digestive upset even when fed in large amounts. However, oats tend to be bulkier than corn, containing only half the amount of energy on a volume basis. Horses that require larger amounts of energy, such as Standardbreds, as well as picky eaters and nervy or smaller framed horses, may not be able to consume the bulk of oats required to meet energy needs. Therefore, substitution of part of the oats by energy rich grains, such as corn and barley, can reduce the volume of the ration to within a horse's appetite limit. In my experience, high levels of oats, above 10 pounds (4.5 kg) daily, may also increase the risk of tying-up in some horses, such as nervy, young fillies. Oats can vary tremendously in protein content from season to season so an additional protein source is usually recommended to meet daily requirements, especially as horses build-up in early training.

HINT

In young fillies prone to tying-up on high oat diets, reduce oats initially to half volume, replacing half the remaining volume with a 50:50 mix of corn and rolled barley. In severe cases, change slowly to a corn/barley mix and add a teacup of corn oil to morning and evening feeds. Ensure that adequate calcium and 1000iu Vitamin E (eg such as White-E) is provided. (See ration guideline.) In nervy or heavy sweating horses, add one tablespoon of salt, 1½ scoops of an electrolyte supplement (such as Humidimix), and one tablespoon of Epsom salts (magnesium sulfate) to the morning and evening feeds. Exercise the horse every day, and on rest days cut all grain to one third, commencing the night before. Reintroduce the full grain ration over two days once exercise is recommenced. Take extra time to warm up and cool out these horses before and after exercise.

The administration of supplementary alkaline buffer salt, such as contained in 2oz (60ml) Neutradex over the tongue after each fast workout appears to be of practical benefit in horses that tie-up in early training, where dietary intake is inadequate or urinary loss is increased. (See Cooling Down Procedure, page 51.)

Corn

Corn contains more energy than oats. In fact, on a volume basis, one quart (about one liter) of corn has about the same energy as two quarts (two liters) of oats. Corn is useful to reduce the bulk of the ration in picky eaters to ensure they consume adequate energy. In hot weather, additional corn mixed into the ration will reduce waste heat during digestion, compared with a more fibrous grain such as oats. (See page 48.)

Corn is often considered a heating grain, because its higher and more soluble carbohydrate content can increase the risk of playful and excitable behavior in some horses, particularly young Thoroughbreds in training. However, in most cases hot manners are due to an individual horse's character, or simply too much energy in relation to workload, rather than the corn itself. Feed corn by weight, and only to exercise level, and reduce to half or less on light work days.

HINT   *Some young fillies find corn unpalatable at first. Introduce corn slowly to the ration in a sweet feed type mix, replacing 3/4 of the weight of oats removed with corn in a step-wise manner.*

Barley

Horses tend to find whole barley less palatable due to the sharp awns on the grain. Steam rolled barley is more palatable and in my experience, is less likely to affect the temperament than oats or corn in young Thoroughbreds. Barley has an energy content between that of oats and corn. A combination of corn and barley, because these grains have reduced heat waste on fermentation, is ideal as the major energy source in hot weather, along with added fat. (See page 25.)

Fat

Over recent years, there has been much interest in feeding fat or oil as a source of energy for racing and performance horses. Fat contains 2.25 times the amount of energy of carbohydrates and proteins, so vegetable oils added to the diet can reduce the bulk of the ration. As fats take more time to metabolize and release their energy, they can provide a useful slow release form of energy for nervy horses, and a less bulky ration for picky eaters.

Oils, such as corn oil, are becoming more widely used as an energy source in galloping and sprint horses, although fat has been used for some years as an energy booster in standardbred rations. (See also pages 25 and 173 for substitution rates.)

Fat can be added to the diet to reduce bulk of feed during early training and between races. Some authorities recommend that the fat be reduced and replaced by carbohydrates such as grains for energy (eg corn) in the 3-4 days leading up to a race. This change back to carbohydrates is now considered unnecessary once the racehorse is conditioned to fat. (See page 25.)

About 8oz (250ml or 2 teacups) of oil daily is considered to be the minimum amount that is worthwhile adding to the ration as an alternative energy source. Where larger volumes of oil are used as an energy source, additional protein, calcium and phosphorus as well as Vitamin E (such as in White-E) must be added to the ration. (See page 26.)

The replacement of some of the oats with corn and corn oil in Standardbred rations during the summer months, may be helpful in reducing the amount of waste heat, and hence sweat loss and risk of dehydration. (See also page 49.)

HINT   *Oils are also very effective in reducing dust in rations, and 2-3½oz (60-100ml) or 4-6 tablespoons daily will help maintain good coat condition in racing horses. Whole sunflower seeds contain about 25% oil, as well as protein, and 2-3 teacups of sunflower seeds each day will promote coat condition in racing horses.*

Commercially Prepared Feeds

Commercial sweet feeds containing grains, protein meals, minerals, and vitamins in a damp molasses mix, have become popular as an evening feed in many racing stables. Generally, sweet feeds replace the grain portion of the ration, with hay and other supplements provided as needed. Sweet feeds and pelleted feeds are convenient, provide a uniform intake of energy, protein and fiber, and are well accepted by most horses.

HINT   *Although the sweet feeds contain added vitamins and minerals in amounts claimed to match the requirements of racing horses, long term storage, particularly in a damp feed mix, may affect the potency of the vitamin content. An additional general vitamin and trace mineral supplement such as Feramo-H, given daily, plus supplements of calcium, electrolytes and iron, will help ensure an adequate intake of minerals and vitamins that may be low or inadequate in the diet to meet the needs of a racing horse.*

Protein Meal Substitution

On alfalfa and mixed hay diets there is usually no need for additional protein, but extra protein should be provided to meet needs on grass hay based diets. (See individual Ration Guidelines.) Although soybean meal is well balanced in amino acid content to make up shortfalls on grass hay based rations, some horses may not find it as palatable initially as linseed, cottonseed or peanut meal. Soybean meal should be added to the ration in a step wise manner over 7-10 days to ensure acceptance in young horses.

HINT   *Soybean meal can be diluted with other protein meals to improve palatability on the basis of 5½ oz of linseed or peanut meal to replace every 4 oz of soybean meal, to give an equivalent amount of protein.*

It is common practice to increase the level of protein by adding 8oz (230g or 4 teacups) extra of soybean meal, or equivalent in other protein meals or pellets, during the first six weeks of training as the horse builds up muscle mass and its blood count. Once the horse is fit and ready to race, the protein level can be reduced to levels normally required to meet exercise requirements. After a hard race, extra soybean 8oz (230g or 4 teacups) may be added for two meals to replace protein lost during hard exercise. If horses go off their feed after hard racing, supplementary B-Complex vitamins, (such as contained in 2oz (60ml) Pulse-8 liquid) over the tongue or mixed into the feed, may be helpful to maintain the feed intake.

Fiber

Adequate hay or roughage cubes must be supplied to provide an open mixture for efficient digestion. However, bulk must be limited so that the horse will consume the concentrate portion to meet energy needs.

Poor Adaptation to Training

A low blood count in racing horses is most commonly due to heavy burdens of bloodworms and redworms, insufficient all-out fast work in training, and an inadequate content of iron in cereal grain and hay based rations. Deworm at the start of training, and repeat in 3 weeks, and again at the start of fast work. This will help ensure that heavy burdens of Small Redworms (Cyathostomes) are reduced and gut reservoirs of encysted stages are depleted. (See page 19.)

As grain and grass hay based diets are often inadequate in iron, copper and cobalt content to meet needs in early training, many trainers provide a daily iron supplement (such as in 2oz (60ml) Ironcyclen liquid) for the first 6-8 weeks of training. After this initial period, reduce the iron to a maintenance level, particularly if other iron containing supplements, (such as Feramo-H) are also being added to the ration. Ensure the horse is given short bursts of all out speed over 350-450 yards (300-400 meters) at the end of a breeze or fast work training run so as to stimulate red cell production.

> **HINT**
>
> *Alternatively, the full dose of an iron supplement, can be given on a 3 days on, 3 days off basis. Some horses on cereal grass based rations benefit from extra supplementary iron during early training, if they sweat heavily during exercise, or are raced repeatedly.*

Loss of Appetite

There are a number of reasons for loss of appetite and picky eating in horses in work. Many of these horses fail to do their best due to underlying problems such as worms, poor teeth, or inadequate feed intake. Introduction to fast work commonly results in loss of appetite particularly in finely built nervy fillies. Affected fillies often become sour or bitchy, and pick at their feed. (For a full discussion on how to overcome loss of appetite at the start of fast work refer to page 51.)

Electrolyte Supplements

A daily supplement of electrolytes mixed into the feed, together with access to cool, clean water, will help ensure horses in work drink sufficient water to prevent tucking-up and dehydration. Extra electrolytes may be provided in the drinking water [maximum 2 tablespoons in 4 gallons (16 liters)] in hot weather. An oral rehydration solution, such as Recharge made up as directed, may also be provided as a post-exercise drink in hot weather.

> **HINT**
>
> *After hard training, racing and travelling, offer a first drink of 1 gallon (4 liters) of made-up electrolyte drink (such as Recharge) to assist rapid replenishment of fluid and electrolyte levels lost in sweat. Some trainers provide a bucketful of made-up electrolyte drink and a bucketful of water side*

-by-side overnight as a choice after hard work, race or long distance travel.

Additional salts as a pre-race or post-race saline drink or tube drench in heavy sweaters during hot weather, is used by veterinarians to correct dehydration and aid recovery after a race. A saline drench may benefit horses that are racing again within 5-7 days. However, to be most effective in correcting pre-race dehydration in hot weather, a saline drench should be administered at least 36-48 hours before a race. Consult your vet for advice.

> **HINT**
>
> *Generally, saline drenches are not required unless clinical signs of dehydration (eg slow skin return on pinch test, tucked-up belly, pebbly dung, or dull dry coat) are seen within 48-60 hours prior to racing. It is unwise to give excessively strong saline drenches - it is a job for your veterinarian.*

In most cases, gallopers trained under cool to moderate climates benefit from feed supplementation with a half dose of an electrolyte replacer, (such as Humidimix)in addition to salt, given as a half a dose in the morning and evening feeds. Supplementation with a non-bicarbonate source of alkaline buffer salts, (such as given by 2oz (60ml) of Neutradex over the tongue on breeze and fast work mornings) is also widely used. However, because Standardbreds are worked for longer periods during LSD or conditioning training, a 50% increase in the electrolyte supplement is recommended to correct feed levels that would be inadequate to replace electrolytes lost in sweat during work. In horses that are exceptionally heavy sweaters under hot conditions, an extra 1½oz salt (45g or 3 tablespoons) may also be provided.

> **HINT**
>
> *Recent studies have shown that in hot, humid climates, all horses in work may develop an imbalance of electrolytes in the blood due to heavy sweat output over a period of time. This can be confirmed, if necessary, using a blood sample taken by your vet early in the morning before the horse is worked or fed. The sample should be submitted for analysis by your vet within two hours of collection.*

> **HINT**
>
> *Many Standardbred trainers routinely give an alkaline citrate supplement, (such as 2oz (60ml) of Neutradex over the back of the tongue on return to the stables on fast work mornings as well as for the two mornings following each time-trial or race, to ensure adequate levels are maintained in the system during the recovery period.*

Nervous Horses

Young inexperienced horses may suffer from pre-race excitement or raceday nerves. This often results in them passing cow pat manure or running their race before the start when being transported or stabled prior to a trial, or on race day.

> **HINT**
>
> *A drink of made-up rehydration fluid (such as Recharge) may also help to replenish salts and fluids following transport in nervy travellers and during hot weather.*

> **HINT**
>
> *I have found that many highly strung, nervy horses, particularly those that are stabled fulltime without access to green pasture, will often settle down once they are given a supplement of high potassium electrolyes to replace sweat loss, and*

increased doses of vitamin E prior to travelling or racing. I routinely recommend a daily feed supplement of a potassium boosted electrolyte, (such as one scoop of Humidimix each morning and evening) particularly in horses that sweat heavily due to excitement. I recommend that these horses are also supplemented with at least 1,000iu vitamin E daily. On the morning before, and morning of travelling, trialling or racing, I advise to increase the feed supplement of vitamin E to 3000-4000iu. I have found that vitamin E derived from natural sources (ie. d-alpha tocopheryl - such as in White-E) appears to be of most benefit, perhaps because it maintains higher blood levels of vitamin E.

Regular Assessment

It is important to continually assess an individual horse's appetite, condition and response to training, and adjust the ration accordingly.

| HINT |

Recent surveys indicate that racing horses perform more consistently when maintained within ± 20lb (about 10kg) of their last winning race weight.

However, avoid training and feeding to maintain these weight limits - always consider the individual horse's appetite, response to exercise and attitude.

| HINT |

Keep a close watch on the color and thickness of the urine, and skin condition, as a guide to dehydration. Darker and syrupy urine or reluctance to stretch out, may indicate dehydration and also muscle soreness particularly after racing. Supplementation with electrolytes, rehydration drinks, and alkaline buffers as discussed previously, will help ensure adequate intake to correct low feed levels in high energy diets.

| HINT |

Check the manure each day - assess amount, color, smell, form and consistency (amount of fiber, whole grain and moisture level) as an indication of the horse's general digestive function. For example, dry pebble like dung, with a thick scum or mucus skin may indicate dehydration. Sour smelling, pasty cow pats may indicate too much grain or other digestive upset. Hints to correct these conditions are given in the guidelines above. (See also page 186.)

First 6-8 weeks of training. 1000-1100lb (450-500kg) bodyweight. Confined to stalls most of the day. LSD conditioning program with moderate intensity jogging exercise for 45 minutes daily and 15 minute walk, to cool out. Three feeds daily.

INGREDIENT	FORM/MIX	DAILY AMOUNT			PROVIDES
		AM	NOON	PM	
CORN	Whole or freshly cracked. If purchased cracked store in bag, fold down top after each use. Dust free, non rancid.	1½lb (700g)	1lb (450g)	1½lb (700g)	ENERGY, PROTEIN - ideal high energy grain to reduce bulk of ration in small framed horses. Cut out on light work and rest days.
OATS	Whole, heavy, dust free.	2lb (900g)	2lb (900g)	3lb (1.4kg)	ENERGY, PROTEIN, FIBER - traditional safe grain but bulky in small framed horses in early training. Cut to one third on rest days. May be replaced with rolled barley or milo - 6½lb (3kg) replaces 7lb (3.4kg) oats.
COMMERCIAL MIXED GRAIN SWEET FEED (Optional)	Good quality, sealed bags.	-	-	5lb (2.3kg)	Alternative night feed - sweet palatable night feed - convenient, no mixing required. Replaces corn and oat mix.
SOYBEAN MEAL (Optional)	Heat treated, free flowing, non rancid.	8oz (230g)	-	10oz (285g)	Optional - provides ENERGY and PROTEIN, should be given with grass hay roughage based diets to meet protein and amino acid requirements.
POLY-UNSATURATED OIL eg Corn Oil (Optional)	Non rancid, keep well sealed. Mix well into feed.	8oz (250ml) (2 teacups optional)	-	8oz (250ml) (2 teacups)	Optional - high ENERGY source to concentrate diet in picky eaters, small framed horses, and hot weather heavy sweaters (see text). Reduce oats by 1½lb (700g) per two cups of oil added. Introduce in a step-wise manner over 7-10 days. If more than two cups added - add 3oz (85g) soybean meal per cup of oil to maintain protein intake (see text).
ALFALFA pellets/ crumbled cubes (Optional)	Commercial pellets/cubes. Dry, no mold.	1lb (450g)	1lb (450g)	2lb (900g)	Optional - ENERGY, PROTEIN, CALCIUM - bulks out feed for horses that eat grain quickly. Chopped alfalfa or mixed hay may be fed - substitute weight for long hay.
MOLASSES	Mix 50:50 with warm water, mix well into feed.	4oz (115g) (3/4 teacup)	-	4oz (115g) (3/4 teacup) (Not required if commercial sweet feed given.)	ENERGY and some CALCIUM. Damp sweetened feed improves acceptance, reduces dust, prevents selection and sifting of ingredients. If dry morning feed preferred, add total amount (8oz) (230g) to evening feed, especially if alfalfa pellets mixed with grain.
GREEN FEED/ HAND GRAZE	Fresh grass		3lb (1.4kg) grass or 30 mins grazing mid afternoon if possible.		Relieves boredom, sharpens appetite.
VITAMIN/TRACE MINERAL SUPPLEMENT	Mix well into feed.			2oz (57g) ½ scoop	Supplements low feed levels with essential vitamins, including Vitamin A & D and trace minerals for muscle, bone and tendon development. Additional Vitamin A & D important on grass hay diets.
IRON SUPPLEMENT (Optional)	Iron, copper and cobalt supplement. Mix well into feed.			eg Ironcyclen liquid 2oz (60ml)	Supplements low feed levels with IRON, COPPER and COBALT - blood building minerals - give daily in horses with history of worms or poor condition - continue daily to beginning of fast work.
ELECTROLYTE SUPPLEMENT	Mix well into feed.	eg Humidimix 3/4oz (22½g) (1 scoop)		eg Humidimix 3/4oz (22½g) (1 scoop)	Supplements low feed levels to replace sodium, potassium and chloride salts lost through sweating (hot humid weather, hard exercise). Aids palatability of ration. In hot weather with heavy sweat loss, give 50% increase in dose (eg extra scoop in evening feed).
VITAMIN E SUPPLEMENT	Mix well into feed.	eg White-E 1000iu (1 scoop)	-	-	Supplements low feed levels with essential Vitamin E to promote muscle function and aerobic capacity - NRC (1989) recommendation. Higher doses if fats are used as energy sources. (See text.)

INGREDIENT	FORM/MIX	DAILY AMOUNT			PROVIDES
		AM	NOON	PM	
DICALCIUM PHOSPHATE	DCP Free flowing, dry. Mix well into feed.			All hay alternatives add 1oz (30g) 2 tblsp. If poly-unsaturated oil substituted for grain, for each 2 teacups oil add ½oz (15g, 1 tblsp) DCP.	Provides extra CALCIUM and PHOSPHORUS to ensure adequate phosphorus. Important in young horses in training to assist in bone strengthening to adapt to fast work. When oil used as an energy source to replace grain, extra calcium and phosphorus is needed.
CALCIUM CARBONATE	Ground limestone. Free flowing, mix well into feed.			Grass hay only - add 1oz (30g) (2 tblsp).	Extra calcium suggested in heavy sweating horses or during training under hot humid conditions.
ALKALINE CITRATE SUPPLEMENT (Optional)	Sodium acid citrate supplement. Mix well into feed.	eg Neutradex 1oz (30ml) in feed			Supplements inadequate feed levels with non-bicarb source of alkaline buffer to help combat effects of lactic acid in blood and muscles of unfit horses in early training.
B-COMPLEX SUPPLEMENT (Optional)	Concentrated vitamins given in feed or over the tongue. Mix well into feed.		eg Pulse-8 liquid 2oz (60ml) (Every second day)		Supplements inadequate feed levels. Can be given directly over tongue with a syringe in horses that are poor eaters. In early training, supplementation every second day is usually adequate.
ALFALFA, HAY or alternatively	Leafy, no dust - dampen if necessary	2lb (900g)	3lb (1.4kg)	5lb (2.3kg)	Provides ENERGY, PROTEIN, FIBER and CALCIUM. Contributes higher protein than mixed or grass hay - ideal for building up horses in early training. Dampen cubes.
MIXED HAY or alternatively	Leafy, clean, no dust - dampen if necessary.	2lb (900g)	2½lb (1.1kg)	6lb (2.7kg)	Well accepted. Use depends on price - more wastage than alfalfa and more bulky for given weight.
GRASS HAY	Leafy, no weeds, no dust - dampen if necessary.	2lb (900g)	2½lb (1.1kg)	5lb (2.3kg)	Actually feed 9½lb (4.3kg) as up to 5% wastage of grass hay. More bulky than alfalfa hay and intake limited by appetite of horse.

NUTRITIONAL INFORMATION: This ration is formulated for a Standardbred in early training to provide energy, protein and calcium levels to meet practical demand in LSD type training programs, which is higher than NRC (1989) guidelines for 1000lb (450kg) horses. Each 21½lb (9.8kg) of concentrate/hay alternative contains approximately 26.5 Mcals (111MJ) digestible energy, 1100-1250g (ave 12%) crude protein, and a minimum of 35g calcium and 26g phosphorus.

Advanced Training/Regular Racing. 1000-1100lb (450-500kg) bodyweight. Confined to stalls most of the day. Fast work (hobbled) two-three times weekly, racing once every 7-10 days. 3-4 feeds daily.

INGREDIENT	FORM/MIX	DAILY AMOUNT				PROVIDES
		Early Morn	Mid Morn to Noon	Mid Aft-n	Evening Supper	
CORN	Whole soaked or cracked every 2-3 days. Dust free, non rancid.	2lb (900g)	1lb (450g)	1½lb (700g)	2lb (900g)	ENERGY, PROTEIN - ideal high energy grain to reduce bulk of ration in small framed horses. Cut out on light work and rest days.
OATS	Whole, heavy, dust free.	2lb (900g)	2lb (900g)	2lb (900g)	3lb (1.4kg)	ENERGY, PROTEIN, FIBER - traditional safe grain but bulky in small framed horses. Cut to one third on rest days. May be replaced with rolled barley or milo - 8lb (3.6kg) replaces 9lb (4.1kg) oats
COMMERCIAL MIXED GRAIN SWEET FEED (Optional)	Good quality, sealed bags.	-	-		4½lb (2kg)	Alternative night feed - provides ENERGY, PROTEIN, FIBER - sweet palatable night feed - convenient, no mixing required. Replaces corn and oat mix.
SOYBEAN MEAL (Optional)	Heat treated, free flowing, non rancid.	8oz (230g)			10oz (285g)	Optional - should be given with grass hay roughage based diets to meet protein and amino acid requirements in hard racing horses.
POLY-UNSATURATED OIL eg Corn Oil (Optional)	Non rancid, keep well sealed.	8oz (250ml) (2 teacups) optional	-		8oz (250ml) (2 teacups)	Optional - high ENERGY source to concentrate diet in picky eaters, small framed horses, and hot weather heavy sweaters (see text). Reduce oats by 1½lb (700g) per 2 teacups of oil added - introduce in a step-wise manner over 7-10 days. If more than 2 cups of oil added - add 3oz (85g) soybean meal per cup of oil to maintain protein intake (see text).
ALFALFA pellets/cubes (Optional)	Commercial pellets/cubes. Dry, no mold.	1lb (450g)	1lb (450g)		2lb (900g)	Optional - ENERGY, PROTEIN, CALCIUM - bulks out feed for horses that eat grain quickly. Chopped alfalfa or mixed hay may be fed - substitute weight for long hay.
MOLASSES	Mix 50:50 with warm water, mix well into feed.	4oz (115g) (3/4 teacup)	-		4oz (115g) (3/4 teacup) (Not required if commercial sweet feed given.)	ENERGY and some CALCIUM. Damp sweetened feed improves acceptance, reduces dust, prevents selection and sifting of ingredients. If dry morning feed preferred, add total amount (8oz) (230g) to evening feed, especially if alfalfa pellets mixed with grain.
COMMERCIAL VITAMIN/TRACE MINERAL SUPPLEMENT	Mix well into feed.				eg Feramo-H 2oz (57g) ½ scoop	Supplements low feed levels with essential vitamins, including Vitamin A & D and trace minerals for muscle, bone and tendon development. Additional Vitamin A & D beneficial on grass hay diets for tendon strength.
IRON SUPPLEMENT (Optional)	Iron, copper and cobalt supplement. Mix well into feed.				eg Ironcyclen liquid 2oz (60ml)	Supplements low feed levels with essential IRON, COPPER and COBALT - blood maintenance minerals.
ELECTROYTE SUPPLEMENT	Mix well into feed	3/4oz (22½g) (1 scoop)			3/4oz (22½g) (1 scoop)	Supplements low feed levels with sodium, potassium and chloride salts lost through sweating (hot humid weather, hard exercise). Aids palatability of ration. In hot weather with heavy sweat loss, give 50% increase in dose (eg extra scoop in evening feed).
VITAMIN E SUPPLEMENT	Mix well into feed.	eg White-E 1000iu (1 scoop)	-		-	Supplements low feed levels with essential Vitamin E to promote muscle function and aerobic capacity - NRC (1989) recommendation. Higher doses if fats are used as energy sources (see text).

INGREDIENT	FORM/MIX	DAILY AMOUNT				PROVIDES
		Early Morn	Mid Morn to Noon	Mid Aft-n	Evening Supper	
DICALCIUM PHOSPHATE	DCP Free flowing dry. Mix well into feed.				All hay alternatives add 1oz (30g) 2 tblsp. If poly-unsaturated oil substituted for grain, for each 2 teacups oil add ½oz (15g, 1 tblsp) DCP.	Provides extra CALCIUM and PHOSPHORUS to ensure adequate phosphorus. Important in young horses in training to assist in bone strengthening to adapt to fast work. When oil used as an energy source to replace grain, extra calcium and phosphorus is needed.
CALCIUM CARBONATE	Ground limestone. Free flowing, mix well into feed.				Alfalfa - nil. Mixed hay - 3/4oz (20g) (1½ tblsp) Grass hay only - add 1½oz (42g) 3 tblsp.	Essential to balance mixed and grass hay based diets. Add an extra ½oz (15g) 1 tablespoon to diets of heavy sweating horses, and in humid conditions.
ALKALINE CITRATE SUPPLEMENT	Sodium acid citrate supplement.	eg Neutradex 2oz (60ml) over tongue after fast work or racing.				Supplements inadequate feed levels with sodium and citrate salts to help buffer lactic acid in muscle cells after fast work. Encourages horse to drink more water in hot weather. Alkalinizes urine and may help to conserve calcium in body after hard or fast exercise.
B-COMPLEX VITAMIN SUPPLEMENT (Optional)	Concentrated vitamins. Mix well into feed.	eg Pulse-8 liquid 2oz (60ml) mixed into feed or over tongue.				Supplements inadequate feed levels with multi-vitamin concentrate - aids appetite in horses off feed after fast work or racing. Give dose over tongue if horse off feed after fast work.
GREEN FEED/ GRAZING	Fresh grass			3lb (1.4kg) grass or 30 mins hand grazing mid-afternoon if possible.		Relieves boredom, sharpens appetite.
ALFALFA, HAY or alternatively	Leafy, no dust - dampen if necessary	1½lb (700g)	1½lb (700g)	1lb (450g)	4lb (1.8kg)	Provides ENERGY, PROTEIN, FIBER and CALCIUM. Contributes higher protein than mixed or grass hay. Ideally feed alfalfa in day feeds, grass hay overnight.
MIXED HAY or alternatively	Leafy, clean, no dust - dampen if necessary.	1½lb (700g)	1½lb (700g)	1lb (450g)	5lb (2.3kg)	Well accepted. Use depends on price - more wastage than alfalfa and more bulky for given weight.
GRASS HAY	Leafy, no weeds, no dust - dampen if necessary.	1½lb (700g)	1½lb (700g)	1lb (450g)	4lb (1.8kg)	Actually feed 9½lb (4.3kg) as up to 5% wastage of grass hay. More bulky than alfalfa hay and intake limited by appetite of horse.

NUTRITIONAL INFORMATION: This ration is formulated for a Standardbred in advanced training that is racing on a regular basis, providing adequate energy to meet practical needs. Each 27lb (12.3kg) provides 35.3-36.4 Mcals (147-152MJ), 1360-1520g (11.7%) crude protein, and a minimum of 40g calcium and 29g phosphorus (extra iron and calcium allowances made for heavy sweating horses - see text).

DIETARY GUIDELINES - FLAT, SPRINT OR JUMP RACEHORSE, Thoroughbred, Quarter Horse, Paint, Appaloosa, Arabian

First 6-8 weeks training. 1050-1150lbs (475-525kg) bodyweight. Confined to stalls most of the day. Moderate intensity conditioning exercise 25 minutes daily. Walking 40 minutes. Three feeds daily. For smaller framed breeds - adjust grain and hay intake in proportion to bodyweight and exercise.

INGREDIENT	FORM/MIX	DAILY AMOUNT			PROVIDES
		AM	NOON	PM	
CORN	Whole or freshly cracked. If purchased cracked - store in bag, fold down top after each use. Dust free, non rancid.	1lb (450g)		2lb (900g)	ENERGY, PROTEIN - adds energy with reduced bulk as compared to oats - ideal for small framed horses or poor, picky eaters. Cut out corn on rest or light work days, replace with hay.
OATS	Whole, heavy, dust free.	2lb (900g)	2½lb (1.1kg)	3lb (1.4kg)	ENERGY, PROTEIN, FIBER - palatable and dilutes ration to avoid digestive upset. Cut to one third on rest days. May be replaced with rolled barley or milo - 7lb (3.2kg) replaces 7½lb (3.4kg) oats.
COMMERCIAL MIXED GRAIN SWEET FEED (Optional)	Good quality, sealed bags.	-	-	4½lb (2.0kg)	Alternative sweet palatable night feed - convenient, no mixing required - replace corn and oats.
SOYBEAN MEAL (Optional)	Heat treated, free flowing. Non rancid.	8oz (230g)		14oz (400g)	Optional - provides ENERGY, PROTEIN.
POLY-UNSATURATED OIL eg Corn Oil (Optional)	Non rancid, keep well sealed.	8oz (250ml) (2 teacups)		8oz (250ml) (2 teacups)	Optional - high energy source to concentrate diet in picky eaters. Reduce oats by 1½lb (700g) per 2 teacups of oil. Introduce in a step-wise manner over 7-10 days (see text). If more than 2 teacups added, add 3oz (85g) soybean meal per cup of oil to maintain protein intake.
ALFALFA pellets/cubes	Commercial cubes. Dry, no mold.	1lb (450g)	1lb (450g)	2lb (900g)	Optional - ENERGY, PROTEIN, CALCIUM - bulks out feed for horses that eat grain quickly. Chopped alfalfa or mixed hay may be fed - substitute weight for long hay.
MOLASSES	Mix 50:50 with warm water, mix well into feed.	4oz (115g) (3/4 teacup)	-	4oz (115g) (3/4 teacup) (Not required if commercial sweet feed given.)	ENERGY and some CALCIUM. Damp sweetened feed improves acceptance, reduces dust, prevents selection and sifting of ingredients. If dry morning feed preferred, add total amount (8oz) (230g) to evening feed, especially if alfalfa pellets mixed with grain.
COMMERCIAL VITAMIN/TRACE MINERAL SUPPLEMENT	Mix well into feed.			eg Feramo-H 2oz (57g) ½ scoop	Supplements low feed levels with essential vitamins, including Vitamin A & D and trace minerals for muscle, bone and tendon development. Additional Vitamin A & D important on dehydrated grass hay diets.
IRON SUPPLEMENT (Optional)	Mix well into feed.			eg Ironcyclen liquid 2oz (60ml)	Supplements low feed levels with IRON, COPPER and COBALT - blood building minerals, give daily in horses with history of worms or poor condition - continue daily to beginning of fast work.
ELECTROLYTE SUPPLEMENT	Mix well into feed	eg Humidimix 3/4oz (22½g) (1 scoop)		eg Humidimix 3/4oz (22½g) (1 scoop)	Supplements low feed levels to replace sodium, potassium and chloride salts lost through sweating (hot humid weather, hard exercise). Aids palatability of ration. In hot weather with heavy sweat loss, give 50% increase in dose (eg extra scoop in evening feed).

INGREDIENT	FORM/MIX	DAILY AMOUNT			PROVIDES
		AM	NOON	PM	
VITAMIN E SUPPLEMENT	Mix well into feed.	eg White-E 1000iu (1 scoop)	-	-	Supplements low feed levels with essential Vitamin E to correct dietary deficiencies so as to promote muscle function and aerobic capacity - NRC (1989) recommendation. Higher doses if oil is used as energy source (see text).
DICALCIUM PHOSPHATE	DCP Free flowing dry. Mix well into feed.			All hay alternatives add 1oz (30g) 2 tblsp. If poly-unsaturated oil substituted for grain, for each 2 teacups oil add ½oz (15g-1 tblsp) DCP.	Provides extra CALCIUM and PHOSPHORUS for horses in training to assist in bone remodelling and strengthening to adapt to fast work and minimize risk of bucked shins (see text for details). When oil used as an energy source to replace grain, extra calcium and phosphorus is needed.
CALCIUM CARBONATE	Ground limestone. Free flowing, mix well into feed.			Grass hay only - add 1oz (30g) 2 tblsp as well as DCP	CALCIUM - essential to meet calcium needs on grass roughage diets in young two year old horses in training.
ALKALINE CITRATE SUPPLEMENT (Optional)	Sodium acid citrate supplement. Mix well into feed.	eg Neutradex 1oz (30ml) in feed			Supplements feed with non-bicarb source of alkaline buffer to combat effects of lactic acid in blood and muscles of unfit horses in early training.
B-COMPLEX VITAMIN SUPPLEMENT (Optional)	Concentrated vitamins. Mix well into feed or over the tongue.		eg Pulse-8 liquid 2oz (60ml) (Every second day)		Supplements low feed levels. Can be given directly over tongue with a syringe in horses that are poor eaters. In early training, supplementation every second day is usually adequate.
GREEN FEED/ HAND GRAZE	Fresh grass		3lb (1.4kg) grass or 30 mins graze on lead in mid-afternoon if possible.		Relieves boredom, sharpens appetite.
ALFALFA HAY or alternatively	Leafy, no dust - dampen if necessary	2lb (900g)	3lb (1.4kg)	5lb (2.3kg)	Provides ENERGY, PROTEIN, FIBER and CALCIUM. Contributes higher protein than mixed or grass hay - ideal for building up horses in early training. Dampen cubes.
MIXED HAY or alternatively	Leafy, clean, no dust - dampen if necessary.	2lb (900g)	3lb (1.4kg)	6lb (2.7kg)	Well accepted and use depends on price - more wastage than alfalfa and more bulky for given weight.
GRASS HAY	Leafy, no weeds, no dust - dampen if necessary.	2lb (900g)	2½lb (1.1kg)	4½lb (2.1kg)	Actually feed 9½lb (4.3kg) as up to 5% wastage of grass hay. More bulky than alfalfa hay and intake limited by appetite of horse. Lower in protein and calcium relative to alfalfa or mixed hay.

NUTRITIONAL INFORMATION: This ration is formulated for a Flat, Sprint or Jump racehorse in early training providing 100% of the daily requirement based on NRC (1989) guidelines. Each 20lb (9.1kg) of concentrate/hay alternative contains approximately 24.5 Mcals (103MJ) digestible energy, 1050-1200g (ave 12%) crude protein, and a minimum of 33g calcium and 30g phosphorus. The ration is also suitable for a two year old in training, with corn, oil and alfalfa feed options (see text).

DIETARY GUIDELINES -   FLAT, SPRINT OR JUMP RACEHORSE, Thoroughbred, Quarter Horse, Paint, Appaloosa, Arabian.

Advanced Training/Regular Racing. 1050-1150lbs (475-525kg) bodyweight. Confined to stalls most of the day. Breezed one or twice weekly, 3-4 feeds daily. For smaller framed breeds - adjust grain and hay intake in proportion to bodyweight and exercise.

INGREDIENT	FORM/MIX	DAILY AMOUNT				PROVIDES
		EARLY MORN	MID MORN	MID AFT-N	EVENING SUPPER	
CORN	Whole or freshly cracked. If purchased cracked - store in bag and fold down top after use. Dust free, non rancid.	2lb (900g)	1lb (450g)	1lb (450g)	2lb (900g)	ENERGY, PROTEIN - ideal high energy grain to reduce bulk of ration in small framed horses. Cut out on light work/rest days.
OATS	Whole, heavy, dust free.	3lb (1.4kg)	2lb (900g)	2lb (900g)	4lb (1.8kg)	ENERGY, PROTEIN, FIBER - traditional safe grain but bulky in small framed horses in advanced training. Cut to one third on rest days. May be replaced with rolled barley or milo - 6½lb (3kg) replaces 7lb (3.4kg) oats.
COMMERCIAL MIXED GRAIN SWEET FEED (Optional)	Good quality, sealed bags.	-	-		5lb (2.3kg)	ENERGY, PROTEIN, FIBER - sweet palatable night feed - convenient, no mixing required. Replaces corn and oat mix.
SOYBEAN MEAL (Optional)	Heat treated, free flowing, non rancid.	8oz (230g)			14oz (400g)	Optional - should be given the grass hay roughage based diets to meet protein and amino acid requirements to build blood and muscle.
POLY-UNSATURATED OIL eg Corn Oil (Optional)	Non rancid, keep well sealed.	8oz (250ml) (2 teacups)	-		8oz (250ml) (2 teacups)	Optional - high ENERGY source to concentrate diet in picky eaters, small framed horses, and hot weather heavy sweaters. May aid performance. (See text.) Reduce oats by 1½lb (700g) per 2 teacups of oil added - introduce in a step-wise manner over 7-10 days. If more than two cups added - add 3oz (85g) soybean meal per cup of oil to maintain protein intake (see text).
ALFALFA pellets/ crumbled cubes (Optional)	Commercial pellets/cubes. Dry, no mold.	1lb (450g)	1lb (450g)	1lb (450g)	2lb (900g)	Optional - ENERGY, PROTEIN, CALCIUM - bulks out feed for horses that eat grain quickly. Chopped alfalfa or mixed hay may be fed - substitute weight for long hay.
MOLASSES	Mix 50:50 with warm water, mix well into feed.	4oz (115g) (3/4 teacups)	-		4oz (115g) (3/4 teacups) (Not required if commercial sweet feed given.)	ENERGY and some CALCIUM. Damp sweetened feed improves acceptance, reduces dust, prevents selection and sifting of ingredients. If dry morning feed preferred, add total amount (8oz) (230g) to evening feed, especially if alfalfa pellets mixed with grain.
COMMERCIAL VITAMIN/TRACE MINERAL SUPPLEMENT	Mix well into feed.				eg Feramo-H 2oz (57g) ½ scoop	Supplements low feed levels with essential vitamins, including Vitamin A & D and trace minerals for muscle, bone and tendon development. Additional Vit A & D important on grass hay diets for tendon strength.
IRON SUPPLEMENT (Optional)	Iron, copper and cobalt supplement. Mix well into feed.				eg Ironcyclen liquid 2oz (60ml)	Supplements low feed levels with IRON, COPPER and COBALT - blood maintenance minerals.
ELECTROLYTE SUPPLEMENT	Mix well into feed.	eg Humidimix 3/4oz (22½g) (1 scoop)			eg Humidimix 3/4oz (22½g) (1 scoop)	Supplements low feed levels to replace sodium, potassium and chloride salts lost through sweating (hot humid weather, hard exercise). Aids palatability of ration. In hot weather with heavy sweat loss, give 50% increase in dose (eg extra scoop in evening feed).

INGREDIENT	FORM/MIX	DAILY AMOUNT				PROVIDES
		EARLY MORN	MID MORN	MID AFT-N	EVENING SUPPER	
VITAMIN E SUPPLEMENT	Mix well into feed.	eg White-E 1000iu (1 scoop)	-		-	Supplements low feed levels with essential Vitamin E to promote muscle function and aerobic capacity - NRC (1989) recommendation. Higher doses if fats are used as energy sources. (See text.)
DICALCIUM PHOSPHATE	DCP Free flowing dry. Mix well into feed.				All hay alternatives add 1oz (30g) 2 tblsp. If poly-unsaturated oil substituted for grain, for each 2 teacups oil add ½oz (15g-1 tblsp) DCP.	Provides extra CALCIUM and PHOSPHORUS for horses in training to assist in bone remodelling and strengthening to adapt to fast work and minimize risk of bucked shins (see text for details). When oil used as an energy source to replace grain, extra calcium and phosphorus is needed.
CALCIUM CARBONATE	Ground limestone. Free flowing, mix well into feed.				Alfalfa - nil Mixed hay - add 3/4oz (20g) (1½ tblsp) Grass hay - add 1½oz (42g) (3 tblsp).	CALCIUM - essential to meet elevated calcium needs on both mixed and grass hay roughage diets in young horses. Add an extra ½oz (15g) 1 tablespoon to diets of heavy sweating horses, and in humid climates.
ALKALINE CITRATE SUPPLEMENT (Optional)	Sodium acid citrate supplement.	eg Neutradex 2oz (60ml) over tongue after breezing/racing.				Supplements inadequate feed levels with sodium and citrate salts to help buffer lactic acid in muscle cells after fast work. Often encourages horses to drink more water in hot weather. Alkalinizes urine and may help to conserve calcium in body after hard or fast exercise.
B-COMPLEX VITAMIN SUPPLEMENT (Optional)	Concentrated vitamins. Mix well into feed.	eg Pulse-8 liquid 2oz (60ml) mixed into feed or over tongue				Supplements inadequate feed levels with vitamin concentrate - aids appetite in horses off feed after breezing; picky eaters. Give dose over tongue if horse off feed after fast work.
GREEN FEED/ HAND GRAZE	Fresh grass			3lb (1.4kg) grass or 30 mins hand graze in mid-afternoon if possible.		Relieves boredom, sharpens appetite.
ALFALFA, HAY or alternatively	Leafy, no dust - dampen if necessary	2lb (900g)	1½lb (700g)	1½lb (700g)	5lb (2.3kg)	Provides ENERGY, PROTEIN, FIBER and CALCIUM. Contributes higher protein than mixed or grass hay. Ideally feed alfalfa in day feeds, grass hay overnight. Dampen cubes.
MIXED HAY or alternatively	Leafy, no weeds, no dust - dampen if necessary.	2lb (900g)	1½lb (700g)	1½lb (700g)	6lb (2.7kg)	Well accepted. Use depends on price - more wastage than alfalfa and more bulky for given weight. Low in PROTEIN and CALCIUM relative to alfalfa.
GRASS HAY	Leafy, no weeds, no dust - dampen if necessary.	2lb (900g)	½lb (700g)	1lb (450g)	4½lb (2.1kg)	Actually feed 9½lb (4.3kg) as up to 5% wastage of grass hay. More bulk than alfalfa hay and intake limited by appetite of horse.

NUTRITIONAL INFORMATION: This ration is formulated for a Flat, Sprint or Jump racehorse in advanced training and racing on a regular basis, providing 100% of the daily requirement based on NRC (1989) guidelines. Each 27½lb (12.5kg) provides 33.5-34.0 Mcals (140-142MJ) digestible energy, 1330-1480g (11.2%) crude protein, and a minimum of 46g calcium and 33g phosphorus (extra mineral and calcium allowances made for heavy sweating horses - see text).

EQUESTRIAN SPORT HORSES

Although the nutritional requirements are not as high as racing horses, horses used in upper levels of equestrian sport undergo demanding training programs in preparation for competition. This group includes upper level three-day event horses, showjumpers, competitive fox hunters, polo and polocrosse horses and western performance horses used for reining, barrel racing, cutting and rodeo competition.

The demand for high standards of competition require that the majority of sport horses be stabled full-time during the competitive season, with access to grazing for psychological relief and an opportunity for limited free exercise, if available.

A well balanced diet, formulated to meet the specific needs of each class of horse is essential for health and fitness and to maximize response to training.

Upper level competitions are demanding on a horse's stamina, and stress of travelling and regular competition can often result in a lack of performance during the lead up to the season's final competitions and championships. As many of these horse sports rely on team performance, all horses must be well conditioned, fit and be able to recover quickly between competitions.

EVENTING/TRIAL HORSES

Three-day eventing, or horse trialing, is one of the most demanding types of equine athletic activity. The horse has to be well conditioned and physically fit, yet calm and obedient to compete successfully, and score well in all three phases.

Initial training is usually conditioning-type work, with nutritional requirements similar to that of a Showjumper. However, once conditioning for the speed and stamina of cross-country and steeplechase phases is commenced, the energy, protein, mineral and vitamin content of the ration must be increased in proportion to exercise.

Traditionally, most Eventers are crossbreds and warmblood breeds, and expertise is required to manipulate the ration to maintain calm behavior and control in the dressage and showjumping phases. Most upper level Eventers are stabled full-time, where dietary intake can be more closely supervised. These horses are specifically trained to higher fitness standards than required for other competitive team sports, such as polo and showjumping.

Nutritional Requirements

The requirements in the showjumping and dressage phases match those of Show horses, with increases to match those of racehorses and polo horses in the strenuous steeplechase and cross-country competitions.

Energy

The relative energy demand changes in proportion to the speed and duration of exercise. Energy levels must be increased for steeplechase and cross-country exercise to ensure performance, without making the horse playful, over energetic or likely to rush its movements in the dressage phases.

Eventers that are trained out of the paddock require only about half the grain level to maintain condition and performance. The "fret" factor in confined horses increases their energy requirements.

Protein

Protein requirements for exercise increase in proportion to the energy level, and adequate protein is usually provided by the increased grain intake on a base of alfalfa and mixed roughage. Where high levels of fat are substituted for cereal grain used as an energy source, extra protein should be added to make-up the shortfall as grain content is reduced. (See Fats page 26.)

Fiber

Adequate fiber as good quality hay is required for Eventers that are stabled full-time with little access to pasture.

Minerals

As the contribution of pasture is reduced, extra minerals must be provided. A daily supplement of iron helps maintain performance and stamina in Eventers on high grain and fat boosted rations, once faster, anaerobic training is commenced. Extra calcium is usually needed on high grain rations where grass hay is used as the primary source of roughage. Supplementary calcium may also be required to replace calcium lost in heavy sweat output and bone turnover, which occurs in hard cross-country training. Supplementary selenium may benefit hard-worked horses on high grain or fat rations. Reports suggest that responses to selenium are manifested by improved stamina and performance. However natural selenium intake from feeds must be determined prior to adding supplementary selenium. Consult your local Agricultural Advisor, or vet for specific advice.

Vitamins

In heavily stressed and high-performance horses such as the competitive eventing horse, vitamin requirements match those of a racing horse, particularly the need for Vitamins A, E and B Complex. (See page 86.)

Electrolytes

Body salt need and losses are related to climatic condition, sweat output and speed of exercise. In early training, long slow distance (LSD) aerobic type exercise at speeds of less than 325-400 yards (about 300-350 meters) per minute for 40-60 minutes daily helps to increase stamina and strength for cross-country competition. Hard or prolonged exercise results in heavy sweat loss and dehydration, particularly during warmer weather.

After 4-6 weeks of this type of conditioning training without adequate salt and electrolyte replacement, horses can be slow to recover, nervy and spooky, and puff hard after exercise (often referred to as thick in the wind) due to blood electrolyte imbalances. Studies indicate that extra potassium and chloride salts are necessary to replace continual or heavy sweat loss during hard training. Once horses begin regular speed work in excess of 400 yards (350 meters) per minute, then a supplement of an alkaline citrate buffer, after fast work, is useful to assist return to normal acid-base levels in muscles and blood during the recovery period.

Ration Guidelines and Nutritional Management - Refer to pages 105-109.

SHOWJUMPERS AND FOX HUNTERS

In recent years, both local amateur and professional Showjumping to international or world cup standard, is becoming more popular due to improved sponsorship, higher prize money and more shows per season. Consequently, the standard of training, feeding and general care has also improved.

Showjumpers train and perform at higher average speeds than most other competitive ring event horses, such as show horses and Dressage horses. Although in some countries Warmbloods and their crossbreds are becoming more popular because of their robust conformation, many Showjumpers are ex-Thoroughbred racehorses. Showjumpers are usually fed on a more individual basis than most other equine athletes.

Many riders prefer a well-conditioned, responsive mount, without too much energy and excitable behavior that makes handling and control of the horse difficult when jumping. Consequently, many of the more docile Showjumpers receive much higher grain rations than their nervy counterparts. Horses confined to stalls full-time require more energy to counteract fretting than those with daytime access to pasture.

Hunters are generally schooled in flat work and over fences during the week and competed on weekends where they are expected to be docile but athletic. For this reason, they too are fed according to their temperament and training method rather than nutritional requirements alone. The fox hunter must be quiet enough to gallop along in a large pack but athletic at the same time; hurdling obstacles at speed. A diet formulated for the particular needs of each horse is essential.

Nutritional Requirements

Many of the comments made under the Show/Dressage horse feeding section apply to the general nutritional needs of the Showjumper. However, some of the more specific nutritional requirements applicable to Showjumpers are outlined below.

Energy

An adequate amount of energy is required to maintain the horse in good condition and provide energy for hard training and competitive jumping without making the horse hard to handle or control. The use of fat as a slow release energy feed is becoming more popular for horses worked hard during an extended season or ridden mainly on weekend hunts.

Protein

Some form of protein supplement, usually good quality soybean meal is recommended on low grain or fat based diets with a grass hay roughage base to provide amino acids for muscle development and maintenance of body tissues.

Fiber

Showjumpers trained from the pasture usually receive adequate fiber. However, as most competitive horses are confined full time to stables, provision of good quality hay and green feed if available, is important to balance grain rations particularly when travelling. Whilst low energy, bulky rations may reduce excitable behavior, they can lead to hay belly and increased gut weight that can reduce a jumper's competitive ability.

Minerals

The mineral requirements of mature Showjumpers and Hunters are less than that of other performance horses such as racehorses and Eventers. However, adequate calcium must be provided to balance the calcium to phosphorus intake where a combination of grain and grass hay is used as the main diet. As calcium is lost in sweat particularly in hot weather, extra calcium, up to 1oz (30g) or 2 tablespoons of calcium carbonate per day is recommended in heavily sweating horses worked or hunted for more than 60 minutes a day.

Vitamins

A complete range of vitamins will help ensure balanced nutrition and optimum performance.

Supplements of vitamin E will help correct low feed levels deficiencies and may assist in maintaining a calmer more relaxed attitude in nervy horses during competition.

Electrolytes

Electrolyte requirement is related to the sweat output, duration of work and environmental conditions. For horses that sweat heavily or are required to travel regularly, supplementary electrolytes will help maintain better coat condition, vitality and overall performance, particularly under warmer conditions.

Ration Guidelines and Nutritional Management - refer to pages 105-109.

WESTERN PERFORMANCE HORSES

Reining, Roping, Cutting, Rodeo

Western pleasure horse sports such as cutting, roping, barrel racing, and reining demand a high standard of physical fitness and a well balanced ration. Rodeo competition and ranch or stock work command highly trained and well cared for horses, although previously most were only lightly trained and kept at pasture. They have similar nutritional demands as a fox hunter in full training.

These horses are required to work at various exercise speeds of trot, canter and gallop, with turning, reining to a sliding halt, and rapid acceleration in stock and rodeo competition.

If a horse is being competed on a regular basis, then supplementary concentrate feeds must be fed to ensure speed and stamina, as well as good condition and turnout. The large variation in breeds, and wide variety of training methods, require horses to be fed on an individual basis.

Nutritional Requirements

Energy

The energy level of the ration will depend on the speed, duration and frequency of exercise, the condition of the working surface, and temperament of the horse. The weight of the rider, which influences relative energy demand in strenuous exercise, is also an important consideration. There are probably larger variations in rider size and build in western competition than in any other horse sport.

The use of energy-dense rations containing corn oil or fat is recommended in hot weather or when horses are worked hard on a regular basis. (See Feeding in Hot Weather, page 48.)

Protein

Cereal grains for energy, with alfalfa and mixed hay as the roughage base will generally provide enough protein for light to moderate exercise. When fat replaces grain as an energy source, and the ration is based on grass hay, additional protein as oil seed meal should be provided for hard working horses. (See Fats, page 25.)

Fiber

As with all other horses in work on a concentrate ration, adequate fiber must be provided to prevent grain overload and digestive upsets, particularly if corn is used as the main energy source. Horses grazing on dried off pasture with minimal concentrate intake often eat large amounts of fiber, which can result in a mild hay belly, and reduce their appeal in western halter and breed classes. These horses may have to be confined to stalls overnight to ensure they consume concentrate feeds, and use grazing as a top-up during the day.

Minerals and Vitamins

Access to good quality pasture should provide adequate minerals and vitamins for light or weekend pleasure work. However, once concentrate feeds constitute 50% of the total ration intake, or exercise exceeds 30 minutes daily, then additional calcium is needed to balance grain based diets, replace sweat losses and maintain bone strength, particularly when grass hay is used as the primary roughage.

| HINT | *In ranch horses and rodeo horses that are constantly turning sharply, and sliding to a halt, a daily supplement of 50,000iu Vitamin A may help maintain tendon and ligament strength in horses grazing dry pasture or given stored hay for roughage that is low in this vitamin.* |

Electrolytes

Electrolyte needs are related to climatic conditions and duration of exercise, which in turn influence sweat loss. In most cases, when horses are on concentrate feed and being trained for 30 minutes or more daily, or are hauled long distances to compete on a regular basis, an electrolyte supplement, will replace body salts lost in sweat where sufficient is not available from the feed.

Ration Guidelines and Nutritional Management - refer to pages 105-109.

POLO PONIES AND POLOCROSSE HORSES

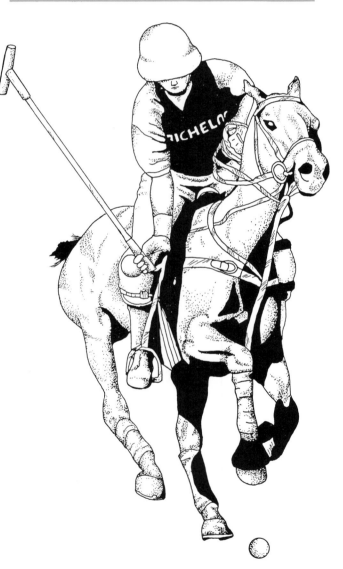

Polo exercise encompasses a wide variety of exercise speeds, with sudden stops, starts and fast sprints to keep up with the flow of the game. The popularity of Polo and the increased standard and frequency of competition has highlighted the need to train and feed horses to a competitive level. Traditionally, Polo competition was a social or amateur sport, where horses were fed and trained from the paddock.

In recent years, the Australian derived game of Polocrosse has been introduced to the United States. Polocrosse is a horse sport combination of Polo and lacrosse where a racket or net on a stick, is used to scoop and throw a large, soft ball. Only one horse per player is used for Polocrosse, which is played in 8 minute chukkas on a smaller field than polo. Polocrosse is a game that can be played by the rich and poor alike, from children to adults, with a team of six horses or ponies per side. A Polocrosse horse may be required to perform for 30-50 minutes per day, so nutrition must be adequate to satisfy requirements for relatively strenuous exercise.

Although Polo ponies are competed for shorter periods, the large playing field and faster speed of the game places a similar demand on fitness and nutritional intake.

Training regimens vary, but often horses are exercised at the trot and canter, with bursts of galloping, for 45-60 minutes daily to condition them for competition. Polocrosse horses may play for up to an 8 month season, with 8 chukkas daily on a weekend carnival. Regular competition and travelling often interrupts normal feeding routines.

The nutritional intake must be tailored to suit the individual horse's size, temperament, feeding habits and training program.

Nutritional Requirements

Energy

Studies have shown that the energy needs for strenuous Polo-type exercise is roughly similar to that required by a racehorse in training. Like many other sporting-type horses, most Polo and Polocrosse horses are pastured during the day, and stabled overnight, with a concentrate feed night and morning. As the majority of Polo horses are fully grown and mature, adequate energy is required to maintain weight and condition as well as meet the needs for exercise.

| HINT | *Many Polocrosse players feed a commercially prepared working horse feed or sweet feed mix for convenience, especially on weekend carnivals. However, additional grain and supplements may be added to match each horse's needs relative to the intensity of training.* |

Tying-up is a relatively common problem in horses that are unfit for the speed of competition, or on the day after a rest day on full grain rations.

Protein

Protein needs are similar to those of racehorses in training, with adequate amounts provided by a grain/alfalfa or mixed hay in a home mixed, or prepared commercial ration. Where horses have access to pasture, protein intake can vary depending on pasture species and seasonal growth rates. For a Polo horse in full training, the twice daily concentrate feed should contain adequate protein to meet daily needs, with pasture as a bonus.

| HINT | *A fit Polo/Polocrosse horse should be maintained in a sleek condition - with outline of ribs and pin bones not obvious, but ribs able to be felt through the skin.* |

Fiber

Adequate fiber is required to ensure proper digestive function. Horses trained from the paddock may have a variable pasture intake, so hay should be provided on an ad-lib basis. Hay should be given as an overnight feed to stabled horses as it also helps to reduce boredom.

Minerals

As the amount of work is increased, extra amounts of most minerals, including iron and calcium, are required. Studies have shown that for horses working in excess of 10 miles (16kms) per day, calcium turnover in bone increases by up to 20%. As long-distance conditioning exercise also increases sweat loss of calcium, a supplementary source of calcium should be added to the ration. Additional selenium may also improve performance in horses on marginally deficient diets. Consult your vet for advice on the need to supplement selenium.

Vitamins

Polo type exercise is strenuous, resulting in large amounts of energy being metabolized. Increased levels of vitamins, particularly Vitamin A, E and B-Complex, may be beneficial in ensuring repeated good performance, recovery and maintenance of appetite, even in Polo ponies or Polocrosse horses with daily access to good pasture.

Electrolytes

Because of the extended distances and training times required to fully condition Polo horses to the level of fitness required for repeated competition, sweat loss of electrolytes must be replaced. A supplement of electrolytes will correct inadequate feed levels and assist in maintaining levels depleted during training and competition. Adequate water must be provided, particularly in heavily sweating horses grazing dry pastures or given a large bulk of dry hay in their diet.

Ration Guidelines and Nutritional Management - refer to pages 105-109.

NUTRITIONAL MANAGEMENT

The majority of the problems in this group of horses relate to temperament on high energy diets, the effects of strenuous exercise and loss of appetite, particularly after hard competition.

Hot manners, hard to control behavior

Once the grain and concentrate level in the diet is increased to meet the demand of higher intensity exercise during training and for competition, sport horses may become playful and hard to control. Obviously, energy in excess of exercise needs will be expended in playful behavior, so concentrates must only be fed in proportion to exercise on any particular day, rather than planned exercise.

| HINT | *The use of rolled barley as a substitute for corn and oats, and replacement of grain with polyunsaturated fats or tallow, will often assist in controlling over energetic behavior. I also recommend increasing the supplementary dose of Vitamin E on the morning before and morning of competition in horses that are quiet and settled at home, but become nervy and hyperactive during travelling, when waiting prior to competition, or unpredictable and hard to control when competing.* |

In my experience, maintaining a horse on 1000iu Vitamin E daily to supplement inadequate feed levels is beneficial in advanced training. On the morning before, and morning of travelling or competition I recommend an increase in supplementary Vitamin E to 3000-4000iu. I have found that most horses will settle and keep their mind on competition after one or two such increases in the supplementary levels of Vitamin E, which can be repeated prior to each competition if necessary. I have found that natural source Vitamin E (d-alpha-tocopherol - such as in White-E) appears to have a more beneficial effect than other forms of Vitamin E.

Avoiding risk of Tying Up

High energy rations in excess of exercise need, particularly when maintained on a light work or rest day, or if training is interupted by travelling prior to competition increase the risk of metabolic problems such as tying up (and playful behavior), when full exercise is resumed. Fillies and mares tend to be more prone to tying up when fed on a diet containing oats as the major energy source.

The risk of tying up in these horses can be reduced by cutting the amount of oats to one third or less, and substituting corn and rolled barley, with additional corn oil, as the primary energy sources.

HINT

As a guideline, cut the weight of oats to one third, substituting each 1lb of oats removed with 13½oz corn or alternatively 14oz barley, to give a roughly equal amount of energy. I normally recommend a 50:50 corn and barley mix. On rest days, cut out the corn and half the barley, commencing the night before, and on light work days, cut out the corn. Increase to full grain again over two day period once exercise resumes after a planned rest day, or on return to work after downtime due to lameness etc. Daily supplementation with Vitamin E, and an electrolyte mix (such as Humidimix), and ensuring adequate warm up and cool down exercise for at least 10 minutes prior to and following intense exercise or competition is also helpful in reducing the incidence of tying up in many horses (see also page 51).

Use of Fat as an Energy Source

Corn oil, other polyunsaturated oils, and even warm liquid tallow, can be used as alternative energy sources, particularly in horses in hard training, during hot weather, or in small framed horses or picky eaters that find it difficult to consume the bulk of concentrate feeds to meet exercise demands. (See pages 25 and 173 for substitution details.)

Supplementary Electrolytes

Many horses are prone to dehydration and tucking up when travelling to and from competition, particularly those that have a nervy disposition, or during hot weather. Loss of fluid and body salts through sweating, can result in reduced stamina, poor recovery between competitions or matches, and drying out of the coat. A routine supplement of electrolytes (such as in Humidimix), will help correct inadequate feed levels, particularly in horses that do not have regular access to green pasture. A daily supplement of electrolytes will also help maintain water intake, and combat the effects of dehydration.

HINT

A drink of an oral rehydration fluid (such as one gallon (4 liters) of made-up Recharge), before and after long distance travelling, or during the cool down period after hard exercise, may help maintain adequate blood fluid and body salt levels. Many competitors provide a bucket of oral rehydration fluid, and a bucket of plain, clean water, side-by-side overnight as a choice.

Feeding after Competition

Many horses will be tired after hard competition, and a few hours in the paddock to graze and exercise, will often aid recovery. If a horse is off its feed after hard competition then a supplment of B complex vitamins (such as 2oz (60ml) of Pulse-8) given over the tongue prior to the evening feed, may be of benefit. If a light day is to be given after competition, then the grain concentrate should be reduced in proportion to the exercise demand.

After fast competition, a supplement of alkaline salts is often recommended to counteract the effects of lactic acid accumulation in the muscles resulting from intense exercise. Allowing a horse to walk for one minute or so, followed by cool down exercise at the trot for at least five minutes, will assist in utilization of lactic acid in the muscle cells as a fuel for this exercise, and reduce stiffness and soreness that can lead to general discomfort and loss of appetite.

HINT

I have found a supplement of alkaline citrate salts can assist in reducing risk of muscle soreness and stiffness, and help to maintain the appetite, particularly if a horse is hauled for 2-3 hours after competition. I recommend a dose of non-bicarbonate liquid buffer, containing citrate salts, (such as 2oz (60ml) of Neutradex) be given over the tongue after each fast workout in training, and within 20-30 minutes of competition. Access to adequate volumes of 3-4 gallons (12-16 liters) or more of cool clean water must be provided after this supplement of acid-base buffer.

Feeding Hints - Polocrosse Horses

The Australian derived game of Polocrosse is becoming more popular in North America, as it is a highly skilled and fast flowing team game. The game is played by teams of six players over weekend meetings, called carnivals.

Polocrosse is played on a smaller playing field, and a single horse is used to play 6-8 short intensive eight minute chukkas per day. Generally it is less expensive to maintain a single horse and play than compared to polo, and in Australia it is played by children on ponies, as well as by highly competitive interstate championship players.

As Polocrosse is bein played more widely in the United States, I have provided some additional hints on Australian feeding and management program for a competitive polocrosse horse during the season.

Day	Exercise	Feeding Level
Monday	Traditional rest day after weekend carnival	Horse turned out to green pasture. Check state of dehydration after overnight transport. if skin pinches up - provide evening feeding of dampened hay, about 4lb of concentrate feed with added electrolytes.
Tuesday	Light exercise such as trotting and cantering for 20-30 minutes.	Increase concentrates to 60% of normal full exercise level. Provide good quality pasture and hay to appetite.
Wednesday	Higher intensity exercise - cantering, galloping with stick and handling practice for 30-40 minutes.	Concentrate feed to full regular working level. Ensure to cool down horse for 5-10 minutes at trot after fast exercise. May supplement with alkaline buffer. (See page 108-109.)
Thursday	20-30 minutes of trotting, cantering, skill/ball handling practice.	Feed concentrates to exercise level. Check for dehydration if hot weather and long distance travel to carnival. Provide electrolytes/rehydration drinks.
Friday	Tapering off exercise, sufficient trotting and cantering to match concentrate feed level.	Feed concentrates to exercise level. If horses is playful, give 5-10 minutes longeing, or evening trot/canter work out if no access to pasture.
Saturday	Travel to carnival (see Travelling Horses page 53). 6-8 chukkas. Cool out exercise or trot after last chukka.	Dampened hay to at lunchtime or hand graze on grass. Evening feed - normal concentrate with electrolytes. Oral B complex liquid vitamins over tongue to encourage appetite.
Sunday	Carnival play as for Saturday.	Feeding routine similar to Saturday. Ensure cool down exercise and rest before hauling.

1000-1100lb (450-500kg). Confined to stalls full-time, with 1-2 hours, access to grazing during the day . 30-40 minutes moderate to intense exercise daily. Two feeds if grazing provided, three feeds if stabled full time. If horse access to pasture, divide noon feed equally between morning and evening feeds. See foot note for early training.

INGREDIENT	FORM/MIX	DAILY AMOUNT			PROVIDES
		AM	NOON	PM	
CORN	Whole or freshly cracked. If purchased cracked, store in bag - fold bag down after use. Dust free, non rancid.	2lb (900g)	1lb (450g)	4lb (1.8kg)	ENERGY, PROTEIN - increases energy density of ration for small framed or picky eaters. Cut out on rest days. Not heating if horse worked daily.
OATS or alternatively	Whole, heavy. Dust free	2lb (900g)	2lb (900g)	4lb (1.8kg)	ENERGY, PROTEIN, FIBER - Traditional, palatable, safe grain. Cut to half on rest days.
ROLLED BARLEY CRUSHED MILO or alternatively	Rolled - dust free. May need to be dampened to ensure acceptance.	2lb (900g)	1½lb (700g)	3½lb (1.6kg)	ENERGY, PROTEIN, FIBER - may replace some or all of oats depending on availability and cost. On an energy basis, 1lb (450g) oats can be replaced by 14½oz (410g) barley or milo.
COMMERCIAL SWEET FEED MIX (Optional)	Good quality sealed bags.	Feed corn and oats or alternatives as above.		7lb (3.2kg)	Alternative night feed to replace corn and oat home mix. ENERGY, PROTEIN, FIBER - sweet palatable night feed, particularly after competitions, convenient no mixing required.
SOYBEAN MEAL (Optional)	Heat treated. Free flowing, non rancid.	1lb (450g)		1lb (450g)	Optional - not required when alfalfa or mixed hay roughages fed, but should be given to meet protein requirements of grass hay roughage based diets.
POLY-UNSATURATED OIL (eg Corn Oil) (Optional)	Non rancid. Keep well sealed. Mix well into feed.	8oz (250ml) (2 teacups)		8oz (250ml) (2 teacups)	Optional - high ENERGY source to increase energy density for small framed picky eaters, and for slow release energy in nervy horses, or "cool" energy source during hot weather for heavy sweating horses. Introduce in a step-wise manner over 5-7 days (see text). Reduce oats by 1½lb (700g) per 2 teacups of oil added.
ALFALFA PELLETS/ CRUMBLED CUBES (Optional)	Commercial pellets/cubes. Dry, no mold	1lbs (450g)	1lb (450g)	2lb (900g)	Optional - ENERGY, PROTEIN and CALCIUM - bulks out grain feed for horses that eat concentrates quickly. Chopped alfalfa or mixed hay may be fed - substitute for long hay.
MOLASSES	Mix 50:50 with warm water. Mix well into feed.	4oz (115g) (1 teacup)		4oz (115g) (1 teacup)	ENERGY and some CALCIUM. Not required if evening feed replaced with commercial sweet feed. Damp sweetened feed improves acceptance, reduces dust, prevents selection and sifting of ingredients. If dry morning feed preferred, add total amount (8oz) (230g) to evening feed, especially if alfalfa cubes mixed with grain.
COMMERCIAL VITAMIN/TRACE MINERAL SUPPLEMENT	Mix well into feed.			eg Feramo-H 2oz (57g) (½ scoop)	Supplements low feed levels with essential range of vitamins, including vitamin A and D to fortify grass roughage based rations; iron, copper, cobalt and zinc for blood and coat condition, and optimum muscle function.
IRON SUPPLEMENT (Optional)	Iron, Copper and Cobalt supplement. Mix well into feed.			eg Ironcyclen 2oz (50mL)	Supplements inadequate feed levels - may be given three days on, three days off to horses in advanced training to assist blood production in response to high intensity and regular competitive exercise.

INGREDIENT	FORM/MIX	DAILY AMOUNT			
		AM	NOON	PM	
VITAMIN E SUPPLEMENT	Mix well into feed.	eg White-E 1000iu (1 scoop)			Supplements low feed levels with essential Vitamin E to boost levels in grain - aids in muscle function and aerobic efficiency. Higher doses if fats are used as energy sources (see text).
ELECTROLYTE SUPPLEMENT	Mix well into feed.	eg Humidimix 3/4oz (22½g) (1 scoop)		eg Humidimix 3/4oz (22½g) (1 scoop)	Supplements inadequate feed levels with electrolytes lost in sweat. Increase dose in evening feed (ie 2 scoops) in hot weather, when travelling, or for heavy sweating horses.
B COMPLEX SUPPLEMENT (Optional)	Concentrated vitamins. Mix well into feed, or give over the tongue.	eg Pulse-8 Liquid 2oz (60ml)			Supplements inadequate feed levels with B Complex vitamins. Can be given directly over the tongue after hard exercise to horses that are slow or poor eaters. Commence 3-4 days before upper level or hard competition, particularly if travelling long distances.
DICALCIUM PHOSPHATE (Optional)	DCP. Free flowing, dry. Mix well into feed.			Not required on all hay mixes. If polyunsaturated oil substituted for grain, for each 2 teacups oil, add ½oz (15g - 1 tblsp) DCP.	Optional - all hay mixes contain adequate phosphorus when oil used as an energy source to replace grain, extra calcium and phosphorus is needed.
CALCIUM CARBONATE	Ground limestone. Free flowing dry. Mix well into feed.			Grass hay only - add 1oz (28.5g) 2 tblsp.	Calcium to meet calcium needs required to maintain bone density and strength, and to replace sweat losses.
ALKALINE CITRATE SUPPLEMENT (Optional)	Sodium acid citrate alkaline supplement			eg Neutradex 2oz (60ml) over tongue after fast exercise.	Supplements inadequate feed levels with supplementary sodium and citrate to buffer lactic acid formed in muscles. Often encourages horses to drink water after hard exercise.
ALFALFA HAY or alternatively	Leaf, no dust, dampen if necessary.	2½lb (1.1kg)	3lb (1.4kg)	6½lb (3kg)	Provides ENERGY, PROTEIN, FIBER and CALCIUM. Higher protein than mixed or grass hay - ideal for building up horses in early training, or after hard competition. Dampen cubes to soften (see text).
MIXED HAY or alternatively	Leafy, clean, no dust, dampen if necessary	2½lb (1.1kg)	3lb (1.4kg)	7½lb (3.4kg)	Well accepted. Use depends on availability and price - more bulk than alfalfa - may need to limit amount to appetite of horse.
GRASS HAY	Leafy, no weeds, no dust, dampen if necessary.	2½lb (1.1kg)	3lb (1.4kg)	5½lb (2.5kg)	Low in nutrients relative to alfalfa - but usually palatable. Bulk must be limited to ensure full consumption and protein source added (see text). If horse is hungry, add more hay as bulk.

NUTRITIONAL INFORMATION: This ration is formulated for a 1000-1100lb (450-500kg) horse in regular training and high intensity exercise in equestrian sport competition providing 100% of daily requirement based on NRC (1989) guidelines. If good pasture is available, feed the evening hay to appetite. Each 27.5lb (12.5kg) of ration provides approximately 30.3 Mcals (127MJ) digestible energy 1325-1400g (11%) crude protein, and a minimum 43g calcium and 32g phosphorus.

NOTE: Adjustment to the individual rations may be necessary to match exercise demand, appetite and individual temperament. In early training feed approximately 35-40% concentrate to 60-65% good quality hay, adjusting concentrate level in proportion to exercise demand. Refer Nutritional Management notes for further recommendations.

ENDURANCE HORSES

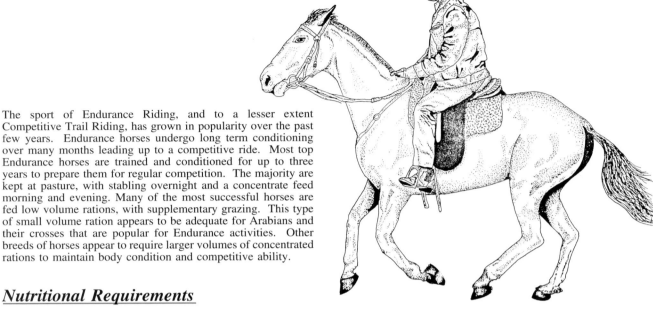

The sport of Endurance Riding, and to a lesser extent Competitive Trail Riding, has grown in popularity over the past few years. Endurance horses undergo long term conditioning over many months leading up to a competitive ride. Most top Endurance horses are trained and conditioned for up to three years to prepare them for regular competition. The majority are kept at pasture, with stabling overnight and a concentrate feed morning and evening. Many of the most successful horses are fed low volume rations, with supplementary grazing. This type of small volume ration appears to be adequate for Arabians and their crosses that are popular for Endurance activities. Other breeds of horses appear to require larger volumes of concentrated rations to maintain body condition and competitive ability.

Nutritional Requirements

Energy

Most Endurance horses being trained for competition are mature four year olds or older. Therefore, the dual demand for energy for both growth and exercise is not required. However, adequate energy must be provided for work and tissue repair in horses training over long distances.

> **HINT**
> *Generally, if a horse is maintaining bodyweight and is performing well, the energy intake is adequate.*

Energy is obtained from carbohydrates, proteins and fats in the diet.

As most Endurance horses are trained out of the pasture, they need only relatively small amounts of grain each day as a concentrate feed. This is in part due to the absence of the "fret factor" in pastured horses. Endurance horses that are confined to stalls would require higher levels of concentrates to provide adequate energy for exercise. Arabian horses often perform well on 3-4½lb (1.5-2kg) oats or even less corn daily. Although Endurance horses are trained over distances of 12-15 miles (about 20-25km) daily, many horses will satisfy up to 50% of their requirements just on good quality pasture, if available.

> **HINT**
> *Endurance horses seem to be more sensitive to over supply of energy in grains than other performance horses, with an increased risk of tying-up and lameness.*

Slow release energy feeds that can be broken down during exercise provide a continuous source of energy for the working muscles. Therefore, fat, such as corn oil or other vegetable oil, can provide a reservoir of energy for endurance exercise. Recent studies have shown that once conditioned to fat intake, fit horses are able to utilize fat efficiently as an energy source for slow, long distance exercise.

> **HINT**
> *Fat has a much higher calorific value than carbohydrates, enabling consumption of energy dense or less bulky feeds by smaller framed Arabian-type horses.*

Once conditioned to a high fat diet, volumes of 1-1½ pints (up to 1 liter) of corn oil or blended vegetable oils, have been fed twice daily to competitive horses without risk of digestive or metabolic upset. However, usually about 10% of energy needs, provided by half a pint (2 teacups) in the morning and evening feeds is the standard amount. (See Fats, page 25.)

Protein

Most Endurance horses do well on a 10-12% protein diet, which is usually provided as grain and alfalfa or mixed hay based diets. Where fat is substituted for grain as an energy source, extra protein must be added to meet requirements, particularly where grass hay is used as the roughage base. (See Fats page 26.) Adequate protein intake is necessary to maintain muscle mass, especially after a hard ride. Protein requirements are increased by long distance and stressful exercise, particularly when fat is used as a major energy source. Higher levels of protein (14-16%) may be beneficial for 1-2 days after a hard ride.

Fiber

Adequate fiber intake from hay or grazing is essential to maintain efficient digestive function on high grain or fat diets.

> **HINT**
> *Fiber also traps water in the large bowel which acts as an essential fluid reservoir to replace sweat loss and prevent dehydration during a long distance ride.*

Minerals

Adequate intake of a wide range of minerals is required by the hard working Endurance horse. The requirement for minerals such as iron and copper for blood cell production is not as high as for speed horses, as endurance horses predominantly use slow speed aerobic energy pathways in working muscles.

Recent studies have indicated that calcium turnover in bone is increased dramatically when a horse is exercised for more than 10 miles (16km) per day. The rate of calcium deposition in bone was increased by up to 20% when long distance exercise was given, triggering reduced calcium excretion in the urine and increased body retention of calcium.

> **HINT**
>
> *Excessive calcium intake during training, particularly from high amounts of alfalfa hay, can cause suppression of parathyroid gland function, which normally controls mobilization of calcium stores from the bones to maintain blood calcium levels. During competition in excess of four hours duration, sweat loss lowers blood calcium, which is not replenished by parathyroid hormone action. Low blood calcium causes a high risk of tying up and the "thumps" during competition.*

Recent recommendations advocate that minimal alfalfa should be provided during training, and grass hay and pasture be provided as the roughage source. In the 2-3 days prior to competition, the amount of alfalfa can be increased to provide a reserve of calcium and water for use during the ride. This feeding method will maintain parathyroid action which will be activated during long distance competition. The amount of supplementary calcium and phosphorus added to the diet should only be sufficient to balance the ration to meet daily requirements.

Vitamins

Studies have indicated that when large amounts of energy are metabolized, particularly where increased levels of fat are provided, extra Vitamin E and B-Complex vitamins are required. It has been reported that up to 5000iu of Vitamin E is supplemented daily to top Endurance horses. Conservative doses of 1000-2000iu are considered to be of practical benefit to maximize stamina and muscle function in Endurance horses.

Electrolytes

Endurance horses have elevated requirements for electrolytes, particularly potassium, chloride and calcium due to the large amounts of these salts that are lost in sweat. Studies have shown that salt alone is not sufficient to replace sweat loss. Sweat losses of 70-110 pints (40-60 liters) per day have been measured in Endurance horses performing over distances of 60-100 miles (100-160km).

Water

Adequate water intake and ability to store a reserve of water in roughage in the large bowel, is important to meet body requirements and replace sweat loss, particularly when electrolytes are being supplemented. Dehydration in Endurance horses can severely affect performance and delay heart rate recovery. Hot and tired horses are unable to efficiently lose heat during a rest period if sweating is reduced by dehydration. In this case, heart rate recovery will be slow, and may result in vetting out due to failure to recover to the ride standard.

Nutritional Management

A ration consisting of 3-4lbs (1½-2kg) grain, with good quality grass hay and access to pasture, would meet the needs of most Endurance horses in early conditioning training.

However, once a horse commences long distance work exceeding 6 miles (10km) daily, the inclusion of corn and fat to increase energy density of the ration will help ensure that a small framed horse can consume sufficient feed without exceeding its appetite limit. Corn and fat will also reduce waste heat from fermentation during digestion, and may be helpful in reducing overall sweat loss in long distance rides.

> **HINT**
>
> *About half a pint (275ml or 2¼ teacups) of corn oil mixed into each of the morning and night feeds is considered the minimum amount that makes use of oil worthwhile and economic in Endurance horses. Commence on 2oz (60ml) twice daily increasing by 2oz (60ml) every 3-4 days to ensure acceptance until the desired dose is reached.*

> **HINT**
>
> *Mix oil or fat thoroughly into ration. Clean out left-overs after each feed. Avoid pouring oil over vitamin supplements before mixing. Mix oil into feed, then add vitamins to the top layers of feed and mix them in.*

When grains are replaced by corn oil or other polyunsaturated oils in the diet, additional protein, some calcium and phosphorus, and Vitamin E, should be added to the diet. (See page 26 for full details.)

> **HINT**
>
> *Doses of up to 4000iu Vitamin E, (such as White-E) daily starting 3-5 days before a ride may help energy utilization and maintain stamina during long distance rides in Endurance horses. However, a normal dose of Vitamin E (1000iu) daily should be fed for at least 7-10 days before increasing to this level.*

Sweat Loss and Dehydration

Sweat loss during long distance training and competition, particularly during warm or humid weather, results in depletion of vital body salt reserves and symptoms of dehydration. Supplementation with a heavy sweat salt electrolyte mix with extra potassium and chloride, such as in Humidimix, is recommended to replace electrolyte loss and encourage horses to drink adequate amounts of water to maintain optimum fluid balance. For example, Humidimix is usually supplemented as one scoop in the morning feed, and two scoops in the evening feed.

> **HINT**
>
> *A drink of 1-1½ gallons (about 4-6 liters) of a commercial rehydration formulation mixed as directed (such as Recharge) after hard exercise will help to rapidly replace lost salts and fluid, and maintain rate of recovery. (See Checkpoint Rest page 112.)*

> **HINT**
>
> *As calcium is lost in sweat, additional calcium carbonate to balance the ration to meet daily needs should be added to the feed of heavy*

sweating horses. (See Ration Guidelines page 115.) For horses with broken away or cracked hooves, or those that lose their shoes easily, a supplement of 15mg biotin daily may be useful.

Grazing Contribution

The nutritional contribution from grazing varies from season to season, and the appetite of the individual horse. Where a horse has access to good pasture during the day, only minimal amounts of grain are required in concentrate feeds. Generally, horses are confined to stalls or corrals overnight to ensure they consume the higher energy concentrate feeds. Good quality alfalfa or mixed hay can be provided in a hay rack in the pasture, particularly as the pasture dries off.

Feeding For Competition

Theoretically, whilst it would be an advantage to reduce gut fill and hence bodyweight in the lead up to a long distance ride, concentrating the diet by reducing roughage increases the risk of colic, tying up, dehydration and early fatigue during competition.

HINT
It is now common practice to replace grass hay with alfalfa hay during the last 2-3 days of a competitive ride. This helps to maintain a valuable reservoir of fluid in the bowel, and provide additional calcium, to counteract sweat loss during the ride. (See Minerals, above, and ration guideline table for details.)

On day of the ride:

About 6-8 hours before the ride, feed a soaked mixture of 4lb (1.8kg) crushed corn for energy, half a pound (225g) of wheat bran or chopped hay, and 4lb (1.8kg) alfalfa hay to trap water in the gut. Mix in an electrolyte and Vitamin E supplement. Allow access to water right up to ride.

HINT
If available, allow the horse to drink small quantities of fresh water from creeks, dams etc during a ride under hot, humid conditions. Some horses will not drink a lot at checkpoints due to fatigue, or sometimes excitement. However it is essential that horses be given water first, then feed, at every opportunity. Topping up with cold water in this way will not cause colicky signs, provided the horse is continued on the ride.

HINT
Some riders carry an oral syringe of electrolyte paste or liquid (eg such as 1 scoop of Humidimix mixed up in honey or molasses, or 1oz (30ml) Recharge concentrate) in their saddlebags. This salt mix is administered over the tongue just prior to the horse drinking from a creek, pond or trough. The horse must be allowed to drink at least ½-1 gallon of water (4 liters) after the salts are given in this way.

At each Vet Check:

Ensure the horse is cooled out as quickly as possible after unsaddling, particularly if the horse is puffing and panting in humid weather. This will help to lower the body temperature and ensure a faster heart rate recovery. (See Cool Down Procedure, page 51.)

HINT
Prepare two buckets of drinking water. In one bucket, mix up a commercial rehydration drink, such as Recharge as recommended. (Ensure the horse is accustomed to drinking the drink during training.) Fill the other bucket with plain, cool water.

If the water is very cold take the chill off by adding a small amount of hot water. Allow the horse to take as much of the rehydration drink as it wishes, then place the bucket of plain water in reach of the horse to allow it to drink freely.

Allow the horse to rest and rehydrate by drinking before offering feed. At a Vet Check Point, the first priority is water or fluid replacement, then access to feed.

It is unwise to give grain and carbohydrate energy feeds during a vet check rest period, as it can cause earlier fatigue once the ride is resumed.

HINT
Many riders provide a sloppy mash of alfalfa meal with salts to help provide additional fluid intake as a refill at vet checks. This will encourage the continued use of body and gut fats for energy as the ride continues.

Some horses may prefer to pick at good quality greenfeed or dampened hay provided in a hay net hanging on the trailer, or in a tree. Others prefer to walk around and nibble at grass (if available), which may also help a horse settle and reduce the tendency to stiffen up in the joints and legs at the last checkpoint in a long ride prior to the vet check.

After a ride:

Repeat the cool out procedures at the completion of the ride and give fluid and electrolyte replenishment (such as a Recharge drink) as described above, prior to the final vet check. Ensure the horse is taken for a walk to cool down and prevent stiffening up before the final vet check.

Once the horse has settled down and is ready to eat, provide a dampened feed of grain and hay. Mix a standard dose of electrolytes into the concentrate feed to help encourage the horse to drink more fluids during recovery.

HINT
Many riders provide a concentrate feed of 4lb (1.8kg) of cracked corn every 3-4 hours, with access to grazing and good quality hay in between feeds. The uptake of carbohydrates is encouraged after a ride to replenish muscle energy stores. Up to 12-16lb (5½-7kg) of corn can be given in the first 18 hours after a ride, particularly if a horse has to compete again within a few days.

HINT
Mix an extra 4oz (115g) of protein meal (eg soybean meal) into the feed to boost protein levels, and sweeten with molasses if necessary. Studies suggest that additional protein may be useful to help replace damaged muscle protein after a long ride. Feed the increased protein for two days, then revert to normal rations.

Ensure the horse is rested overnight if possible before long distance travel.

Avoiding Heat Stress

Endurance exercise during hot, humid weather can result in the risk of heat exhaustion syndrome, which is increased when horses sweat heavily and dehydrate during a ride. Horses may become fatigued, and develop symptoms of tying-up, and in severe cases, physical exhaustion and collapse.

The onset of physical and heat stress can be detected by increased respiratory noise, blowing following relatively easy hill climbs, and loss of coordination and gait pattern.

If symptoms develop when riding between vet checks during hot, humid weather, then it is best to slow down in pace, and if necessary dismount and walk the horse until it recovers.

HINT

If water is available, then the horse can be allowed a few mouthfuls, walked for 2-3 minutes, and then allowed a larger drink. The horse can be washed over with water, and scraped off with the hands after 30 seconds, to allow steaming off and enhance evaporative cooling.

At the next vet check, seek advice from the ride veterinarian. However the horse should be cooled down with an efficient strapping method, and allowed to relax with access to water as the primary need, then feed with added electrolytes. Heart rates will remain elevated if the horse is not cooled down as efficiently as possible. If the horse continues to pant and blow, repeat the strapping procedures - but avoid excessive chilling.

HINT

Under hot, humid, still air conditions, fanning the horse with a towel to enhance evaporative cooling is helpful. Do not leave a horse dripping wet after strapping, as during humid conditions, heat will be retained in the coat, and heart rates will remain elevated. Consult the ride veterinarian for advice if necessary.

In my experience, once a horse has suffered from a heat stress or exhaustion problem, it seem to be more prone to them in the future, so expert check point management is necessary to avoid possible future heat stress problems.

Horses weighing 900-1000lb (400-450kg) or 1050-1150lb (475-525kg) total bodyweight, including 150lb (70kg) rider. Stabled overnight, access to grazing during day. Two feeds daily if at grass.

Note: The distance travelled, the weight of the rider, and terrain during training and competition will greatly influence the energy intake required. The following guideline is based on calculations and practical experience for a 10-12 mile (15-20km) ride daily, but the ration must be adapted to suit duration and distance of exercise. Smaller Arabian type breeds appear to be able to perform well on 60-70% of the grain level suggested. Extra amounts should be given in proportion to the weight of the rider and distance of ride.

INGREDIENT	FORM/MIX	DAILY AMOUNT		PROVIDES
		AM	PM	
CORN	Whole or freshly cracked. If purchased cracked, store in bag - fold bag down after use. Dust free, non rancid.	3lb (1.4kg)	4lb (1.8kg)	ENERGY, PROTEIN - increases energy density to reduce bulkiness of ration for smaller framed horses. Cut out on rest or light-work days. Non heating if horse worked daily.
OATS or alternatively	Whole, heavy. Dust free	4lb (1.8kg)	4lb (1.8kg)	ENERGY, PROTEIN, FIBER - Limit bulk of feed by feeding 50:50 oat:corn mix.
ROLLED BARLEY CRUSHED MILO	Rolled - dust free. May need to be dampened to ensure acceptance.	3½lb (1.6kg)	4lb (1.8kg)	ENERGY, PROTEIN, FIBER - may replace some or all of oats depending on availability and cost. On an energy basis, 1lb (450g) oats can be replaced by 14½oz (410g) barley or milo.
COMMERCIAL SWEET FEED MIX (Optional)	Good quality sealed bags.	Feed corn and oats or alternative as above.	7½lb (3.4kg)	Replaces corn and oat home mix. ENERGY, PROTEIN, FIBER - sweet palatable night feed, particularly after competition, convenient, no mixing required.
SOYBEAN MEAL (Optional)	Heat treated. Free flowing, non rancid.	8oz (230g)	8oz (230g)	Optional - ENERGY, PROTEIN adds extra protein to meet needs on grass hay diets. Also add one cup per cup of oil in excess of first cup added to ration (see text).
SUNFLOWER SEEDS (Optional)	Whole, clean, plump, dust free.		8oz (230g)	Optional - Provides ENERGY, PROTEIN, FIBER and POLYUNSATURATED OIL for coat condition. Palatable.
POLY- UNSATURATED OIL (eg Corn Oil) (Optional)	Non rancid. Keep well sealed. Mix well into feed.	8oz (250ml) 2 teacups up to 1lb (500ml) 4 teacups	8oz (250ml) 2 teacups up to 1lb (500ml) 4 teacups	Optional - ENERGY - high density, minimum bulk. Although included as an optional feed, oil is an excellent source of high density energy in place of oats to reduce bulk of ration and gut content/weight. Introduce in a stepwise manner over 10-14 days equally for larger amounts. Vitamin E, calcium, phosphorus and protein must be added. See text for full details.
ALFALFA PELLETS/ CRUMBLED CUBES (Optional)	Commercial pellets/cubes. Dry, no mold.	2lbs (900g)	3lb (1.4kg)	Optional - ENERGY, PROTEIN and CALCIUM - bulks out grain feed for horses that eat concentrates quickly. Chopped alfalfa or mixed hay may be fed - substitute for long hay. Note: Adds suitable roughage base for high levels of oil (1lb - 500mL) each feed.
MOLASSES	Mix 50:50 with warm water. Mix well into feed.		8oz (230g) (1½ teacups) (Not required if commercial sweet feed given.)	ENERGY and some CALCIUM. Damp sweetened feed improves acceptance, reduces dust, prevents selection and sifting of ingredients. If dry morning feed preferred, add total amount (8oz) (230g) to evening feed, especially if alfalfa cubes mixed with grain.
COMMERCIAL VITAMIN/TRACE MINERAL SUPPLEMENT	Mix well into feed.		eg Feramo-H 2oz (57g) (½ scoop)	Supplements low feed levels with range of essential vitamins, including vitamin A and D to fortify grass roughage based rations; iron, copper, cobalt and zinc for blood and coat condition, and optimum muscle function.
VITAMIN E SUPPLEMENT	Mix well into feed.	eg White-E 1000iu minimum (1 scoop)		Supplements low feed levels. Vitamin E is important for aerobic energy pathways and muscle formation. Up to 4000iu daily may be beneficial in preparation for long distance rides (see text).
ELECTROLYTE SUPPLEMENT	Mix well into feed.	eg Humidimix 3/4oz (22.5g) (1 scoop)	eg Humidimix 3/4oz (22.5g) (1 scoop)	Supplements inadequate levels in diet - particularly potassium and chloride to replace sweat loss over long distance exercise. Double doses in hot weather, heavy sweat output or long distance competition. (See also Recharge drink after exercise - in text.)

INGREDIENT	FORM/MIX	DAILY AMOUNT		PROVIDES
		AM	PM	
B COMPLEX VITAMIN SUPPLEMENT (Optional)	Concentrated vitamins. Give as oral drench or mix well into feed.	eg Pulse-8 2oz (60ml) (1oz Part A, 1oz Part B)		Supplements inadequate feed levels to help maintain appetite during and following hard competition. Can be administered orally by syringe over tongue - see text.
DICALCIUM PHOSPHATE	DCP. Free flowing, dry. Mix well into feed.		All hay alternatives add 1oz (30g) 2 tblsp. If poly-unsaturated oil substituted for grain, for each 2 teacups oil add ½oz (15g - 1 tblsp) DCP.	An adequate amount to ensure calcium and phosphorus to replace heavy sweat loss of calcium, and bone turnover losses during long distance exercise is essential to prevent bone weakness. Do not give excess calcium during training. When oil used as an energy source to replace grain, extra calcium and phosphorus is needed.
CALCIUM CARBONATE (Optional)	Ground limestone. Free flowing dry. Mix well into feed.		Grass hay - 1oz (30g) 2 tblsp.	Extra calcium to meet daily needs and provide extra for heavy sweat loss and grass hay diets. Do not give excess calcium during training.
ALFALFA HAY	Leafy, no dust, dampen if necessary.	4lb (1.8kg)	6lb (2.7kg)	Do not feed alfalfa hay routinely during training (see text). Replace grass hay with alfalfa hay only during the 2-3 days prior to a ride to boost calcium reserves.
CLOVER HAY or alternatively	Leafy, clean, no dust, dampen if necessary	4lb (1.8kg)	7lb (3.2kg)	Hay provides roughage and should constitute at least 50% of grain based rations by weight, and 60% of oil-containing rations by weight. Roughage traps water in the large bowel as a reserve against dehydration (see text).
GRASS HAY	Leafy, no weeds, no dust, dampen if necessary.	4lb (1.8kg)	5lb (2.3kg)	

NUTRITIONAL INFORMATION: This ration is formulated for an endurance horse in training, with access to pasture. Horses with access to good quality pasture may train and perform well on 2/3 of the suggested grain level. Horses that are stabled for longer periods may need more grain to counteract fretting due to confinement under similar training programs. Because of the wide range of training distances and speeds, adjustment to maintain optimum static bodyweight may be necessary. Each 26.5lb (12kg) ration provides approximately 30.5-31.6 Mcals (127-132MJ) digestible energy, 1200-1400g (ave 1300g) (10.8%) crude protein, and a minimum 42g calcium and 33g phosphorus. Do not feed excess calcium during training.

SECTION SIX

SHOW HORSES
PLEASURE HORSES

Show and pleasure horses are probably the best cared for class of horse in terms of feeding and health awareness. Most owners want their horses to be contented, and look their best, and this often results in overfeeding in relation to maintenance and exercise needs.

Many of the common behavioural problems are a result of excess energy in relation to exercise requirements, which can fuel a naturally nervous temperament and result in playful, hot manners. However, with experience gained in the show ring, and relatively minor adjustments to the dietary composition, many of these horses develop into controlled, highly trained competitors.

In recent years, interest in breeding and showing draft horses has been rekindled, with many heavy horse breeds being raised and trained for show and demonstration team work. Many of the long forgotten skills of feeding and management of draft horses are being revived. Owners are often amazed at the smaller relative amount of feed that the quieter, slower moving working draft horses require when compared to the amount consumed by exercising light horse breeds.

Ponies are also popular both for recreational use by children, and as specific breeds in the show ring. True pony breeds are often good doers, and even on relatively poor pasture, they are prone to gaining weight when only exercised on an occasional leisure time basis. Crossbred ponies can be considered as small horses and often they need more feed on a weight basis compared to purebred ponies.

SHOW HORSES,
WESTERN PLEASURE HORSES,
DRESSAGE HORSES

English and Western pleasure and Show horses and lower level equitation horses are traditionally well cared for in terms of general health, feeding and grooming. These horses are trained to exhibit faultless manners and movement, and most show standards require them to be robust and well conditioned with a shiny hair coat. In order to maintain adequate condition and a high standard of coat hair it is necessary to stable, groom, rug and hood these horses for most of their competitive life.

Surveys have shown that show and equitation horse owners feed a large variety of ration mixes. Many competitors have developed complicated rations and their own ways of feeding to maintain optimum show condition.

Traditionally, re-schooled Thoroughbreds constituted a large proportion of English Pleasure and Dressage horses. In recent times Warmblood breeds and their Thoroughbred crosses have been preferred because of their quieter temperament, size and natural, flowing movements.

Nutritional Requirements

Whilst speed is not required, adequate nutrition must be provided to allow for daily training sessions of sixty minutes or more, and to maintain optimum body and coat condition. Feeding should be individually modified to help ensure a calm, well mannered, but responsive horse in the show ring. When horses are travelled extensively to compete they must maintain their appetite and be prevented from dehydrating during travelling, as this will dry out the coat, and reduce general vitality.

Energy

Energy level in the ration must be adequate to maintain robust body condition, without making a horse hot mannered, playful and above the bit. The amount and type of energy feed used depends on the individual horse's temperament, work load and acceptance of feeds. Fats are becoming popular as a source of slow release energy for pleasure and show horses.

Feeding of Grain

Some horses have a reputation for becoming hot mannered and nervy on highly fermentable carbohydrate feeds, even when offered relatively small amounts of grains, such as oats. In many cases, this is due to excessive grain relative to the amount of work given to the horse. If a show horse is not being worked regularly, then the amount of grain in the ration should be minimal.

HINT
Many racehorses that are purchased off the track for re-schooling for showing and equitation, are accustomed to smaller volume, high energy dense rations. They have not had their digestive tracts stretched by a largely hay or pasture diet, and may take up to six months or longer to fill out into the proportions required in the show ring, eat a larger volume of feed, and efficiently use the higher roughage diets. However, with time, many become much quieter and settled as a show horse with adequate condition. Higher grain rations will encourage such horses to put on fat over the ribs and round off the rump, but may make them harder to handle and less manageable in the show ring.

Some horses maintain a better appetite when a small amount of grain is given as concentrate feed to supplement hay, so it may not be practical to initially withdraw grain from the ration.

Protein

The protein requirement in show and dressage horses is generally less than for performance horses, but adequate protein must be provided for exercise and body development. Most rations based on alfalfa or mixed hay will provide more protein than is required. For show and equitation horses, it is unnecessary to add extra protein meals such as soybean or linseed meal, unless the horse requires building up.

HINT
Once the horse reaches the desired bodyweight, and is in good show condition, there is normally no need to add extra protein meal. However, about 1lb (450g) of linseed meal, or alternatively, ½lb (about 230g) of sunflower seeds may be mixed into the ration to provide polyunsaturated fats for coat condition.

Fiber

As many higher level equitation and Dressage horses are stabled with limited access to pasture during the show season, adequate fiber must be provided in the ration. Insufficient fiber in the ration will reduce digestive function and increase the risk of stabled horses developing habits or vices such as eating their bedding, wood chewing, and eventually, wind sucking. These pastimes commonly develop because of boredom when horses are confined to stables without adequate exercise or companionship, or are fed on low bulk feeds.

HINT
In stabled horses it is best to provide the bulk of hay with the overnight feed to keep the horse occupied. In some areas, wheat bran is popular as a laxative feed for show horses on dry rations, but it actually has little laxative effect in the amounts given in dry feeds. However, bran is palatable to most horses, and a couple of cups a day mixed into a damp feed will often help increase the general acceptance of the ration.

Calcium

Adult horses maintained on alfalfa and mixed hay based rations, and receiving only small amounts of grain or wheat bran, do not generally need additional calcium to meet requirements. However, in heavily sweating show horses, and those receiving cereal based rations (grains and grass hay) or grazing on grass based pastures, then extra calcium should be added to the ration.

HINT
In these horses, a supplement 3/4oz (20g or 1½ tablespoon) calcium carbonate will help to balance the calcium:phosphorus ratio and maintain an adequate intake of calcium and essential bone forming minerals. As calcium is lost in sweat, show horses that sweat heavily require more calcium, which is normally satisfied by 1-1¼oz (28.5-36g or 2-2½ tablespoons) of calcium carbonate daily. (See Ration Guidelines.)

Electrolytes

Although 2-3 tablespoons of salt will improve the palatability of the ration, it is not a complete electrolyte replacer for heavy sweating horses. Supplementation with a range of electrolytes is recommended during hot weather or when horses are travelling over long distances. Highly strung or nervy horses that anticipate competition and "compete before their class", particularly when waiting around at shows, will often break into a nervy sweat. This can cause dry out and dull the coat, detracting from its appearance.

HINT
In cooler weather, or when horses are not sweating heavily, only half the recommended rate of an electrolyte supplement given morning and evening will meet daily needs. During the warmer months, when horses are travelling regularly, for horses that sweat up when worked, or sweat up when excited at shows, increase the amount (such as one scoop of Humidimix morning and evening) to meet needs.

Water

All horses must be provided with an adequate supply of clean, fresh water at all times. It is especially important to provide adequate water during hot weather or travelling, when they sweat heavily.

A typical Thoroughbred Showhorse requires at least 5-6 gallons (about 20-25 liters) of water per day. Up to double this amount may be consumed during hot weather or when large amounts of dry feed are given.

Rehydration drinks (such as Recharge mixed into water) are also available for use after travelling or competition to rapidly replenish fluid and electrolyte levels.

I have found these commercial supplements help to restore vitality and coat condition after a workout in the show arena.

Nutritional Management

The above dietary guidelines are based on scientific and practical feeding recommendations. Many experienced Western, Show and Dressage horse owners have developed successful diets that condition their horses for the show ring and as a consequence, may be reluctant to modify their own rations or ideas on feeding show horses. The information below is provided to enable diet changes to suit individual horses or local availability of feeds.

Feed Substitutions

Oats

Oats is still the traditional grain fed to horses in many areas, and most horses find it palatable. It is a safe grain that is unlikely to cause digestive upset even when gorged. However, even small amounts of oats have a reputation for making horses playful hot mannered and above themselves. This is more likely in horses that are not worked on a regular basis. In my experience, some horses become less excitable when rolled barley is given as the major energy source instead of oats.

> HINT
>
> *Many Thoroughbred show horses become playful, hard to control, nervy or above themselves within 3-4 hours of being fed grain or other soluble carbohydrates. This is thought to be due to the slow control of blood sugar levels in the Thoroughbred, resulting from a delayed release of insulin in response to elevated blood sugar levels as the grain is digested. To avoid this problem, don't feed grain on the morning of a show or event.*

Barley

Whole barley is generally not palatable to most horses due to sharp awns on the grain. Whole barley softened by mixing into a damp feed, or steam rolled barley is more palatable and in my experience, seems to have a less heating or nerving effect than either oats or corn, despite having an intermediate energy content. Boiled barley may be less likely to cause over energetic behavior as fermentation of starch is retarded by cooking.

Commercially Prepared Feeds

There is a large variety of good quality commercially prepared farm/ranch mixes, working horse mixes and feed mixes formulated from low energy ingredients as **cool** feeds, available through produce stores. These feeds are time saving and convenient to feed, palatable, and provide a uniform intake of energy, protein and fiber. Check the analysis table on the bag and match the type of mix to the needs of your horse.

> HINT
>
> *Although some of these feeds have added vitamins and minerals, long term storage, particularly in a damp sweet feed type mix, may affect potency of the vitamin content in particular. A daily supplement of a mineral/vitamin mix (such as Feramo-H), will help ensure adequate intake of essential minerals and vitamins to correct losses in these feeds during storage, and maintain good coat condition.*

Fat

A daily supplement of 2oz (60ml) of polyunsaturated oil (eg corn oil) will provide essential fatty acids to ensure a shiny and well conditioned coat in the show ring. However, larger volumes of corn oil, and other polyunsaturated oils added to the diet can provide a useful slow release energy food that can reduce hot tempered behavior in some nervy or highly strung show horses.

> HINT
>
> *About half a pint (275ml) of corn oil has the same energy value as 1½lb (700g) of whole oats. At least half a pint (275ml) daily is recommended as a energy source for nervy types of horses; remember to reduce grains accordingly. See also page 25 for feeding details.*

Hot tempered or Nervy Horses

The ideal show mount should be calm and not go to pieces during competition. Feeding rations that are excessively high in energy will increase the risk of playful and hard-to-handle behavior. Always feed energy in proportion to the work load for the day. Feed each horse as an individual. Hard keepers may need more energy to maintain condition without causing handling problems.

> HINT
>
> *On forced rest days, (including lameness or sickness), feed only good quality hay. On planned rest days, cut out the concentrate the night before, and re-introduce it over two days once regular exercise resumes. This will help reduce hot behavior and the risk of tying-up after a rest day.*

> HINT
>
> *Some horses are quiet, well mannered and easy to handle at home, but change their temperament on show day. Some owners work such a horse hard for 30-40 minutes before travelling to use up excess energy and tire the animal to calm its nervy behavior. However, this can put unnecessary strain on the musculo-skeletal system in horses that are given little or only light work during the week.*

Vitamin E

As tranquilizers, sedatives and other drug-induced calming agents are banned on competition days, manipulating the diet can be a useful way of settling down nervy behavior. The use of barley-based concentrate feeds and fats have been discussed above. Over recent years, high doses of supplementary Vitamin B1 and Vitamin E have been used successfully to maintain quiet, predictable temperaments for competition in horses that are nervy or upset by show day travelling, crowds or the stress of competing.

In my own experience as an owner of show and dressage horses, I have found that supplements of natural Vitamin E may help to maintain a more settled attitude in horses during travelling and competition. Whilst there are both synthetic (dl-alpha tocopherols) and naturally derived sources (d-alpha tocopherols) of vitamin E available, I consider supplements of natural source vitamin E to be more effective for this purpose.

I normally recommend an initial feed supplement of 1000iu of natural Vitamin E (such as White-E) in the morning feed for at least 7-10 days prior to the show or event. Then on the morning before and the morning of the competition, I advise

increasing the dose to 3000-4000iu. One or two courses of supplementary Vitamin E in this way may be required to get the best results in a horse that is unsettled on show or competition days.

Alternatively, supplementation with Vitamin B1 (about 3000mg) in the feed daily for 3-4 weeks may help settle some horses where the diet is low or inadequate in this vitamin. However, overall I have had best results with natural source vitamin E using the regimen described above. In a horse that sweats heavily during exercise or travelling, I also recommend a supplement of body salts (such as in Humidimix) to maintain adequate electrolyte intake, particularly for horses that are stabled without regular access to green pasture. If adequate electrolytes are not supplemented, I have found that heavy sweating horses will often become spooky and more nervy after 4-6 weeks of daily arena training, especially during hot weather.

DIETARY GUIDELINES - ENGLISH AND WESTERN PLEASURE, SHOW, DRESSAGE HORSES AND EQUITATION HORSES.

1100-1200lb (500-550kg) adult horse. Confined to a stall with access to a corral. 45-60 mins light arena exercise at trot and canter or dressage training under saddle each day. Two concentrate feeds daily. Hay at lunchtime.

INGREDIENT	FORM/MIX	DAILY AMOUNT		PROVIDES
		AM	PM	
BARLEY or MILO	Rolled. Dust free. Crushed milo.	2lb (900g)	3lb (1.4kg)	ENERGY, PROTEIN, FIBER - in practice appears to be less likely to make horses hot tempered and playful as compared to oats.
OATS or alternatively	Whole. No dust.	1lb (450g)	3lb (1.4kg)	ENERGY, PROTEIN, FIBER - 50% may be replaced by oil for horses with nervy temperaments. Cut to half on rest days.
CORN (Optional)	Cracked/dust free. If purchased cracked, store in bag - fold down after use. Non rancid.	1lb (450g)	2½lb (1.1kg)	ENERGY, PROTEIN. Many riders consider corn as a "heating" feed - reduces bulk in horses that are picky eaters. If horse is working regularly, corn is an economical energy source. Cut out on rest days. Feed barley with additional oil to nervy horses.
COMMERCIAL SWEET FEED MIX (Optional)	Good quality sealed bags.		5½lb (2.5kg)	Alternative night feed - palatable, no mixing, convenient, particularly when travelling or competing.
SOYBEAN MEAL (Optional) or alternatively	Heat treated. Free flowing, non rancid.		8oz (230g)	Optional - ENERGY, PROTEIN - adds extra protein to meet needs on grass hay diets (see text).
SUNFLOWER SEEDS (Optional)	Plump, clean, dust free.	8oz (230g)	8oz (230g)	Alternative ENERGY and PROTEIN to soybean meal on grass hay diets - palatable. Also adds oil for coat condition.
POLY-UNSATURATED OIL (eg Corn Oil) (Optional)	Non rancid. Keep well sealed. Mix well into feed.	8oz (250ml) (2 teacups)	8oz (250ml) (2 teacups)	Optional - 2oz (60ml) daily promotes coat condition. Higher amounts as energy source for nervy horses, or during hot weather. Increases energy density for picky eaters. Reduce oats by 1½lb (700g) per 2 teacups of oil added. Introduce in a step-wise manner over 7-10 days (see text).

INGREDIENT	FORM/MIX	DAILY AMOUNT		PROVIDES
		AM	PM	
MOLASSES	Mix 50:50 with warm water. Mix well into feed.		8oz (230g) (1½ teacups) (Not required if commercial sweet feed given.)	ENERGY and some CALCIUM. Damp sweetened feed improves acceptance, reduces dust, prevents selection and sifting of ingredients. If dry morning feed preferred, add total amount (8oz) (230g) to evening feed, especially if alfalfa cubes mixed with grain.
ALFALFA PELLETS, CHOPPED HAY, CRUMBLED CUBES (Optional)	Commercial pellets/cubes. Dry, no mold.	2lb (900g)	2lb (900g)	Optional - ENERGY, PROTEIN and CALCIUM - bulks out grain feed for horses that eat concentrates quickly. Chopped alfalfa or mixed hay may be fed - substitute for long hay.
COMMERCIAL VITAMIN/TRACE MINERAL SUPPLEMENT	Mix well into feed.		eg Feramo-H (57g) (½ scoop)	Supplements low feed levels with a range of vitamins, particularly Vitamin A & D for grass roughage based diets, combined with iron, copper and zinc for optimum coat bloom and condition, working vitality and performance.
VITAMIN E SUPPLEMENT	Mix well into feed.	(eg White-E) 750-1000iu (3/4-1 scoop)		Supplements inadequate feed levels with Vitamin E for optimum muscle function. Higher doses can be used to help settle nervy horses on deficient diets in the pre-competition period (see text).
ELECTROLYTE SUPPLEMENT	Mix well into feed.	(eg Humidimix) 3/4oz (22.5g) (1 scoop)	(eg Humidimix) 3/4oz (22.5g) (1 scoop)	Provides salt and other electrolytes to meet needs and replace sweat loss in hard worked, heavily conditioned horses or during hot weather/travelling.
VITAMIN B COMPLEX SUPPLEMENT (Optional)	Concentrated vitamin supplement. Give as an oral drench or mix well into feed.		(eg Pulse-8) 2oz (60ml)	Supplements low feed levels with high levels of B complex vitamins to help maintain the appetite in horses that become picky eaters after hard exercise, travelling or competition. Very stable under storage - a handy supplement to have on hand for any horse off its feed.
DICALCIUM PHOSPHATE (Optional)	DCP. Free flowing, dry. Mix well into feed.		Full grain no DCP. Half grain 1oz (30g) (2 tblsp). Hay only 2oz (60g) (4 tblsp).	Not required on full grain diets. Essential to provide adequate phosphorus on half grain or full roughage diets. If polyunsaturated oil substituted for grain (see text), for each 2 teacups oil add ½oz (15g) (1 tblsp) DCP.
CALCIUM CARBONATE (Optional)	Ground limestone. Free flowing, dry. Mix well into feed.		3/4oz (20g) (1½ tblsp)	Provides extra calcium to make up the relative deficiency on grass hay based roughage diets. For heavily sweating, or young horses in training, add 1-1¼oz (28.5-36g) (2-2½ tblsp) daily to meet elevated needs.
MIXED HAY or alternatively GRASS HAY	Good quality, leafy, no dust or mold.	4lb (1.8kg) Lunchtime 3lb (1.4kg) 4lb (1.8kg)	5lb (2.3kg) 4lb (1.8kg)	ENERGY, PROTEIN, FIBER - Hay is essential roughage to bulk the diet and maintain digestive function. This diet does not contain alfalfa hay as the only hay source because of its higher protein content that exceeds the protein needs of the animal. A mixture of 50:50 alfalfa and grass hay, or mixed hay, is the ideal blend.

NUTRITIONAL INFORMATION: This ration is formulated for Show or equitation horse in training for dressage, or English or Western pleasure activities. The amount of grain must be adjusted to match the exercise level, temperament, and the desired body condition required in the horse. Access to grazing is considered a bonus and gives psychological relief from stable confinement or exercise routine. Each 22lb (10kg) of ration provides approximately 25Mcals (105MJ) digestible energy, 1000-1050g (ave 1025g) (10.25%) crude protein, and a minimum 33g calcium and 24g phosphorus. Additional hay may be provided to appetite overnight.

DRAFT HORSES

Over recent years, there has been renewed interest in heavy horse or draft horse breeds for pleasure, showing and team work. Draft horse teams are maintained by some corporations for promotional needs, and more heavy horses are being used for tillage and haulage work on farms.

Draft horses are built for strength and bulk of body and muscle, rather than speed. Early observations indicate that draft horses perform most efficiently when pulling and plowing at 2-2½ (3-4km) per hour.

In the show ring, heavy breeds are usually presented in a fleshy condition, with adequate bulk and development to meet breed standards for a working draft horse.

Nutritional Requirements

The nutritional requirements are related to use and type of work, the individual horses feeding efficiency, environment, and skill of the driver in handling a team. The guidelines given below refer only to adult heavy horse breeds.

Energy

Various studies have shown that draft horses require 15% less energy or approximately 1.27Mcal/100lb (45kg) bodyweight at rest, compared with 1.48Mcal/100lb for a lighter horse breed. Draft horses usually have a quieter natural temperament, move more slowly, and have a lower metabolic rate during exercise than lighter horses.

In most cases, draft horses can be maintained on good quality pasture, with a supplement of mixed or grass hay during periods of poor pasture availability or quality. Only when a horse is working regularly or being conditioned for showing, is grain required to provide energy in proportion to exercise on any particular day.

Heavily muscled horses, such as draft horses are prone to azoturia or "Monday Morning Disease" (a severe form of tying-up or exertional myopathy or acute muscle damage following hard work), if maintained on full grain rations over weekend rest days. It is essential that grain be reduced by at least half on a rest day, preferably from the night before, and resumed again over two days in proportion to the work load on the next full work day.

 HINT *Slow warm-up exercise of walking for at least 10 minutes should be given before hitching to plow or haul after a rest day.*

Although feeding fat would be suited to overall aerobic type of energy utilization in draft horses, it is not popular as most owners prefer to feed their animals adequate bulk of feed to keep them filled out in the gut, and trap adequate water reserves for sweat loss during hard work.

Protein

Observations suggest that draft horses performing haulage or plow work require a 10-11% protein diet, provided that adequate energy is fed to meet work needs. Some owners of working draft horses feed their horses on a corn and grass hay diet which usually has a protein level lower than 10%.

Fiber

Plenty of fiber is required for efficient digestion and most draft horses can be maintained on a full roughage diet of good quality grass or mixed hay. In years gone by, working draft horses were provided with 3 feeds per day, with the midday feed given in a nose bag in the field with a 70% grain to 30% chopped hay mix. The majority of hay (60-65%) was provided overnight. Morning and midday meals had higher proportions of grain to reduce gut bulk during work. The bulk of hay overnight is also useful to keep horses occupied and content by eating.

Electrolytes

The fluid and electrolyte loss in the sweat of draft horses is influenced by work load, climatic conditions and duration of work. Supplementation with salt should be adequate for lighter work loads for periods up to three hours daily. However, during hot weather when horses sweat heavily during work and rest, supplementation with additional calcium, potassium and magnesium, in addition to salt, is recommended to maintain vitality and water intake. Heavy horses require up to 20 gallons (about 80 liters) of water daily for plow or haulage work of 4-5 hours daily in moderate to warm conditions.

Vitamins/Minerals

Good quality pasture and hay will provide adequate vitamins and minerals for the type of light haulage work most heavy horses are used for nowadays. However, draft horses kept for demonstration and show purposes may benefit from supplementation with a wide range of these nutrients (such as in Feramo-H) to maintain coat condition and vitality required for exhibition or showring competition.

Nutritional Management

Grain Substitutions

Although the traditional diet for heavy horses was oats for energy and grass hay for bulk, draft horses can be fed on a variety of feeds including a corn and alfalfa diet. However, where alfalfa is used as the major source of roughage,

protein levels would exceed standard needs, so a 50:50 grass hay alfalfa mix would perhaps be more suitable. Where grass hay and corn are fed as the major feed, additional protein such as one pound (450g) of soybean meal may be required in working heavy horses.

Electrolytes

As outlined above, a supplement of salt 1½-2oz (43-57g or 2-3 tablespoons) daily should meet the needs of a draft horse performing up to 4 hours of work with access to pasture. However, once more grains are added for longer work periods, or if the animal is a heavy sweater under warm to hot conditions, then additional electrolytes, such as 2oz (60g or 3 scoops) of Humidimix, 3oz (90g or 6 tablespoons) of magnesium sulfate, and 3oz (90g or 6 tablespoons) of calcium carbonate may be required to meet needs on hard work days.

DIETARY GUIDELINES - DRAFT HORSES.

1400-1500lb (630-680kg) bodyweight. Exhibition work, light work, speed 2½ miles (4km) per hour. Stabled overnight. Training/handling exercise 1½-2 hours daily. One concentrate feed daily at night. Hay in morning and midday.

INGREDIENT	FORM/MIX	DAILY AMOUNT		PROVIDES
		AM and NOON	EVENING	
OATS or alternatively	Whole, heavy. Dust free.		7lb (3.2kg)	ENERGY, PROTEIN - increases energy density of ration for small framed or picky eaters. Cut out on rest days. Not heating if horse worked daily. Note: If no exercise - cut out grain, increase hay at night by 2lb (900g).
BARLEY	Rolled - dust free.		6½lb (3kg)	ENERGY, PROTEIN FIBER - may replace some or all of oats depending on availability and cost. On an energy basis 1lb (450g) oats can be replaced by 14½oz (410g) barley or milo.
MOLASSES (Optional)	Mix 50:50 with warm water. Mix well into feed.		4oz (115g) (3/4 teacup)	Aids palatability of ration, and ensures acceptance.
DEHYDRATED ALFALFA PELLETS/ CHOPPED HAY/ CUBES	Commercial pellets/cubes. Dry, no mold.		3lb (1.4kg)	Provides ENERGY, PROTEIN, FIBER and bulks out grain ration for fast eaters.
POLYUNSATURATED OIL (eg Corn Oil)	Non rancid. Keep well sealed. Mix well into feed.		4oz 114g (5½ tablespoons)	Provides essential fatty acids for coat condition for exhibition.
COMMERCIAL VITAMIN/TRACE MINERAL SUPPLEMENT	Mix well into feed.		(eg Feramo-H) 3oz (72g) (3/4 scoop)	Supplements low feed levels with range of vitamins, including vitamins A and D to fortify grass roughage based rations; iron, copper, cobalt and zinc for blood and coat condition, and optimum muscle function.
ELECTROLYTE SUPPLEMENT	Mix well into feed.		(eg Humidimix) 1¼oz (35g) 1½ scoops	Maintenance - give 2oz (60g or 4 tblsp salt). Extra salt mix supplements inadequate feed levels to provide electrolytes lost in sweat during light work or hot weather. Heavy sweaters, give 1½oz (42g) (2 scoops).
DICALCIUM PHOSPHATE	DCP. Free flowing, dry. Mix well into feed.		1oz (30g) (2 tablespoons)	Calcium and phosphorus to balance Ca:P ratio and correct phosphorus deficiency. Important in heavily sweating horses - give extra 1oz (30g) daily.
ALFALFA HAY and GRASS HAY mix	Leafy, no dust. Dampen cubes to soften (see text). (Mix of alfalfa and Grass Hay.)	3lb (1.4kg) morning and midday 4lb (1.8kg)	2½lb (1.1kg) mixed evening 2½lb (1.1kg)	Provides ENERGY, PROTEIN, FIBER and CALCIUM. Alfalfa adds extra protein than mixed or grass hay - ideal for building up horses. Dampen cubes to soften (see text). Alternatively, the total morning and midday feed (6lb or 2.8kg) alfalfa hay may be fed as a morning feed, and all the grass hay (8lb or 3.6kg) at midday or early afternoon.
MIXED HAY	Leafy, no weeds, no dust, dampen if necessary.	7lb (3.2kg)	5lb (2.3kg)	Low in nutrients relative to alfalfa - but usually palatable. Bulk must be limited to ensure full consumption and protein source added (see text). If horse is hungry, add more hay as bulk.

NUTRITIONAL INFORMATION: This ration is formulated for a 1400-1500lb (650kg ave) draft horse doing light exercise in training for exhibition or driving and team work as a hobby. Each 26lb (12kg) of total ration contains approximately 26Mcals (109MJ) digestible energy, 1330g (11%) crude protein, and a minimum 44g calcium and 26.5g phosphorus.

PONIES

Riding Ponies can be either ridden daily, or kept at grass and ridden for pleasure by children on the weekend.

In most cases, a mature pony at grass will maintain itself on pasture for light exercise each day, and pony club activities on the weekend. Many pony breeds are easy keepers, and it is often difficult to prevent them becoming overweight even on pasture.

> **HINT** *Grazing intake can be restricted, and exercise encouraged, by fitting a mesh muzzle for 8-20 hours per day (as used for racehorses on race day) to decrease grazing without confinement. Actually increases exercise as ponies walk more when muzzled in the search for longer grass.*

In the Spring, with the increased growth of pasture with soluble sugar and protein intake, overweight ponies are prone to laminitis or grass founder.

> **HINT** *Heavily conditioned pony breeds with a cresty neck and long toes, are more likely to founder on spring pastures. Pasture intake in these ponies must be restricted to a maximum of 2-3 hours of grazing daily.*

If possible, shift high-risk ponies to poorer pasture, or confine them to large corrals with daily exercise or fit a mesh muzzle as described above. A ration consisting of chopped grass hay, 5% wheat bran, and 1% salt, offered at the maintenance rate of 1.5% bodyweight is useful to limit energy and protein needs without starving the animal.

Long shelly toes should be cut back to improve the comfort of walking and general hoof circulation. Consult your farrier or vet. Long toes should be avoided in grazing ponies by regular hoof trimming to reduce the tendency to founder.

> **HINT** *A daily supplement of selenium is recommended for ponies grazing legume or clover pastures on selenium-deficient areas. Many veterinarians report that supplementation with selenium under these conditions appears to help reduce the incidence of founder in ponies. More research is required to establish such a relationship. Initially, a course of weekly injectable selenium may be prescribed by your veterinarian, in conjunction with a daily maintenance level provided by a feed supplement.*

High risk ponies should be given exercise by riding or light longeing to utilize energy and reduce the risk of founder. However, if a pony is lame with founder do not force it to exercise, as tearing and severe damage to the hoof laminae may result. Consult your vet for advice.

NOTE: Overweight pony breeds should not be suddenly starved or drastically cut back in feed as a means of preventing or treating founder. When a pony is starved or fasted for more than 12 hours, mobilized body fat reserves can accumulate in the blood. These fats can deposit in the liver, and in extreme cases can lead to severe sickness and death within ten days of starvation. (See page 149.)

The condition can be triggered by withdrawal of food in grazing ponies due to sudden flooding snow falls, heavy summer rains destroying dried grass pastures, lameness that hampers grazing, and bossing away from feeders of newly introduced ponies, particularly young mares at stud. Ponies that are hauled for more than 8 hours without food are also at risk. It can affect fat or thin ponies that are starved, and pregnant pony mares are more likely to develop the problem. The condition has also been reported in Thoroughbreds on starvation diets.

> **HINT** *The symptoms include depression, muscle tremors, weakness, loss of appetite and vitality. If you notice these symptoms in your pony, consult your veterinarian immediately for advice. It may be that a pony was accidentally starved of feed during the previous few days by inclement weather, lameness, injury, sickness, misadventure or long distance travelling. (See page 149.)*

Nutritional Requirements

Traditional pony breeds, such as the Welsh Mountain Pony, Shetland etc require relatively small amounts of feed to maintain themselves. It is considered that harsh environment have adapted these animals to a lower comparative energy need on a bodyweight basis than horse breeds. Cross bred ponies can be considered as little horses on a direct bodyweight comparison.

DIETARY GUIDELINES - SHOW, WORKING, PLEASURE PONY.

600-700lb (270-320kg) adult Crossbred pony. Stabled overnight, yard or small paddock. 30 minutes light exercise daily with competition or Pony Club on weekends. Two feeds daily.

Note: *Purebred pony breeds can be maintained on 1.3% of bodyweight of good quality hay. Many ponies are easy keepers, and the grain content of the diet may need to be reduced to maintain the desired bodyweight and avoid obesity.*

INGREDIENT	FORM/MIX	DAILY AMOUNT		PROVIDES
		AM	PM	
BARLEY or alternatively	Rolled. No dust.	2lb (900g)	2½-3lb (1.1-1.4kg)	ENERGY, PROTEIN, FIBER - less likely to make ponies playful - suitable energy source for ponies with nervy temperaments. Higher amount if pony is to be kept in show condition. Cut to one third on rest days.
OATS or alternatively	Whole, heavy. No dust	2lb (900g)	3-3½lb (1.4-1.6kg)	ENERGY, PROTEIN, FIBER - traditional energy feed but may make some ponies playful even with adequate exercise. Cut to one third on rest days - feed extra hay.
COMMERCIAL SWEET FEED MIX (Optional)	Good quality sealed bags.		3lb (1.4kg)	Alternative night feed - palatable, no mixing, convenient, particularly when feeding in riding schools, when travelling or competing. Cut to one third on rest days - feed extra hay.
POLYUNSATURATED OIL (Optional) or alternatively	Non-rancid. Keep well sealed. Mix well into feed.		1½oz (45ml) (2½ tblsp)	Essential fatty acids for coat bloom and condition. Can be used as an energy source - 1 teacup (120ml) replaces 12oz (340g) oats in feed. Introduce in a step-wise manner over 7-10 days (see text).
SUNFLOWER SEEDS (Optional)	Plump, clean, dust free.		5½oz (160g)	Alternative source of oil for coat condition - adds extra protein, recommended when grass hay is provided (see grass hay below).
MOLASSES	Mix 50:50 with warm water. Mix well into feed.		4oz (115g) (3/4 teacup) (Not required if commercial sweet feed given.)	ENERGY and SWEETENER - improves palatability of ration, reduces dust and prevents sifting out. Some ponies do not like sweet tastes - add 3-4 drops vanilla essence to feed (see text).
ALFALFA PELLETS/ CHOPPED HAY, CRUMBLED CUBES (Optional)	Commercial pellets/cubes. Dry, no mold.	1lb (450g)	1½lb (700g)	Optional - ENERGY, PROTEIN, CALCIUM - bulks out grain feed for horses that eat concentrates quickly. Reduce weight of hay offered with meal accordingly.
COMMERCIAL VITAMIN/TRACE MINERAL SUPPLEMENT	Mix well into feed.		(eg Feramo-H) 1oz (28.5g) (¼ scoop)	Supplements low feed levels with a wide range of vitamins and trace minerals to ensure health, vitality and bloom in the coat. Vitamin A & D make up inadequate levels on grass hay based diets.
DICALCIUM PHOSPHATE	DCP. Free flowing, dry. Mix well into feed.		½oz (15g) (1 tblsp)	Provides CALCIUM and PHOSPHORUS to balance diet and meet minimum requirements for bone and muscle development. In practice, an extra ½ oz (15g) (3 tspns) of calcium carbonate (ground limestone) could be added to diets of heavy sweating ponies.
SALT	Fine salt. Mix well into feed.		1/3oz (10g) 2 tspns	Improves palatability of ration and encourages water intake. NOTE: If pony is a heavy sweater when worked or during hot weather, add 2 3/4oz (22.5g), (1 scoop) of Humidimix acid salt mix to feed in place of salt (see text).
MIXED HAY or alternatively	Good quality, leafy, no dust or mold.	3lb (1.3kg)	4lb (1.8kg)	ENERGY, PROTEIN, FIBER - Hay is essential roughage to bulk the diet and maintain digestive function. This diet does not contain alfalfa hay as the only hay source because of its high protein, content, which exceeds needs. A mixture of 50:50 alfalfa and grass hay, or mixed hay is ideal.
GRASS HAY	Good quality, leafy, no dust, no mold, sweet.	3lb (1.3kg)	4lb (1.8kg)	Grass hay is lower in energy and protein than alfalfa or mixed hay. Normally, in larger horses, the bulkiness limits the amount that can be consumed. However in ponies, the bulk difference is usually not a problem. A protein source, such as sunflower seeds, is a practical way of providing oil for coat condition, and boosting protein levels in grass roughage based diets.

NUTRITIONAL INFORMATION: The ration is formulated for an adult pony that is exercised daily, or has access to a small sparsely grassed paddock, according to NRC (1989) guidelines. Each 12¼lb (5.6kg) of ration provides approximately 13.5Mcals (56.5MJ) digestible energy, average 575g (10.2%) protein, and a minimum 20g calcium and 16.5g phosphorus.

Traditional Pony Breeds

As a guideline, provide about one third of the total ration required for a true horse breed, on a bodyweight basis. Research indicates that small pony mares require 10-15% less energy than horses, on a bodyweight basis.

HINT	*As a starting point for hand feeding, a 450lb (about 200kg) pony requires about one third of the maintenance energy needs of a 900lb (400kg) horse. The feed intake can then be adjusted to maintain the animal's most desirable condition and fed in proportion to the daily exercise level. Resting ponies can be maintained on a dietary intake of 1.3% of their bodyweight on good quality hay. However, some individual ponies are*

easy keepers. Feed intake must be adjusted to avoid obesity.

Nutritional Management

In ponies used for club and competitive riding, the nutritional management as outlined for hacks is applicable. This includes substitution to rolled barley or fat as an energy source in hot tempered ponies, and use of higher supplementary levels of natural vitamin E (such as White-E 1500-2000iu) on the morning before and morning of competition. If Vitamin E is to be supplemented for this purpose, I have found that a pony should be maintained on 500iu Vitamin E daily for at least 7-10 days before increasing the dose on the two days prior to competition. (See Hints on Management, page 120.)

SECTION SEVEN

BREEDING HORSES

Over recent years, much more research effort has been focused on the nutritional requirements and feeding management of breeding horses. Although large sums of money are often spent on the purchase of breeding farms and stock, in up-grading facilities, promotion of stallions and raising young horses, relatively little attention is given to ensuring optimum nutrition of brood mares.

Fertility and nutrition are inter-related, so careful feeding which supplements grazing to ensure optimum energy intake, and provision of a balanced diet, will set the foundation for success in horse breeding. Even when a well balanced and adequate ration may be provided, the social interaction in groups of grazing mares may result in large differences in feed intake and subsequent fertility and conception rates.

Horse breeders often overfeed pregnant mares and growing horses, but fail to recognize the increased needs of the lactating broodmare, where inadequate nutrition will extend their breeding intervals.

In this section, the nutritional and practical aspects of feeding the broodmare and stallion are discussed, with hints on feeding management of mare groups to help ensure that nutrition is not a limiting factor to breeding performance.

OPEN, NON PREGNANT MARES

Adequate nutrition is essential to enable a mare to breed regularly. Although large investments are often made to purchase breeding mares, there is little attention paid to their specific nutrition. Valuable brood mares are put in foal annually, often with only a month or so between pregnancies onto which is superimposed the drain of lactation. Mares are often bred beyond 20 years of age, with little time for restoring body stores during their breeding lifetime. Spring, with its seasonal boost to pasture growth, and increasing day length, initiates the breeding cycle. In spring, mares lose their winter coats, and the increasing day length during the late spring and summer months is the ideal time to breed mares. In good seasons, the green pasture flush during March to May increases nutritional intake and helps maximize fertility and conception rates.

Inadequate nutrition is one of the main underlying reasons for infertility in mares. Some stud farms overseed pastures with oats or barley during the winter time to provide green pasture in the lead up to the breeding season.

Well fed, but not overly fat mares have been shown to ovulate earlier, with more regular cycles, than fat and overweight mares on a maintenance or poor quality diet. Studies have shown that fat and overweight mares will cycle and conceive successfully if their nutritional intake is maintained. It is unwise to start weight reducing programs on obese mares within the last couple of months before breeding.

HINT *Newly introduced mares often suffer nutritional stress when bossed away from feeders, losing condition and failing to cycle and conceive early in the season. It is best to segregate new and maiden mares away from socialized and older mares on larger breeding farms.*

In practical terms, a rising plane of nutrition appears to improve fertility and conception rates of mares in light to medium condition. The gradual build-up of the feed intake should commence at least 4-6 weeks prior to mating. Heavier mares should be maintained at a constant bodyweight, without obesity.

Nutritional Requirements

Energy

Mares should be maintained in reasonable condition over the winter months. Increasing the energy level on a rising plane prior to the breeding season may improve fertility. There is no practical advantage from a "flushing" feeding program, but thin mares should be fed to achieve a fleshy but not fat condition by the time of breeding.

HINT *Surveys indicate that mares have higher conception rates when maintained at a bodyweight score of 5 or above (see page 166 for Condition Score Appraisal).*

Protein

A maintenance level is required, with a gradual increase in parallel with energy levels at the onset of the breeding season.

Fiber

Adequate fiber is essential to match grain intake in concentrate feeds. Excessive amounts of poor quality roughage in grazing mares may reduce the beneficial response to a rising plane of nutrition before the start of the breeding season.

Minerals

A balanced level of all minerals, including calcium, is required, particularly once the mare conceives.

Vitamins

A supplement of Vitamin A, and possibly Vitamin E, may help fertility, particularly on diets containing dried feed and hay that often have low or inadequate levels or an imbalance of these vitamins.

HINT *I have found that mares grazing on predominately alfalfa pastures and hay improve in follicle size and conception rates when supplemented with 1500-2000iu Vitamin E daily for four weeks prior to breeding.*

Exercise

Exercise is important to improve general fitness, feed conversion and health of the mare. Mares grazing on hilly country usually exercise themselves. Spacing out of feeding and watering points also encourages exercise. Where mares are confined to smaller paddocks, light exercise under saddle, or even longeing, will be beneficial as the breeding season approaches.

Nutritional Management

Maintain Body Condition

Regularly observe the mare's condition and quality of the grazing so as to avoid any loss of condition in the 4-6 weeks prior to planned breeding. Some mares will need supplementation with concentrate feed to build up or maintain body condition, particularly during cold, wet, windy weather conditions.

HINT *As a guideline, increase the concentrate by 2oz per 100lb bodyweight (60g/50kg) per week over a 4-6 week period leading up to the breeding season. Do not allow mares to become grossly overweight, but feed sufficient concentrate to maintain condition in fat mares or easy keepers.*

HINT *In older Thoroughbred mares that fall away in condition, their vulva and anus tend to slope inward under the tail area. This increases the risk of vaginal windsucking (pneumovagina) and contamination with their own manure, leading to breeding tract infection. On larger breeding farms, it is best to separate underweight older mares with sunken anal areas into a small group. Check teeth, de-worm and feed a higher energy ration to build-up condition over a 4-6 week period. As they gain condition, their anus and vulva will return to a more upright and normal conformation. The upper vulva area may be stitched closed using Caslick's procedure to reduce the intake of air and fecal contamination when galloping at pasture. Consult your vet for advice.*

Shy Young Mares

On larger breeding farms, it is sound husbandry to separate maiden mares from older mares, and feed them in a separate group. New mares, or shy timid mares may be bossed away from feeders, and fall away in condition. Sudden nutritional stress of this type may lead to hyperlipidosis in young pony mares. (See page 149.)

HINT *In larger groups of mares, it is a good idea to locate two or more feeders away from the main feed area to help ensure bossed mares are able to consume their supplementary feed in relative peace. (See Feed Tubs, page 29.)*

HINT *On arrival, de-worm a new mare and quarantine in a yard for 24-48 hours to empty out feces after worming. Bring a mare known to be lower in the peck order from the pasture and put her in a yard next to the new mare for 24 hours or so. Often mares will form a friendship which provides security and settles a young or timid mare. They can then both be turned out together into a group of mares.*

Other Helpful Management Hints

☞ If the mare is being sent away to a breeding farm, ask the manager for a feeding program that will coincide with that of the farm. Many managers prefer to receive mares in less than optimum condition and then introduce them to a program of rising nutrition. If mares fall away in condition when sent for breeding their fertility and conception rate may be adversely affected.

☞ Always let down a mare in work being fed on highly-concentrated rations at least 2-3 months before the breeding season. Alternatively, have her mated whilst still on the work ration, and in training. After 90 days of grazing, then slowly reduce the feed by 2oz per 100lb bodyweight (60g/45kg) a week to the level required for mid pregnancy. Overly fat mares should not lose more than 1lb per 100lb bodyweight (1kg/100kg) per week. This will avoid a sudden decrease in nutritional intake that may affect chances of the mare conceiving and maintaining early pregnancy.

☞ Worm grazing mares regularly every 6-8 weeks. It is good practice to worm poorly-conditioned mares twice three weeks apart, and have their teeth checked or rasped, to obtain maximum benefit from the rising plane of nutrition in preparation for breeding.

DIETARY GUIDELINES - OPEN, NON PREGNANT MARE

1000-1100lb (450-500kg) bodyweight. Four weeks prior to breeding. Poor general condition, (Condition Score 3-4) grazing on poor pasture. One concentrate feed, two hay feeds daily. The ration is also suitable for a pregnant mare up to eight months in foal.

INGREDIENT	FORM/MIX	DAILY AMOUNT Morning	DAILY AMOUNT Evening	PROVIDES
OATS or alternatively	Whole, heavy, dust free.		6lb (2.7kg)	ENERGY, PROTEIN, FIBER - traditional safe grain easily fed in feed bins with hay. Increase by 20% in cold weather to maintain a rising plane of nutrition in open mares in poor condition.
BARLEY or alternatively	Rolled, dust free.		5½lb (2.5kg)	Alternative ENERGY, PROTEIN and FIBER sources to oats, selected on availability and price. Adequate energy must be provided to ensure breeding cycles are initiated.
MILO or alternatively	Crushed, dust free.		5½lb (2.5kg)	
50:50 OATS:CORN MIX	Mix whole oats and cracked corn as grain mix.		5½lb (2.5kg)	
ALFALFA CUBES/ PELLETS. CHOPPED HAY (Optional)	Commercial pellets/cubes. Dry, no mold.		3lb (1.4kg)	Optional - Increases bulk of grain concentrate, slows gorging and reduces wastage of grain. Reduce amount of hay accordingly.
MOLASSES (Optional)	Mix 50:50 with warm water.		4oz (115g) (3/4 teacup) Add 8oz (230g) (1½ teacups) if alfalfa cubes/pellet option used.	SWEETENER - useful to dampen grain mix and prevents sifting and loss of dry powder supplements blowing away in wind.
COMMERCIAL VITAMIN/TRACE MINERAL SUPPLEMENT	Mix well into feed.		(eg Feramo-H) 2oz (57g) (½ scoop)	Supplements low feed levels with high levels of Vitamin A which is an important nutrient for fertility. B complex vitamins and trace minerals are included for appetite and general condition.
VITAMIN E SUPPLEMENT	Mix well into feed.		(eg White-E) 1000-1500iu	Supplements inadequate feed levels. The grain mix should be dampened to prevent loss of powder. Mix the Vitamin E into the top portion of the feed to reduce contact with trace minerals in mineral supplement. For difficult breeders, 2000iu daily for at least four weeks prior to breeding season may be provided.
SALT	Fine		2/3oz (20g) (1½ tblsp)	Improves palatability and meets sodium requirements.
MIXED HAY or alternatively	Leafy, no dust or mold.	5lb (2.3kg)	6lb (2.7kg)	ENERGY, PROTEIN and FIBER - mixed hay is preferred as protein content meets needs. Alternatively feed 5lb (2.3kg) alfalfa in morning and 6lb (2.7kg) grass hay in evening.
GRASS HAY	Leafy, no dust	5lb (2.3kg)	7lb (3.2kg)	ENERGY, PROTEIN and FIBER - lower protein than mixed hay but increased amount will meet protein needs (see text).

NUTRITIONAL INFORMATION: The ration is formulated to provide maintenance plus 10% energy and protein to assist in building up a mare in poor condition in preparation for breeding. Adjust ration intake to achieve a "fleshy" condition, Condition Score 5-6 preferably on a rising plane of nutrition. The open mare should be treated for worms twice, three weeks apart, and have her teeth checked. Each 16½lb (7.5kg) provides approximately 17.5Mcals (73MJ) digestible energy, 700-870g (ave 785g) (10.5%) crude protein, and a minimum 27g calcium and 19g phosphorus. Additional hay may be fed to appetite, to improve body condition if necessary particularly in cold weather. A 20% increase in oats is also recommended in cold and wet bleak weather to meet energy needs in open mares in poor condition.

PREGNANT MARES

The pregnant mare should be maintained in a medium, fleshy condition (Condition Score 5-6). Many experienced horse breeders feed to maintain their pregnant mares in working condition rather than heavy show condition. Many hobby owners over feed the pregnant mare in an effort to produce a large strong foal. Whilst studies have not linked overly fat mares with increased difficulty in foaling, many breeders claim that excessive condition can result in a higher incidence of foals with limb deviations. Obese mares at foaling that lose weight because of lack of adequate feed intake to meet lactation demand, are less likely to breed successfully in that breeding season.

As outlined in the dietary guidelines for open mares, an overweight or obese mare should not be put on a weight reduction program until she is bred, conceives and pregnancy is confirmed. Research has shown that pregnant mares which are fed on a diet with energy levels below their needs have a higher risk of abortion during the first three months of pregnancy than mares kept at a constant bodyweight. However, after 90 days of pregnancy, obese pregnant mares may be put onto a weight reducing diet and exercise program. Feed to achieve a weight loss of no more than 1% of bodyweight each week (ie 12lb weekly for a 1200lb mare).

HINT
Slowly reduce the concentrate, feed by about 2oz per 100lb bodyweight, (60g/45kg) per week, or restrict access to grazing and give the mare light exercise for 20-30 minutes under saddle 2-3 times per week.

The mare should not be starved, and not fed on poor quality hays with possible trace mineral deficiencies. She should be provided with adequate good quality protein (eg 2oz (60g) soybean meal per 100lb (45kg) bodyweight daily) and a supplement of vitamins and trace minerals, including copper.

HINT
Most pregnant mares can maintain themselves on good pasture, with minimal supplementary feed, as long as good quality alfalfa or mixed hay is fed during times of reduced pasture availability or quality. Pelleted rations are suitable for maintenance during dry seasons or the early winter months when pasture is poor, particularly as pregnancy progresses.

Unborn foals make half their growth to full-term size during the last 90 days of pregnancy. After the eight month of pregnancy a graded increase in energy, protein and mineral levels is important to provide nutrients for proper development of the foal, as well as to prepare the mare for the high demands of lactation.

During the last three months before foaling, it is best to separate heavily pregnant mares from other mares and horses. Young mares, or timid mares must be able to eat sufficient supplementary feed to meet their needs. Provide one extra feed tub or locate feed tubs away from the main feeder area for these mares.

As a commercial breeding proposition, the mare must be able to breed within 1-2 months of foaling. Failure to supply adequate nutrition to maintain bodyweight after foaling may reduce subsequent fertility and conception. (See Lactating Mares, page 134.)

Nutritional Requirements

Energy

For the first eight months of pregnancy, mares generally need only a ration that maintains them in a reasonable condition.

HINT
Ideally, the pregnant mare should have an overall fleshy cover, with the ribs and pin bones covered, but able to be felt under the skin.

As a guideline, the level of concentrate feed and hay should be increased by an average of 10% per month over the last three months before foaling. (See Ration Guideline for details.) This provides nutrients for increased growth rate of the unborn foal and will help prepare the mare for lactation.

Protein

Protein provides the amino acid building blocks for the development of the unborn foal. Good quality protein with adequate amino acid content is essential for fetal development, with the requirement increasing during the last three months of pregnancy.

Fiber

Fiber is important for efficient digestion. It is good practice to provide more energy dense, less bulky rations during the last couple of months of pregnancy because the enlarged womb reduces digestive capacity, and heavily pregnant mares are unable to eat large quantities of bulky food.

Minerals

All minerals are required in adequate amounts during pregnancy. However, increasing amounts of calcium, for fetal skeletal bone is required in late pregnancy, particularly in older mares (over 16 years of age). Supplementation with grain based concentrate during the last three months of pregnancy should contain extra calcium to provide for bone development in the unborn foal. At the foaling, requirement for calcium is increased by 50% for the forthcoming lactation. In areas where a copper deficiency is known, then a supplement of copper (20ppm) should be considered. Consult your vet for advice.

Vitamins

Vitamins are required to ensure adequate growth of the unborn foal. The requirement for Vitamin A doubles during the last quarter of pregnancy.

During the winter months, pregnant mares at pasture may not be able to synthesize sufficient Vitamin D from sunlight to meet requirements, so it is wise to provide a supplementary source of Vitamin D in the concentrate feed. Provision of good quality sun cured hay will also provide a natural feed source of vitamin D.

Exercise

Exercise is required to keep the mare in a fit condition for foaling. Grazing provides adequate exercise in most cases, although heavily pregnant mares in the last month prior to foaling are often less agile and prefer to graze within easy range of supplementary feed areas. Some breeding farms locate feeders and waterers well apart to encourage exercise. Undulating country also helps grazing mares to exercise. Where mares are confined to small areas, walking for 15-20 minutes daily on a lead is a good idea. It is risky and uncomfortable for heavily pregnant mares to be exercised under saddle, or by longeing.

Nutritional Management

Feed Substitution

High protein pellets (16-18% protein) can be substituted for soybean meal (36% protein) on a 2 for 1 weight basis for mares on a diet base of grass hay as roughage. Pellets are convenient to mix with grain and supplements.

HINT

The inclusion of up to 10% wheat bran in a dampened concentrate sweet feed once a day, is considered beneficial by some breeders for mares in the last month of pregnancy. When mixed with molasses in the concentrate, it may provide some laxative effect for mares grazing on dry summer pastures. If adequate green pasture is present, wheat bran need not be given in the concentrate feed.

NOTE: Where wheat bran and soybean meal are used together in a ration, the availability of calcium, copper and zinc may be decreased. Ensure that adequate calcium, and a trace mineral supplement, are added to the ration. (See Ration Guidelines.)

Old Mares

Brood mares over 16 years of age should receive an extra 1oz (30g or 1½ tablespoons) of calcium carbonate daily because calcium absorption is less efficient in older horses. It is also wise to crush the grain for aged mares with poor teeth to ensure they get the full benefit from concentrate feeds. They should also be provided with a more energy dense ration and additional protein: approximately 8oz (230g) additional soybean meal daily for a 1100lb (500kg) mare as protein utilization is not as efficient.

HINT

It is good practice to pay individual attention to the feeding and daily health of aged pregnant mares, and if necessary, feed them separately from the main group of mares.

Boiled Barley

A sweet feed containing 2-4lb (about 1-2kg) wet weight cooked barley per 1100lb (500kg) mare, may be given twice a week as an appetizing feed in late pregnancy particularly during very cold, wet and windy weather.

Preparation for lactation

Mid-Stage Pregnancy:

Adequate nutrition during the final three months is important. Feed to maintain the mare in a fleshy, but not overweight condition. However, if a mare is in heavy condition, exercise should be increased to maintain her condition, rather than reduce the feed intake if she is gaining weight.

Last Three Months of Pregnancy:

The protein level in the concentrate ration should be boosted to 14-16%, particularly in mares grazing grass based pastures, where the overall protein content is often less than 12% on winter and early spring pasture. The protein content can be economically increased by providing good quality alfalfa hay in self-feeders, plus a 14-16% protein concentrate mix, feed pellets or commercially prepared brood mare feed once or twice daily to maintain condition.

The calcium and phosphorus requirement increases dramatically to foaling, and ideally, the diet should contain 0.5% calcium and about 0.35% phosphorus during the three months prior to foaling.

HINT

A deficiency of phosphorus may not only affect the skeletal development of the unborn foal, but also affect the mare's subsequent milk production and fertility after foaling.

Cereal Based Pastures

The type of grazing pasture influences the amount of calcium and phosphorus available, and the balance between them. Grasses are generally lower in calcium and higher in phosphorus than legumes. Where mares are grazing grass pastures, particularly oxalate rich grasses (such as Setaria,

1100-1200lb (500-550kg). 8-11 months gestation (last 3 months of pregnancy) grazing sparse or poor quality pasture. One concentrate feed daily, hay twice daily or ad lib.

Note: See ration on page 129 for mare in early pregnancy.

INGREDIENT	FORM/MIX	DAILY AMOUNT		PROVIDES
		AM	PM	
OATS or alternatively BARLEY	Whole, heavy, dust free. Rolled, dust free.		7lb (3.2kg) (8-9 months) 7½lb (3.4kg) (9-10 months) 9lb (4.1kg) (10 months - foaling)	ENERGY, PROTEIN, FIBER - traditional safe grain easily fed oat in feed bins with hay.
MILO or 50:50 OATS-CORN MIX	Crushed, dust free. Mix whole oats and cracked corn as grain mix.		6lb (2.7kg) (8-9 months) 6½lb (3kg) (9-10 months) 8lb (3.6kg) (10 months - foaling)	Alternative ENERGY, PROTEIN and FIBER sources to oats, selected on availability and price. Adequate energy must be provided to ensure breeding cycles are initiated.
ALFALFA CUBES/ PELLETS. CHOPPED HAY (Optional)	Commercial pellets/cubes. Dry, no mold.		3lb (1.4kg)	Optional - Increases bulk of grain concentrate slows gorging and helps reduce wastage of grain. Reduce amount of hay accordingly.
MOLASSES (Optional)	Mix 50:50 with warm water. Mix well into feed.		6oz (170g) (1 teacup) (add 8oz (230g) 1½ teacups if alfalfa cube/pellet option used)	Optional - SWEETENER - useful to dampen grain mix and prevents sifting and loss of dry powder supplements blowing away in wind.
SOYBEAN MEAL (Optional)	Heat treated. Free flowing, non rancid.		1lb (450g)	Optional - Important to boost protein level of grass hay based ration to meet lysine requirements.
WHEAT BRAN (Optional)	Flakey, clean, dry, no caking. Pleasant odor.		Last month of pregnancy 1lb (450g)	Optional - provides FIBER, PHOSPHORUS and improves palatability of ration. When mixed in a damp feed with molasses it helps reduce the risk of constipation in heavily pregnant mares. NOTE: On high legume pastures, additional bran will help to provide phosphorus to meet requirements (see text).
COMMERCIAL VITAMIN/TRACE MINERAL SUPPLEMENT	Mix well into feed.		(eg Feramo-H) 2oz (57g) (½ scoop)	Supplements low feed levels with Vitamin A and D to meet needs on grass hay roughage and pasture, as well as trace-minerals including iron, copper and zinc to help ensure bone and muscle development in the unborn foal.
VITAMIN E SUPPLEMENT	Mix well into feed.		(eg White-E) 1000iu (1 scoop)	Supplements low feed levels with Vitamin E, which may reduce the risk of white muscle disease in unborn foals of mares grazing on selenium deficient pastures. Consult your vet regarding need for selenium supplementation.
DICALCIUM PHOSPHATE	DCP. Free flowing, dry. Mix well into feed.		1½oz (42g) (2 tblsp)	Essential to meet calcium and phosphorus requirements in last three months of pregnancy.
CALCIUM CARBONATE	Ground limestone. Free flowing, dry. Mix well into feed.		Grass hay 3/4oz (20g) (1½ tblsp) increasing to 1oz (30g) (2 tblsp) in last month.	From 9 months of pregnancy, on grass hay roughage, or grass pastures, extra calcium is required to meet needs.
SALT	Fine, free flowing		3/4oz (20g) (1½ tblsp)	Palatability and to meet sodium requirement.
MIXED HAY or alternatively	Leafy, no dust or mold.	5lb (2.3kg)	6lb (2.7kg) Last month 5lb (2.3kg) if bran included.	ENERGY, PROTEIN and FIBER - mixed hay is preferred as protein content meets needs. Alternatively feed 5lb (2.3kg) alfalfa in morning, 6lb (2.7kg) grass hay in evening. Mixed hay or a change to alfalfa is preferred when grazing grass based pastures to boost calcium intake (see text).
GRASS HAY	Leafy, no dust	5lb (2.3kg)	6lb (2.7kg) Last month 5lb (2.3kg) if bran included.	ENERGY, PROTEIN and FIBER - lower protein than mixed hay. Limit to volume of hay in last month of pregnancy.

NUTRITIONAL INFORMATION: The ration is formulated to NRC (1989) guidelines for a pregnant mare on little or poor pasture. The amount fed should be in proportion to the bodyweight of the mare to maintain a working, fleshy condition and avoid overfeeding. Each 18.5lb (8.4kg) recommended at 8 months of pregnancy contains approximately 19.5 Mcals (82MJ) digestible energy, 925g (11%) crude protein, and minimum 35g available calcium and 26g available phosphorus. In the last month of pregnancy each 20lb (9.1kg) contains approximately 22Mcals (92MJ) digestible energy, 1025g (11.3%) crude protein, and a minimum 44g calcium and 31g phosphorus.

green or blue panic, buffel grass and argentine or dallas grass) which can lead to calcium malabsorption (see also page 157), then extra calcium must be provided to meet requirements. Provision of good quality alfalfa hay as well as a concentrate feed containing supplementary levels of calcium, zinc and copper is recommended.

Legume Based Pastures

Alfalfa or legume based pastures, whilst usually providing more than adequate calcium, can lead to a relative deficiency of phosphorus in heavily pregnant grazing mares.

In this case, the amount of alfalfa hay should be restricted, and replaced with mixed hay, or a blend of 50:50 alfalfa and grass hay, depending on availability. The concentrate ration should contain a supplement of phosphorus by adding an extra source such as Dicalcium phosphate. (See Ration Guidelines.)

HINT

A general vitamin/mineral supplement should be mixed into the concentrate ration to supplement low feed levels of Vitamins A and D, and trace-minerals such as iron, copper, zinc, manganese, and safe levels of iodine. Adequate Vitamin D is important in mares grazing winter pastures to help control imbalances in the calcium:phosphorus intake. If you are unsure of the balance of minerals in the diets of brood mares, consult an equine nutritionist for advice.

LACTATING MARES

Special attention should be given to the diet of lactating mares. Many owners overfeed young growing horses and pregnant mares, and underfeed lactating mares. Lactating mares should be fed to maintain them in fleshy, well covered condition. It is a common belief that obese mares do not produce as much milk due to fat taking up room in the udder. Studies have shown, however, that obese mares had similar milk yield to moderately conditioned mares, but their foals had a slightly lower rate of growth during the first two months.

At the peak of lactation, which occurs 6-8 weeks after foaling, a 1100lb (500kg) mare can produce 3½-4½ gallons (about 15-20 liters) of milk per day. Young foals suckle about 100 times daily for the first 1-2 weeks, then on average 60-65 times daily. (See page 65 for details on Feeding Habit of Foals.)

Nutritional Needs

Once a mare foals, and starts to produce milk to feed her foal, she needs increased energy, protein, calcium, Vitamin A and other vitamins and minerals. The importance of these nutrients has been outlined in the section dealing with Pregnant Mares.

Studies have shown that during lactation, as compared to late pregnancy, the mare's requirement for energy increases by up to 70%, protein by up to 60%, and calcium by up to 66%. All these are vital components in milk for growth of the foal. A lactating mare requires more of these nutrients than a racing or performance horse in medium-heavy work.

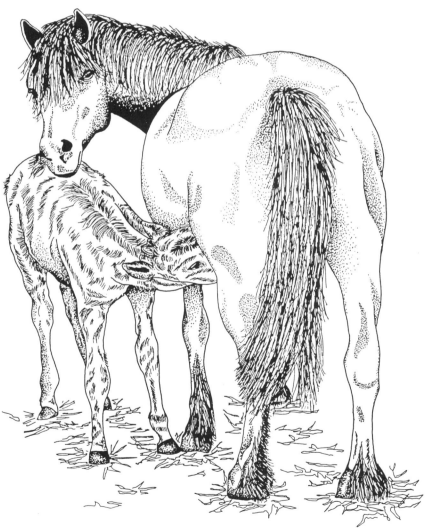

HINT

Inadequate dietary protein intake in lactating mares can result in 20% lower bodyweight of the suckling foal at three months of age. The ration should contain a minimum of 12% protein during the first three months of lactation to maintain the mare's condition and milk supply.

Nutritional stress during the first two months after foaling usually affects fertility first, then milk production and finally body condition. Many authorities believe that failure of early foaling mares to cycle and conceive is largely due to lack of adequate nutrition in mares with a foal at foot.

Observations indicate that mares which lose weight after foaling take up to 30 days extra to come into heat. If a mare is stressed, and in poor condition at foaling, she may take up to eight weeks to recommence her breeding cycles. If a mare is in very poor condition, feeding to gain weight during the early lactation period will help to improve fertility, but rate of conception may be less than optimum. Her milk supply may be lower, and the weight of her foal at three months less than average. If thin mares are put onto higher levels of feed at foaling, they will have conception rates similar to well conditioned mares. An overly fat mare can afford to lose some weight slowly without affecting overall fertility.

In an overly fat mare, it is important to avoid significant weight reduction during the first three months after foaling, otherwise milk production may be reduced and retard the rate of development of her foal. It is important to regularly monitor the body condition of grazing mares in the summer months where reduced pasture quantity and quality may reduce the energy intake and affect fertility and milk production. It is essential to provide supplements of hay or extra concentrate at the first sign of a fall away in condition.

A good quality ration will also serve as a co-feed for the foal to encourage it to develop an individual eating habit and minimize nutritional stress and set back in growth and development at weaning. (See page 135.)

Nutritional Management

In the period between the peak of lactation to weaning, the energy, protein and calcium levels can theoretically be decreased.

HINT

If a mare is bred and conceives during lactation, then after weaning she can be slowly let down over 1-2 months to the ration for a pregnant mare. The mare should not be allowed to become too fat. In an obese mare, the ration intake and exercise level should be adjusted so as to result in weight loss of no greater than 1% of bodyweight each week. After weaning, non-pregnant mares can be let down over a 2-3 week period to the ration levels recommended for an open mare.

Dry Seasons

For a lactating mare at pasture, supplementation with good quality alfalfa or mixed hay will generally provide adequate protein, but result in about a 30% energy deficiency. Therefore, the energy deficiency must be made up with a concentrate feed.

At the peak of lactation a mare can consume daily feed up to the equivalent of 3% of her bodyweight; approximately 33lb per 1100lb (15kg/500kg) bodyweight.

The ration must contain enough phosphorus to ensure fertility, particularly in mares grazing lucerne based pastures.

HINT

Field observations suggest that lactating mares grazing predominantly on alfalfa or legume based pastures appear to breed more successfully when given a concentrate feed containing additional phosphorus (eg made up of 3% wheat bran and 0.5% dicalcium phosphate), 1500iu Vitamin E, additional Vitamin A and trace minerals.

NOTE: Studies have shown that supplementing copper and zinc to lactating mares does not elevate the level of these trace minerals in the mare's blood or milk, or increase uptake by the suckling foal. If copper is supplemented to foals, it should be added to the co-feed, or creep feed. Supplementation at a rate of 25ppm of co-feed is considered worthwhile to provide adequate copper to suckling foals sharing the mare's feed.

Water

It is essential that free access to water be provided at all times for lactating mares. Lack of adequate water will quickly reduce milk production, and if severe, can dry off a mare in 2-3 days.

HINT

When a pregnant mare loses her foal due to accident or sickness within the first three months of lactation, she can be dried up by confinement to a yard, a ration of hay at 1.5% of bodyweight and limited water for 5-7 days.

If a mare is also in early pregnancy, the feed level should be reduced more slowly to avoid losing the fetus. Consult your vet for advice.

Most mares dry up naturally at the normal weaning time of 5-6 months, as, by this age, foals have little reliance on suckling.

DIETARY GUIDELINES - LACTATING MARE - FIRST THREE MONTHS OF LACTATION

1100lb (500kg) bodyweight. Little grazing. Two feeds daily. Ration can be consumed as a co-feed by young foal.

Note: Lactating Mares - 3 months to Weaning.

1)   This ration may be continued to be provided for late lactation where her foal consumes it as a co-feed from a shared feed tub or trough. As the amount the foal eats will increase gradually, the mare's intake will decrease accordingly but should meet her declining lactation demand to weaning.

2) Where a foal is provided with a separate ration (see guideline page 71), then the mares energy, protein and mineral intake can be reduced after the peak of lactation to weaning. From 3 months to weaning, omit the corn from the morning feed, reduce soybean meal to 1lb (450g) on mixed hay rations, omit wheat bran and dicalcium phosphate from the evening feed.

3) Adjust the amount to maintain the mare in a fleshy condition.

INGREDIENT	FORM/MIX	DAILY AMOUNT		PROVIDES
		AM	PM	
OATS or alternatively	Rolled, dust free.	3lb (1.4kg)	5lb (2.3kg)	ENERGY, PROTEIN, FIBER - the processed grain allows the ration to be used as co-feed for foals.
BARLEY or MILO	Rolled, dust free. Crushed, dust free.	3lb (1.4kg)	4½lb (2kg)	
CORN	Freshly cracked/dust free. If purchased cracked store in bag - fold down after use. Non rancid.	3lb (1.4kg)	3lb (1.4kg)	ENERGY & PROTEIN - higher energy density to boost energy levels and reduce bulk of ration, particularly if used as a co-feed for foals.
SOYBEAN MEAL (Optional)	Heat treated. Free flowing, non rancid.		1½lb (700g)	Provides ENERGY and PROTEIN - required to meet protein and lysine requirements for mixed hay or grass based rations and as a co-feed for foal.
ALFALFA CUBES/ PELLETS. CHOPPED HAY (Optional)	Commercial pellets/cubes. Dry, no mold.	2lb (900g)	3lb (1.4kg)	Optional - dampened and should be included if ration is consumed by foals. Provides ENERGY, PROTEIN and CALCIUM - helps prevent separation and sifting - makes ration easier for foals to co-feed with mare. Note: Adjust the hay intake of the mare accordingly.
MOLASSES	Mix 50:50 with warm water. Mix well into feed.	4oz (114g) (3/4 teacup)	4oz (114g) (3/4 teacup)	SWEETENER - useful to dampen grain mix; prevents sifting and loss of dry powder supplements. Sweetens feed for young foals.
WHEAT BRAN	Flakey, clean, dry, no caking. Pleasant odor.		1lb (450g)	Provides additional PROTEIN and PHOSPHORUS and improves palatability as a co-feed for foals.
COMMERCIAL VITAMIN/TRACE MINERAL SUPPLEMENT	Mix well into feed.		(eg Feramo-H) 2oz (57g) (½ scoop)	Supplements low feed levels with a wide range of vitamins and trace minerals to help correct feed deficiencies and provide extra vitamin A for milk production and fertility.
VITAMIN E SUPPLEMENT	Mix well into feed.	(eg White-E) 1000-1500iu (1-1½ scoops)		Supplements inadequate feed levels with Vitamin E which corrects deficiency in feeds to help muscle development in foal. May also help maintain fertility in mares grazing alfalfa based pastures.
DICALCIUM PHOSPHATE	DCP. Free flowing, dry. Mix well into feed.		Alfalfa Hay and Mixed Hay add 1oz (30g) (2 tblsp)	Provides CALCIUM and PHOSPHORUS to balance Ca:P intake and meets phosphorus requirements, particularly as a co-feed for foals.
SALT	Fine		1oz (30g) (2 tblsp)	Aids palatability and meets sodium requirements.
CALCIUM CARBONATE	Ground limestone. Free flowing, dry. Mix well into feed.		Mixed Hay - add 1oz (30g) (2 tblsp).	Provides extra calcium to meet needs on a mixed hay based diet which is lower in calcium than alfalfa hay. If grass (11lb) only available, add 2oz (60g) (3 tblsp).
COPPER SULFATE MIX (Co-feed only)	1 part Bluestone (21% copper) in 9 parts fine or granulated sugar. Mix well.		(15g) (3 teaspoons)	Supplements inadequate feed levels with approximately 25ppm copper in 27lb of feed used as a co-feed by foal. Does not increase copper levels in milk.
ALFALFA HAY or alternatively MIXED HAY	Leafy, no dust or mold.	4lb (1.8kg) 4lb (1.8kg)	6lb (2.7kg) 7lb (3.1kg)	Provides ENERGY, PROTEIN, FIBER - essential roughage to bulk diet. Alternatively feed alfalfa in morning, mixed hay in evening.

NUTRITIONAL INFORMATION: This ration is formulated for a lactating mare to NRC (1989) guidelines for the peak lactation at 2-3 months after foaling, but adjustments to amount fed may be required, depending on pasture intake to maintain a fleshy condition (see text). Each 27lb (12.3kg) of feed contains approximately 31Mcals (130MJ) digestible energy, 1550g (12.6%) crude protein, and a minimum 58g calcium and 40g phosphorus and 25 ppm added copper. It is a suitable co-feed for nursing foals to supplement milk intake. (See also specialized foal rations.)

Stallions turned out during the non-breeding season should be maintained in a reasonable body condition and physical fitness. After the breeding season, it is best to let them down, by a gradual reduction of grain in the diet, to a maintenance ration to match the level of paddock exercise.

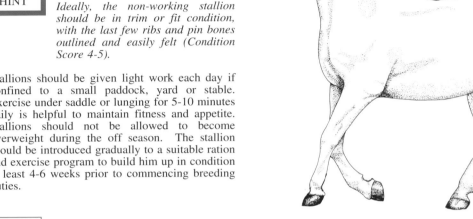

> **HINT**
>
> *Ideally, the non-working stallion should be in trim or fit condition, with the last few ribs and pin bones outlined and easily felt (Condition Score 4-5).*

Stallions should be given light work each day if confined to a small paddock, yard or stable. Exercise under saddle or lunging for 5-10 minutes daily is helpful to maintain fitness and appetite. Stallions should not be allowed to become overweight during the off season. The stallion should be introduced gradually to a suitable ration and exercise program to build him up in condition at least 4-6 weeks prior to commencing breeding duties.

> **HINT**
>
> *As the breeding season approaches, owners of mares may inspect the stallion, so he should be in a fleshy condition with a healthy and fit appearance and a well conditioned coat. Most stallion owners keep their animals well groomed and ready to be inspected and paraded at a few minutes notice. Always ensure the hooves are kept in good condition and trimmed regularly during the off-season.*

Nutritional Requirements

Energy

Adequate energy must be provided for maintenance of body condition, particularly in stallions kept at pasture over the fall-winter period. Regular observation during winter is important to ensure that the ration is maintaining a static bodyweight. If the stallion is kept indoors during winter, provide daily exercise and control the ration intake to maintain him in trim condition.

Protein

Stallions in the off-season require protein at maintenance or sufficient for a resting horse.

Minerals

Calcium is essential to maintain bone strength, particularly in older stallions over 16 years of age. It is recommended that a daily supplement of essential vitamins and minerals (such as contained in Feramo-H), be given during the non-breeding season if pasture intake is limited. It helps maintain coat condition and general vitality.

Exercise

Daily exercise at pasture and during grazing should be sufficient for stallions in larger areas of two acres (about one hectare). However, in smaller areas, exercise under saddle or longeing should be given to maintain reasonable fitness and a trim, fit body condition.

Nutritional Management

* Increase grain (eg oats) by 10% during wet, cold, wintry weather, or as required, depending on seasonal conditions and available pasture. Stallions at pasture can usually be maintained on good quality hay with only minimal concentrate feed.

* Carry out regular worming and hoof care.

* Stallions of Pony Breeds - do not allow them to become cresty on the neck, or obese on lush spring pastures, as these could lead to founder. Limit grazing to 1-2 hours per day, and provide grass hay as the roughage base to the diet. Fit a mesh muzzle to limit pasture intake and encourage exercise as the animal attempts to seek suitable pasture to graze through the muzzle. Exercise the stallion daily for 5-10 minutes. Do not starve pony stallions to take off excess weight, as there is a high risk of a metabolic disease relaxed to rapid mobilization of fat reserves in starved ponies (called hyperlipemia). (See Ponies, page 124 for additional management hints on avoiding founder and hyperlipemia.)

1100lb (500kg). Access to pasture for exercise. Stabled overnight. Adjust feed intake to condition and pasture quality. If stabled full time, allow 15-20 minutes exercise, three feeds daily - hay midday. The total amount of concentrate may be combined into an evening feed, with hay only in the morning if necessary, depending on pasture availability.

INGREDIENT	FORM/MIX	DAILY AMOUNT AM	DAILY AMOUNT PM	PROVIDES
CORN or alternatively	Whole or freshly cracked. If purchased cracked, store in bag; fold down after use.	2lb (900g)	2lb (900g)	ENERGY, PROTEIN, FIBER provides palatable economical source of energy.
BARLEY MILO or alternatively	Rolled or crushed. Dust free.	2lb (900g)	2lb (900g)	ENERGY, PROTEIN, FIBER - alternative energy feed.
OATS	Whole, heavy. Dust free.	2lb (900g)	2¼lb (1kg)	ENERGY, PROTEIN, FIBER - traditional grain - may be replaced by a mix of rolled barley and corn (see above).
SOYBEAN MEAL (Optional)	Heat treated. Free flowing, Non rancid.		8oz (230g)	Optional - should be given on grass hay roughage based diets to meet protein needs.
DEHYDRATED ALFALFA PELLETS, CHOPPED HAY, CRUMBLED CUBES (Optional)	Dust free. Sweet smelling, no mold. Mix into grain mix.	1lb (450g)	1½lb (700g)	Optional - ENERGY, PROTEIN, CALCIUM - bulks out feed for horses that eat grain quickly. Substitute weight by reducing hay intake accordingly.
POLYUNSATURATED OIL or alternatively	Non rancid, keep sealed between uses.		2oz (57ml) (4 tblsp)	Provides essential fatty acids for coat condition.
SUNFLOWER SEEDS (Optional)	Black variety clean and plump.	4oz (115g)	4oz (115g)	Provides essential fatty acids for coat condition, and also protein - may replace soybean meal as protein boost on grass hay diets.
MOLASSES	Mix 50:50 with warm water, mix well into feed.		4oz (115g) (3/4 teacup)	Improves palatability, reduces dust and sifting of supplements.
CONCENTRATED VITAMIN/TRACE MINERAL SUPPLEMENT	Mix well into feed.		(eg Feramo-H) 2oz (57g) (½ scoop)	Supplements low feed levels with Vitamin A, iron, zinc, and copper for coat condition.
VITAMIN E SUPPLEMENT (Optional)	Mix well into feed.		(eg White-E) 1000iu (1 scoop)	Optional - provides Vitamin E to meet needs on grass or cereal based rations. Mix into top of damp evening feed.
CALCIUM CARBONATE	Ground limestone. Select good quality only. Mix well into ration.		Grass Hay ½oz (15g) 1 tblsp	Provides CALCIUM to ensure requirements on grass hay diets.
SALT	Fine grade, mix well into feed.		2/3oz (20g) (1½ tblsp)	Aids palatability and meets sodium need.
ALFALFA HAY or alternatively	Leafy, no dust or mold, dampen if necessary.	5lb (2.3kg)	6lb (2.7kg)	Provides ENERGY, PROTEIN, FIBER and CALCIUM. Contributes excess protein to diet if fed as the only roughage to a horse at rest.
MIXED HAY or alternatively	Leafy, no weeks, no mold, dampen if necessary.	5lb (2.3kg)	7lb (3.2kg)	Well accepted - adequate protein to meet needs. Alfalfa may be fed in morning, and grass hay overnight if good quality mixed hay is not available.
GRASS HAY	Leafy, no weeds, mold or dust. Sweet smelling. Dampen if necessary.	5lb (2.3kg)	6lb (2.7kg)	More bulky and lower protein than alfalfa; intake limited by appetite of horse. Extra protein should be added to meet needs.

NUTRITIONAL INFORMATION: The ration has been formulated to maintain a stallion in a working condition. If grazing, hay only may be provided to appetite and condition. The ration intake should be adjusted to exercise and grazing. For stallions confined indoors, it is recommended that the alternative grain mixes be bulked up by mixing in dehydrated alfalfa cubes or chopped hay, with grass hay provided at lunch (see text for full details). The ration meets NRC (1989) guidelines for maintenance. Each 15lb (7kg) ration provides approximately 17 Mcals (71MJ) digestible energy, 700g (grass hay) - 1000g (alfalfa hay) (ave 12%) crude protein, and a minimum 27g calcium, and 17g phosphorus.

STALLIONS (Breeding Season)

Working stallions require a well balanced diet and adequate exercise to ensure maximal fertility, stamina and vigor for breeding, particularly during the height of the breeding season on larger breeding farms.

> **HINT** *Stallions are usually fed and exercised as if they are in training for light work.*

Adequate exercise must be given to keep the stallion fit so as to maintain his serving stamina and libido. Where possible, stallions can be exercised under saddle. More aggressive stallions should be longed at least once daily, or provided with an opportunity for pasture exercise in a safe, secure paddock.

Excessive exercise, however, may tire stallions and reduce libido. Avoid pasturing stallions anywhere near mares as they may run off their condition or interrupt their grazing time, as well as risking injury trying to join the mares. Although adequate nutrition is important, stallions must not become over fat, as libido and fertility may both be adversely affected.

During the breeding season, stallions are often paraded for mare owners and visitors to the breeding farm - a fit, healthy, well groomed stallion with male character and vitality is required.

Nutritional Requirements

Energy

Adequate energy is required to maintain body condition, sperm production, fertility, libido and overall stamina and vigor. When a stallion is not being bred regularly, then a ration to maintain a desired bodyweight should be fed. If the stallion is being used on average once a day, then the ration may have to be increased to maintain adequate condition and vigor.

Protein

A 14-16% crude protein concentrate containing about 0.1% good quality protein (eg soybean meal) is considered ideal by leading breeding farm managers to maintain fertility in working stallions. Protein rations above 18% are costly and not required.

Minerals

Stallions require a similar mineral intake to a working horse, including possibly a daily supplement of iron and trace-elements. Older stallions, over 16 years of age, may not be able to absorb calcium efficiently. As grain content in the ration increases, extra calcium is required to balance the high phosphorus intake.

Vitamins

A supplement of vitamin A and D is required by stallions stabled for the majority of daylight hours, particularly those that are fed on a grass hay based ration. Vitamin A may be important for fertility. Vitamin E may also be beneficial in hard working stallions although studies have failed to demostrate a positive effect on fertility in stallions. A supplement of B-Complex vitamins may help to maintain appetite in stallions with restricted access to green pastures.

Electrolytes

Regular breeding, exercise and hot weather leads to an increase in electrolyte loss due to sweating, so an electrolyte supplement may be of benefit to help maintain general vigor, coat condition and fluid intake.

Exercise

Stallions must be given adequate exercise to maintain fitness throughout the breeding season. Lunging for about 10 minutes daily will provide sufficient exercise for most stallions that are not over-fed.

Nutritional Management

* If the stallion is not serving mares on a regular basis, then reduce the amount of concentrate to match the exercise level and maintain the stallion in a fleshy condition.

* Stallions are often exhibited to visitors or owners of mares - rug in cold weather to help maintain an acceptable hair coat.

> **HINT** *Daily provision of a general vitamin/mineral supplement (such as Feramo-H) will help supplement low feed levels of these nutrients to maintain vitality and good skin and coat condition.*

Excitable, Hard-to-Handle Stallions

Very excitable stallions make hand breeding difficult and time consuming, risking injury to the mare and handler. Some breeders report that supplementation with high doses of Vitamin B1 (3000mg twice daily) for 7 days, then once daily in the night feed thereafter assists in settling excitable, hard-to-handle stallions if their diets are low in this vitamin.

1100lb (500kg). Covering one mare every 1-2 days. Access to pasture for exercise. Stabled overnight. If stabled full time, provide 15-20 minutes light exercise daily. Three feeds daily, hay at midday.

INGREDIENT	FORM/MIX	DAILY AMOUNT		PROVIDES
		AM	PM	
CORN or alternatively	Whole or freshly cracked. If purchased cracked, store in bag - fold down top after use.	1lb (450g)	2lb (900g)	ENERGY, PROTEIN, FIBER provides palatable economical source of energy with lower bulk.
BARLEY or MILO	Rolled or crushed, dust free.	1lb (450g)	2lb (900g)	ENERGY, PROTEIN, FIBER, alternative feed.
OATS	Whole, heavy. Dust free.	2lb (900g)	4lb (1.8kg)	ENERGY, PROTEIN, FIBER - traditional grain - may be replaced by a mix of rolled barley and corn.
SOYBEAN MEAL (Optional)	Heat treated. Free flowing Non rancid.	8oz (230g)	12oz (345g)	Optional - should be provided on grass hay roughage based diets to meet protein needs. Provides additional essential amino acids to correct minor deficiencies.
DEHYDRATED ALFALFA PELLETS, CHOPPED HAY, CRUMBLED CUBES (Optional)	Dust free. Sweet smelling, no mold. Mix into grain mix.	1lb (450g)	1½lb (700g)	Optional - ENERGY, PROTEIN, CALCIUM - bulks out feed for horses that eat grain quickly. Substitute weight by reducing hay intake accordingly.
POLYUNSATURATED OIL or alternatively	Non rancid, keep sealed between uses.		2oz (57ml) (4 tblsp)	Provides essential fatty acids for coat condition. Can be used as an energy source during hot weather. (See Fats.)
SUNFLOWER SEEDS (Optional)	Black variety clean and plump.	4oz (115g)	4oz (115g)	Provides essential fatty acids for coat condition, and also protein - may replace soybean meal as protein boost on grass hay diets.
MOLASSES	Mix 50:50 with warm water, mix well into feed.		4oz (115g) (3/4 teacup)	Improves palatability, reduces dust and sifting of supplements.
CONCENTRATED VITAMIN/TRACE MINERAL SUPPLEMENT	Mix well into feed.		(eg Feramo-H) 2oz (57g) (½ scoop)	Provides vitamins and trace minerals to correct low feed levels. Vitamin A, iron, zinc, copper to help promote coat condition.
VITAMIN E SUPPLEMENT (Optional)	Mix well into feed.		(eg White-E) 1000iu (1 scoop)	Optional - supplements Vitamin E to meet needs on grass or cereal based rations. Mix into top of damp feed.
HUMIDIMIX	Acid salt electrolyte mix. Mix well into feed.	3/4oz (22½g) 1 scoop	3/4oz (22½g) 1 scoop	Supplements inadequate feed levels with sodium, potassium and chloride to replace sweat losses in hot weather or in hard working stallions and helps maintain water intake.
CALCIUM CARBONATE	Ground limestone. Select good quality only. Mix well into ration.		Grass Hay ½oz (15g) (3/4 tblsp)	Provides CALCIUM to ensure adequate on grass hay diets. If sweating heavily, add an extra 1oz (30g) (2 tablespoons) of calcium carbonate to grass hay diets.
SALT	Fine grade, mix well into feed.		2/3oz (20g) (1½ tblsp)	Aids palatability water intake and meets sodium need.
GREEN FEED (Optional)			Early afternoon 3lb (1.4kg) green feed.	If stabled full time, give 30 minutes grazing on lead in early afternoon if green feed not available. Helps relieve boredom and aids the appetite.
ALFALFA HAY or alternatively	Leafy, no dust or mold, dampen if necessary.	5lb (2.3kg)	6lb (2.7kg)	Provides ENERGY, PROTEIN, FIBER and CALCIUM. Contributes excess protein to diet if fed as the sole source of roughage even in a working stallion.
MIXED HAY or alternatively	Leafy, no weeds, no mold, dampen if necessary.	5lb (2.3kg)	7lb (3.2kg)	Well accepted - adequate protein to meet needs. Alternatively, feed alfalfa in morning, and grass hay in evening.
GRASS HAY	Leafy, no weeds, mold or dust. Sweet smelling. Dampen if necessary.	5lb (2.3kg)	6lb (2.7kg)	More bulky and lower protein than alfalfa; intake limited by appetite of horse.

NUTRITIONAL INFORMATION: The ration is formulated for a working stallion during the breeding season where grain intake has been increased to meet additional energy and protein demand above maintenance based on NRC (1989) recommendations. The stallion should be given regular daily exercise and be maintained in a "fleshy" condition, rather than overweight (see text). Each 20lb (9kg) of ration provides approximately 21Mcals (88MJ) digestible energy, 1000-11150g (ave 12.6%) crude protein, and a minimum of 32g calcium and 23g phosphorus.

PROBLEMS RELATING TO FEEDING

Most of the common ailments and problems associated with feeding result from boredom and confinement, irregular feeding times, restriction of social interaction between horses at feed time, and the feeding of highly concentrated rations without adequate exercise and roughage balance.

Feed related problems can be grouped into five main classes:

1. Behavioral disorders or abnormal eating habits.

2. Metabolic conditions related to feeding.

3. Respiratory conditions caused by dust or allergen inhalation.

4. Gastro-intestinal disorders related to feeding.

5. Plant poisoning and toxic chemicals.

Of these, behavioral disorders are the most common problems that annoy horse owners. These are discussed in detail. A summary of other problems is provided in the tables on pages 146-161.

BEHAVORIAL DISORDERS OR ABNORMAL EATING HABITS

Horses can develop bad manners at meal times, leading to feed wastage, digestive upsets and risk of injury from aggressive behavior. Some of these habits develop as a result of boredom, competition for feed, or simply a bossy nature.

The following outline provides a summary of undesirable eating habits in horses, some of the common terms used by horse owners to describe horses, and possible reasons for the habit. Useful remedies were extracted from an entertaining review of behavioral eating habits entitled Mealtime Monsters, by K. Kopp Du Teil in EQUUS magazine No. 144, October 1989.

Scattering Feed when Eating
Colloquial names: Feed Scatterer,   Grain Slinger,Messy Eater, Feed Flinger

Horses confined for long periods can develop an annoying habit of flinging feed from their feed bins or searching through their rations for palatable morsels, scattering grains and chaff onto the bedding and ground.

After initially scattering feed, they often spend much of their time sifting through the bedding in search of wasted feed, eating bedding and feed contaminated by eggs and larvae of internal parasites from fecal contamination of their living area.

Often, these horses will intercept the feed bucket as it is poured into the tub, or up-end the feeder as soon as it has been filled.

Causes: The reasons for a feed scattering habit are not obvious, but may be related to greediness, sudden feed changes or a desire to search for familiar tastes, grains, sweet pellets or sweet feeds after sudden feed changes. These habits may result from frustration and boredom from being confined in a stable.

Remedies: Practical remedies include making gradual changes over 7-10 days to discourage searching for known tastes. If the habit is extreme, attach wooden, or covered metal bars to the feed tub leaving just enough space for the horse's nose, to restrict sideways movement to minimize food wastage. The use of deep, narrow-sided feed buckets is also useful, providing they are well anchored to the floor or to the wall.

If all else fails, invest in a deep nose bag, attached to the head stall to minimise spillage of feed over the sides during feeding. In intractable cases, seek a more understanding owner for the horse.

Aggression when Feeding
Colloquial names: Over Aggressive Feeder, Possessive Feeder, Grumpy and Mean Feeder

Occasionally, horses become unpredictable and quite defensive if disturbed when feeding. Many of these horses are generally pleasant to handle, but at feed time develop aggressive manners towards other horses, including biting, kicking, charging other horses or humans, and showing their teeth or kicking out when disturbed during a meal.

Often other horses in adjacent stables go off their feed in fear of being harassed by the aggressive feeder. As well, the aggressive feeder may take a long time to finish the feed due to lifting its head between each mouthful to show aggressive and greedy behavior.

Causes: It is considered that the instinctive fight for survival, particularly in mares and aggressive ponies, may lead to competitive feeding habits, particularly when stabled adjacent to more dominant horses. This type of behavior could also occur if the horse has been annoyed by other horses when feeding. Taking the food away before the full amount has been consumed may cause an aggressive reaction. The problem can become worse when a horse is confined to a stable with limited space and set feeding times.

Remedies: Generally, the aggressive and threatening behavior is only confined to feed time. It is helpful to ensure that these horses are fed away from others, and that they are not disturbed during feeding. Groom and attend to these horses other than at feed time. If they become aggressive when handled, then firm discipline is required.

Impatience When Feeding
Colloquial names: Wall Kicker, Tub Striker, Floor Pawer

Some horses kick or strike walls or feed tubs, or paw the floor in anticipation of feed time. The habit and noise usually starts with the appearance of a feed bucket, or the sound of other horses getting fed first. Once fed, most will settle down to eat, but a few will continue pawing and kicking with enjoyment when feeding. Damage to walls, pawing and wearing away of shoes, and self mutilation to the kicker occurs in bad cases.

Causes: The underlying cause is not known, but once tried, the horse learns it can get fed first. Feeding acts as a reward for this type of behavior, so it is often difficult to correct in bad cases.

Remedy: Old time remedies included chains on the legs that caused discomfort as the horse kicked or pawed, but these were often ineffective. The simplest remedy is to feed this noisy horse first. Ignoring the habit and not feeding until it quietens, or attempting discipline, is usually a waste of time.

Dropping of Feed
Colloquial names: Dribbler, Slobberer, Nosy Parker

Horses are gregarious and social animals, and like to have visual contact with other horses when eating. When confined by themselves, they may develop a habit of eating a mouthful of their feed, walking to the stable door, then back for another mouthful, dribbling feed all the way. Some then eat their bedding in an attempt to recover the lost morsels.

Causes: Insecurity in young horses stabled out of sight of other horses at feed time. Observations indicate horses develop this habit if the feed bin is located in a dark area of the stall. Sharp edged cheek teeth may also cause slobbering and quidding. Some horses progress to the "eat-drink" habit, which not only wastes feed, but wets the bedding.

Remedies: Firstly, check the teeth for sharp edges (see page 15). The best way to overcome the problem is to place the feeder on the stable door, or provide a mesh window above the feed tub to let in light. This will enable the horse to view other horses whilst chewing each mouthful - at least the dropped bits will fall back into the feeder. A hay net or rack can be hung above the feeder and any waste then falls into the feeder rather than onto the floor.

If the problem occurs mostly overnight, consider installing a night light (15W protected bulb) above the feeder, or a low wattage security light in the stable itself to benefit all horses.

Shutting the top door often results in a more depressed attitude and loss of appetite. Alternatively, invest in a nose bag so the horse can watch the world, and eat at the same time.

Rapid Feed Intake
Colloquial names: Feed Gorger, Speed Eater, Greedy Horse and Feed Bolter

Most stables have a horse that cleans up before others have started, and fails to thrive despite an adequate diet. These horses are more prone to colic, choking and diarrhea due to feed overload. If whole grain is fed, much of it is passed intact and undigested in the manure.

Causes: Irregularity in feed times with long gaps between meals can cause horses to become very hungry and gulp their food. A bully or aggressive horse in a group of horses may harass those lower in the peck order. They learn to eat quickly in case they are chased away from the feeder. Teeth problems such as sharp edges, bit lacerations and root abscesses may result in pain when chewing. Horses may avoid discomfort by swallowing mouthfuls without proper chewing.

Remedies: Check teeth and attend to any dental problems. Habitual bolters can be slowed by placing a couple of large smooth rocks, (or a salt block in dry weather) in the bottom of the feeder to make it difficult to gulp mouthfuls. Give smaller feeds more frequently and on a regular basis. Feeding a portion of hay 30 minutes prior to a grain feed also avoids digestive overload. Spreading the feed out in a wide tub, with chopped roughage or broken up cubes also slows down intake of grains and pellets.

Slow Food Intake
Colloquial names: Slow Eater, Picky Eaters, Poor Appetite

Horses that take longer than average to finish a meal rarely suffer from digestive upsets and generally utilize their food well. However, many simply run out of eating time and fail to lick clean. They may not take in sufficient to meet exercise demands, and hence lose weight, or lack vitality and performance.

Causes: There are a number of underlying causes of picky eating, or poor appetite, such as nervousness, fatigue and soreness from hard or fast exercise, teeth problems, lack of company, changes in feeds, boredom with the ration, unpalatable feeds and health problems. These are discussed on page 50.

Remedies: Generally, if teeth or health problems are not to blame, then the bulk of the ration should be reduced to increase the energy density by adding grains or fats (see page 25). The ration can be made more palatable by mixing in finely chopped carrots or apples, dampening the ration, or adding flavorings that the horse will accept. (See page xx and 35.)

In a naturally slow eater, ensure there are no distractions or interruptions (eg mucking out boxes) and reschedule training to give more time for the horse to eat the fresh, newly mixed meal.

Eat-Drink Habit/Playing with Water

Young horses confined to stables may start playing with the float or valve on the automatic waterers, or tip over buckets and flood their bedding. Some drink excessive amounts of water, leading to soft cow pat manure, or runny motions. Others deposit feed in their waterers to make a gruel, and then don't eat it anyway. Bad cases will carry mouthfuls of water to the stable door and drop it outside the doorway, bogging the entry to the stable.

Causes: Boredom and confinement are considered to be the most common causes. Although dusty feed, or mouth problems are often cited as reasons for horses mixing water and food, it is unlikely that most offenders would purposely dampen food in this way. Positioning feed tubs and water troughs close together also tends to increase the risk of the "eat-drink" habit.

Remedies: Check the mouth for sharp teeth or lacerations. Dampen the feed and hay to reduce dust. However, if the problem is not medical, then remove the water bucket or shut off the waterer at feed times, and revert to scheduling drinks under supervision at least four times daily. However, don't forget to provide regular access to water, particularly in hot weather, or as a follow-up to cooling down after work.

Coprophagy
Colloquial name: Manure Eater

The urge to sample, and then regularly eat their own manure, is relatively common amongst stabled and confined mature horses. Manure eating is generally a harmless pastime, and does not increase the risk of worm uptake, unless the manure is more than a week old. Some horses develop the dirty habit of stopping to eat fresh manure passed whilst feeding. Manure eating can also lead to a desire to eat sand and bedding.

Causes: The underlying cause is probably boredom in most horses. However, highly concentrated diets can increase the incidence due to low fiber intake. Irregular feeding times, with over 16 hours or longer from the night feed to breakfast, may trigger the habit in some horses if they become hungry between meals. Deficiencies of minerals, such as iron, zinc and calcium have been blamed, but not proven.

Remedies: Provide good quality hay between feeds, particularly overnight to keep the horse occupied. The additional fiber will dilute energy dense rations and help to improve digestive function. In my own experience, weekly injections of Vitamin B12 (5,000ug) for 2-3 weeks, seems to reduce the habit in some horses. Oral B-Complex vitamins, such as 2oz (60ml) of Pulse-8 liquid over the tongue twice weekly, may also be helpful.

Older remedies worth trying include adding 2 teaspoons (10g) of yellow sulfur powder to the evening meal, or alternatively ½ tablespoon meat meal in the morning and evening meals, increasing over seven days to 1 tablespoon twice daily, and continuing for 7-10 days at this dose. Drenching with a single dose of 2 cups of cooking oil in a large syringe may make the manure smelly and less attractive. If all else fails, muzzle the horse between the main meals, or turn out in a paddock with grazing or access to good quality hay.

Nibbling and Eating Wood
Colloquial names: Wood Chewers/Crib Biters

Chewing rails, feeders, doors, and trees is another habit primarily brought on by boredom and confinement with infrequent or irregular meal times. Many horses like to chew soft woods, particularly sweet cedars and even treated pine. Observations indicate that stabled horses spend an average of 8 minutes per day chewing stall fixtures. (See page 31.) Splinters of wood and nails etc. may lodge between the teeth or lacerate the gums or tongue. Some horses confined to outside steel fenced corrals develop a habit of licking the pipes, wearing off the paint and exposing the metal which rusts.

Causes: Some authorities consider a lack of phosphorus in the diet may result in an urge to eat wood. Sweet feed based diets also tend to increase the habit. A lack of adequate fiber and/or protein in the diet is also blamed. Confining a horse to a barn by itself increases insecurity and boredom. Feeding of pelleted rations also increases the risk, possibly due to the low volume ration and boredom between feeds.

Remedies: Provide a balanced ration with a Calcium:Phosphorus ratio of 2:1. Up to 10% bran to provide extra phosphorus may be added to high alfalfa-roughage based rations. Reduce boredom by providing good quality hay between meals, particularly overnight. Replacing soft wood rails with hard lumber deters some nibblers, or covering ledges and door tops with metal strips may reduce damage. Strands of charged electric fence wiring over problem areas may help, but bad cases will be forced to chew elsewhere. Coating rails, door tops and trees with hot, bitter tasting preparations to deter chewing is also worth trying. Dilute pelleted rations with an equal amount of chopped hay to increase bulk and extend feeding time.

Aerophagia/Oral Windsucking
Colloquial name: Windsucker, Cribber

This is the term used to describe the technique developed by horses where they anchor their top teeth on a rail or post, arch their necks, and gulp air. New evidence suggests that stretching the neck and gulping air is a pleasurable sensation. It often leads to excessive teeth wear, resulting in digestive upset and poor condition due to interrupted feeding habits.

Causes: Confinement to stables, resulting in boredom and frustration, may cause a horse to initially nibble or chew wood, and then develop the windsucking habit. Horses and foals can quickly learn the technique from other horses. Occasionally, horses will even windsuck by arching their necks and anchoring their teeth on their own knee joint area.

Remedies: Application of deterrent preparations to all horizontal surfaces or favourite windsucking ledges in stalls, corrals and paddocks, may be helpful. However, as horses only rest their top teeth on horizontal rails or tops of posts, often these preparations are not tasted. Preparations with an offensive smell can be more effective in keeping horses away from rails, and human caretakers out of the stable.

Fitting a 3 inch (75mm) wide leather calf neck strap snugly around the throat latch area appears to be more successful than conventional hinged windsucking straps, which often cause pressure sores on the throat latch.

Provision of metal mirrors to the back of the stall may reduce the frequency of windsucking by nervous, confined horses. In severe cases, a modified Forsells operation to prevent arching of the lower neck muscles to windsuck may be tried. However, it has been observed that only younger horses that have been windsucking for less than a year, have a good chance of being cured from the habit by surgery.

In the mid 1980's, the compound Nalmefene, a specific opioid antagonist was trialled by Tuffs University as a treatment for crib biting and windsucking. Nalmefene, similar to Naloxone in its action, but with a longer duration of activity, was used to block the release of endorphins (morphine-like proteins produced by nerve tissues to block pain). The theory was based on the observation that windsuckers obtained a "high" or feeling of well being from the endorphin release.

Follow-up indicates Nalmefene - released by pellets deposited under the skin - can suppress crib biting and windsucking for up to four weeks. However, further research needs to be carried out on long-term toxicity and drug interaction, as well as to develop the best dosage form to give a slow release of Nalmefene. Unfortunately, once the blocking effects of the drug wear off, most chronic windsuckers and crib biters take up their habit with renewed vigor.

Tail and Mane Chewing
Colloquial names: Tail Chewer and Mane Chewer

These habits are common in young horses, particularly during long nights and cold weather. Chewed tails are a particular problem in weanlings or young horses confined to dry lots or corrals with infrequent feeds. Tail hairs take a long time to regrow, ruining the cosmetic appearance of the animal for months. Chewing hair may lacerate the gums and may lead to digestive disturbances and gut obstruction in severe cases.

Causes: Lack of adequate fiber, salt, phosphorus, copper and other mineral deficiencies have been suggested. Usually only one horse in a group will develop the habit.

Remedies: Ensure horses have adequate roughage as good quality alfalfa hay provided in hay racks or fed out daily. Smear a suitable deterrent preparation on the tails of all young horses at least monthly from weanling onwards,

particularly during colder weather when horses are huddled together in groups, or in sheltered areas. Addition of meat meal to the ration (see Wood Chewing above) is reported to help prevent the habit in some cases.

Bedding Eater

Ingestion of straw bedding can lead to intestinal compaction, plant poisoning and increased risk of worm uptake. Poisoning of horses from eating American Redwood shavings used as bedding has been reported. The habit is most common in horses confined to stalls for long periods of time during preparation, yearling pre-training or racing.

Causes: Boredom, irregular feeding times, lack of adequate fiber in the ration, nervousness and messy eating habits (see page 31), are thought to lead to the habit of eating the bedding.

Remedies: Provision of adequate roughage, with hay between feeds and particularly overnight, usually overcomes the problem. Straw can be sprayed with a bitter preparation to make it unpalatable. If the problem persists on straw bedding, change to sawdust which is less likely to be palatable. Nervous horses, or isolated horses, are best moved to be next to a buddy. In intractable cases, remove bedding materials, and shift horse to a sand floored stable with access to an outside corral, or muzzle the horse between feeds.

Dirt or Sand Eater

Some horses will paw and dig up clay and soil and eat it on a regular basis. Accidental ingestion of sand is common in horses grazing short pastures on sandy soils, particularly during drought conditions, or when confined to dry lots or sandy corrals with hay fed on the ground. Build up of sand in the narrow segments at the bends of the large bowel inevitably leads to sand impaction, colic and fatal bowel rupture.

Cause: This habit is primarily boredom related, but lack of iron, copper, calcium and phosphorus in the diet is claimed to trigger the desire to eat dirt. Gastroduodenal ulceration resulting from highly concentrated or refined diets has also been suggested.

In sandy areas where grazing increases uptake of sand, heavy burdens of hypobiotic or encysted Cyathostome spp. (Small Redworms) in the colon wall is considered to increase the prevalence of sand colic, as bowel movement may be reduced. Different sand types may be more likely to cause accumulation than others, with fine sand being the most dangerous.

Remedies: In sandy areas, horses should be shifted to longer pastures on a regular basis, or provided ad-lib hard feed and hay in hay racks. Regular bimonthly drenching with laxative gels may be suggested by your vet. Stabled horses that eat sand whilst in their outside corrals should be provided with hay in a hay rack located on a compacted area. Mixing of 3oz (100g) psyllium husk into the feed once weekly, or giving 1oz (30g or 2 tablespoons) of Epsom salts (magnesium sulfate) is helpful in preventing sand accumulation in the large bowel.

Where a horse develops a craving for sand or dirt, provision of a daily vitamin/mineral supplement (such as Feramo-H), and a calcium supplement may help control the habit. Alternatively, mixing half a cup of powdered red clay into the night feed may be worth trying, as is a dose of sulphur powder (2 teaspoons daily) or meat meal (see page 143).

A full examination by your veterinarian should be carried out on horses, as mouth lesions and gastric ulceration may cause them to habitually seek out and eat clay or soil. Mixing 1½oz (43g) or three tablespoons of bicarbonate of soda into the evening meal is widely regarded by horse owners as a useful therapy to reduce an uncomfortable stomach burning sensation in horses on high grain diets. However, in racing horses, the dose of bicarbonate should not exceed 1 3/4oz (50g or 4 tablespoons) daily as it may elevate blood bicarbonate levels to above the threshold that constitutes bicarbonate doping. Consult your vet for advice.

Over Eating or Obesity

Horses can overeat in a single meal, leading to founder (laminitis), or other digestive upset. However, obesity can be a long-term problem resulting from provision of high energy rations in excess of exercise demand.

Causes: Horses are not well adapted to high carbohydrate diets available on a continuous basis, and naturally store body fat for leaner periods for seasonal variations which are not forthcoming in horses confined to stalls in training or the over-winter months. The provision of highly palatable, nutritious feeds in large quantities, frequent feeding, decreased roughage intake and restricted exercise all predispose to obesity.

Remedies: The treatment of obesity should be limited to restriction of feed and increased exercise. Decrease in dietary energy density, and controlled, but not excessive slow aerobic type exercise at trot and canter is safe and effective in reducing excess bodyweight. (See page 55 for full details.)

METABOLIC, RESPIRATORY AND DIGESTIVE CONDITIONS RELATED TO FEEDING

Predisposing Cause	Condition	Dietary Management for Prevention
Unaccustomed or sudden increase, or overfeeding of grains	Tying-up (Exertional myopathy)	Feed grain in proportion to exercise. Do not suddenly increase grain. Reduce grain on rest days, take 2 days to reinstate full grain ration once exercise resumes. Avoid feeding high levels to young fillies (see page 88).
	Impaction Colic	Ensure a step-wise increase in grain. Provide adequate roughage as hay, and multiple small meals of grains during day. Do not feed finely crushed corn or wheat.
	Dilation Colic (Gas Colic)	Avoid feeding finely milled feeds or high grain rations to hungry horses. Offer roughage before concentrates in horses that bolt their feed.
	Torsion Colic	Feed adequate roughage 1.0% bwt. at all times. Regular worming every 6-8 weeks, daily feed worming medication.
	Diarrhea	Avoid more than 50% high energy grain in ration. Make all changes to feed slowly (see page 150).
	Hot Behaviour	Feed grain to exercise level. Feed adequate roughage. Remove grain on rest days (see page 41).
Gorging carbohydrates eg Corn, Wheat	Founder (Laminitis)	If gorged, consult vet immediately. Prevent free access to corn storage. Increase corn in increments of half pound (230g) daily to exercise level, withdraw on rest day (see page 41).
Chronic overfeeding of grains or high energy and protein diets in young horses	Limb deformities (Developmental Orthopedic Disease) (DOD)	Avoid feeding excess energy and imbalanced Ca:P ratio diets to growing horses. Restrict starch and protein intake to NRC (1989) levels, and ensure minimum requirements of trace-minerals are provided. Aim at 80% growth rate in bloodlines with prevalence of DOD. Do not restrict growth by feeding poor quality feeds with trace mineral deficiencies (see page 148).
New Season's Grain and High protein diets	Skin Bumps Protein Bumps Hives (Urticaria)	Reduce protein content of ration by feeding grass hay to allergic horses. Store oats for 3 months after harvest prior to use. Mix new season's grain 50:50 with old season's grain and change over 7-10 days (see page 150).
	Excess Ammonia in urine	Avoid excessively high protein diets that can cause excess ammonia in urine and may lead to reduced performance.
Lush Green Forage Grass clippings	Gas (Flatuent) Colic	May lead to flatulence and secondary impaction colic. Avoid sudden introduction to lush legume pastures.
	Diarrhea	Avoid turning out hungry horses onto wet, lush pastures or giving large amounts of greenfeed to horses maintained on dry feeds.
	Founder (Laminitis)	Avoid grazing cresty ponies or horses on lush spring pasture (see page 148).
	Sudden death	Do not feed grass or garden clippings containing poisonous plants.
Pellets	Intestinal Inflammatory Disease (Colic)	Dilute concentrates or pellets 50:50 with chopped hay or dampened cubes to prevent rapid ingestion. Feed small feeds on more regular basis.
	Chewing wood	Increase exercise or companionship to occupy horse. Provide adequate roughage to dilute pellet intake (see page 143).
High Wheat Bran Diets	Bran Disease/Big head Bone Deformities (Nutritional Secondary Hyperparathyroidism - NSH)	Avoid feeding more than 10% wheat bran on a continuous basis as excess phytic acid can bind calcium and reduce absorption. Do not mix calcium supplements into **pure** bran mashes (see page 187).
Grazing Tropical Pastures	Big head, Bone Deformities (Nutritional Secondary Hyperparathyroidism - NSH)	Avoid grazing fast growing, highly fertilized tropical grass containing high oxalate chemicals, such as Panic, Buffel, Setaria, and Paspalum for continuous periods without additional calcium supplements (see page 149).

Predisposing Cause	Condition	Dietary Management for Prevention
Sandy Country Drought Conditions	Sand Colic	Supplement horses with hay in a hay rack when grazing sandy areas, or in drought. Worm-out regularly for Small Redworms (Cyathostomes). Provide feed tubs and hay racks. Feed psyllium laxative or Epsom salts (see page 144).
Cattle or Poultry Growth Promotant Formulations	Monensin Toxicity (Colic)	Consult vet immediately if ingested by accident. Lethal dose Monensin is 1-1½mg/lb. Consumption of 600-1900mg Monensin over 36-48 hours is fatal within 3 weeks. Ensure feeds containing Monensin are not fed to horses - check bag labels.
Silage, haylage or poorly cured hay.	Botulism Poisoning	Ensure horses are not fed poorly cured silage or big bale hay contaminated with dead animal carcasses. Do not feed haylage if plastic bags are torn open for more than 3 days.
Feeding under Stress or Sudden Fasting	Gastroduodenal ulceration (Foals grind teeth)	Foals: Ensure foals are not deprived of feed due to separation, injury or transport. Avoid highly concentrated rations and pellets without adequate roughage. Avoid stress and overcrowding of foals. Adult Racing Horses: Avoid highly concentrated rations, feed adequate roughage in adult horses in training - minimum 50% by weight.
	Hyperlipidemia (subclinical) Hyperlipemia (severe)	Ponies (and Thoroughbreds): Ensure adequate feed is available at all times, particularuly for pregnant and lactating pony mares. Provide hay after storms, floods and snowfalls. Rest ponies during long hauls - provide feed every 4 hours. Do not starve overweight ponies (see page 149).
Dusty Feeds	Heaves (COPD)	Dampen all dusty feeds and brittle dusty hays prior to feeding. Hays may need to be soaked for 12 hours. (See page 43.) Avoid high hay racks in stables unless hay is damp. Avoid dusty feeds during long distance travelling (see page 53).
Excessively dry feeds	Choke (Esophagus obstruction)	Avoid feeding dry hay to hungry horses or those that bolt their feeds. Dampen all feeds for bolters (see page 43). Slow down feed intake - stones in feeder (see page 142).
	Constipation	Ensure adequate access to water and provide electrolytes in heavily sweating, hard working horses fed on dry feeds. Dampen hay.
Whole Fruits/Vegetables	Choke (Esophagus obstruction)	Do not feed whole apples, carrots or potatoes to hungry horses or feed bolters. Chop fruit and vegetables into small pieces.
Poisonous Plants	See pages 155 to 161 for signs associated with ingestion of toxic plants	Avoid letting hungry or new horses out into areas with potentially poisonous plants. Provide hay during poor pasture, drought or overstocking to reduce need to eat poisonous plants. Examine alfalfa hay for blister beetles. Avoid access to home gardens. Do not feed lawn clippings.
High Mineral Intake	Poisoning from high mineral intake in feed or water	Avoid access to areas around ore smelters, petroleum products, heavy metal toxic waste dumps or run-offs, contaminated or heavily mineralized water supplies, insecticide overuse, lead-based painted surfaces or rails.
	Bowel Osbtruction Enteroliths/Fecoliths Constipation	Mineralized formations and accumulation around stones, etc in bowel. If incidence is high in an area - consider relocation. Avoid high magnesium and phosphate diets. (See page 152.)

COMMON METABOLIC CONDITIONS RELATED TO FEEDING

Condition	Predisposing Cause	Underlying Causes	Dietary Prevention
LAMINITIS ("Founder") Inflammation of laminae in hooves	Unaccustomed, or chronic overfeeding of grain, especially high carbohydrates such as wheat, corn in overload levels greater than 12lb/1000lb horse. Lush Spring legume based pastures - ponies more susceptible, especially males or geldings 7-10 years of age. Ingestion of large amounts of very cold water in a hot horse immediately following exercise.	Lactic acidosis and endotoxin production causes blood flow changes in laminae of feet. Unaccumstomed intake of higher energy and protein in rapidly growing grass in susceptible ponies. Possible circulatory shock syndrome resulting in blood flow changes in hoof.	Increase grain in increments of ½lb (225g) daily to match exercise. Prevent access to grain stores. Limit grazing access to lush pasture, to 1 hour morning and evening in fat or heavily conditioned ponies, or "good doers", "easy keepers". Exercise to utilize feed intake. Fit a wire mesh muzzle. Offer dampened hay for 30 minutes after work to cool down. Offer small volumes water only 2 pints every 10 minutes - offer water with chill taken off, 4 pints every 10 minutes.
EXERTIONAL MYOPATHY Syndrome "Tying up" "Set Fast" Also called: Azoturia, Equine Rhabdomyolysis, Syndrome, Paralytic Myoglobinuria, Monday morning disease	1. Faulty substrate metabolism - Carbohydrate overloading - high grain rations; Glycolytic enzyme deficiency; Faulty fat metabolism. 2. Vitamin and mineral deficiencies: Vitamin E and, or, selenium: thiamine. 3. Endocrine abnormalities: Hypothyroidism; Sex related, nervous fillies; Corticosteroid therapy. 4. Electrolyte imbalances: Na+, K+, Ca+, Mg+, pH+, heavy sweat alkalosis; Malignant hyperthermia. 5. Others - Viral infections. 6. Sudden exercise in unfit or sedentary horses, especially cold weather.	Underlying causes still unknown. Mild cases may be associated with lactic acidosis of muscles after sudden exercise or fast work in an unfit horse. New evidence suggests electrolyte imbalances, accumulation of calcium in muscle cells. Various degrees of and occurrence during stages of exercise (during and after) suggest multiple pathogenesis. Exhaustion in heavily dehydrated Endurance horses, high calcium intake during training, such as in alfalfa.	1. Reduce grains to one third level on rest days, starting night before rest days. 2. Reduce level of oats to half in nervous fillies, replace with corn or rolled barley. 3. Feed to exercise level - do not suddenly increase grains. 4. Provide electrolyte supplements in heavily sweating horses. 5. Supplement with Vit.E/Selenium daily. 6. Supplement 1 cupful vegetable oil daily in recurring cases. 7. Warm horses up and cool down at trot after exercise. 8. Work susceptible horses each day with no rest days. 9. Ensure adequate water provision. 10. Do not feed large amounts of alfalfa hay or cubes during training in endurance horses (see page 111).

COMMON METABOLIC CONDITIONS RELATED TO FEEDING

Condition	Predisposing Cause	Underlying Causes	Dietary Prevention
HYPERLIPEMIA (Severe Syndrome) **HYPERLIPIDEMIA** (Subclinical syndrome) Elevated lipids or trigyclerides in blood - Hyperlipemia often fatal - hard to reverse once in severe form	Sudden fasting, starvation in ponies. Also reported in donkeys and Thoroughbreds. Good, well conditioned ponies more susceptible, especially pregnant or lactating mares. Negative energy balance can be caused by: 1. Heavy parasite burdens 2. Demands of pregnancy/lactation. 3. Severe disease. 4. Loss of pasture due to rain storms, snow or floods. 5. Lack of feed when transporting >12 hours. 6. Young mares at stud bossed way from feeders. 7. Chronic diarrhea. 8. Pituitary tumors/insulin insensitivity.	During fasting, fat or adipose tissue broken down into free fatty acids and glycerol into blood. Free fatty acids used by muscle, but majority accumulate in liver. Some converted in liver to low density lipoproteins and released back into blood. Hyperlipemia - serum triglycerides above 50g/L - fat accumulates in liver - fatal in 7-10 days often with metabolic acidosis. Hyperlipidemia - subclinical syndrome - coudy appearance of serum with triglycerides level 5-10g/L.	1. Ensure adequate feed is available at all times, particularly pregnant and lactating pony mares, young mares at stud (provide extra feeder or feed separately). 2. Provide hay or hard feed during winter, or after heavy rains. 3. Rest and allow ponies to eat every 4 hours during transport, or provide damp alfalfa in hay net in truck or trailer. 4. Do not starve overweight ponies - reduce feed level slowly and increase exercise. 5. Seek vet advice on ponies not eating due to laminitis or sickness.
DEVELOPMENTAL ORTHOPEDIC DISEASE (DOD) Also called: Metabolic Cartilage Disease, Metabolic Bone Disease, and individual conditions eg Epiphysitis etc. Open Knees	Combination of genetic, hormonal, nutritional, metabolic and mechanical factors. Genetic influences increase risk of high growth rates when over feeding occurs in susceptible young horses. Poor nutrition, stunted growth corrected by over nutrition.	Underlying cause involves incomplete formation and maturation of cartilage to bone during development.	Carefully formulated diet that specifically restricts starch and protein, whilst supplying NRC (1989) minimum requirements of other essential nutrients, with adequate but not excessive exercise. Adapt feeding program to horses with family or bloodline incidence of DOD to aim at 80% of maximum growth rate. Do not restrict growth by feeding poor quality feeds as trace mineral deficiencies can lead to poor cartilage formation. (See also page 73.)
NUTRITIONAL SECONDARY HYPER- PARATHYROIDISM (NSH) Also called Bran Disease, Big Head	High phosphorus grain based rations in growing horses. High bran content containing phytic acid which forms insoluble poorly absorbed calcium phytate compounds. High oxalate content of tropical grasses, when calcium/oxalate ratio is 0.5:1.0 less in dry matter. Alfalfa contains calcium oxalates ratio at 2-3 times critical 0.5:1.0 ratio and is unlikely to cause NSH itself. Tropical grasses contain 0.23:1.0 Calcium: oxalate. (See page 157.)	Reduction in availability of calcium due to binding affect, reduces blood level, which stimulates release of parathyroid hormone to demineralize calcium stored in limb and facial bones to maintain calcium blood level. Condition may be exacerbated by calcium demand in heavily sweating horses/pregnant/ lactating mares grazing susceptible pastures.	Graze horses on other non-hazardous species of grass where possible. Plant clover with topical grass to balance calcium intake. Avoid over fertilizing grass with high phosphorus mixes - superphosphate and poultry manure. Restrict access to oxalate grass in young horses to prevent DOD - feed hard feeds with calcium 60-90g daily. Feed a calcium supplement 90g daily when grazing hazardous pasture, or feeding high bran diets.

COMMON METABOLIC CONDITIONS RELATED TO FEEDING

Condition	Predisposing Cause	Underlying Causes	Dietary Prevention
URTICARIA "Skin Bumps" "Protein Bumps" "Hives"	Increased protein content of ration. Feeding new seasons grain. Pellet feeds have been incriminated without controlled evidence.	Theory Excess protein leads to non-protein nitrogen level as ammonia in blood stream. New grain contains higher volatile nitrogen compounds. In severe cases, causes generalized allergic reaction.	Reduce protein content in ration - feed grass hay to allergic horses. Store oats for 3 months after harvest before use. Mix new seasons grain 50:50 with old seasons grain and change over 7-10 days.

DIARRHEA RELATED TO FEEDING

Type of Diarrhea	Predisposing Causes	Pathogenesis	Dietary Prevention
ANTERIOR ENTERITIS	**Small Intestine** High grain, low roughage diets cause inflammation with gut flora changes and release of endo or enterotoxins.	Non surgical ileus, loss of smooth muscle co-ordination due to abnormal microflora toxins. Chemical and plant toxins.	Avoid highly concentrated diets, especially of sorghum, wheat and boiled feeds. Feed adequate roughage - 50% by weight with grain or pelleted ration. Provide individual feeders in group of horses to prevent gorging by dominant horses.
DIARRHEA	**Large Intestine** Dietary induced overload, with changes to microflora, fermentation rates. Ingestion of wet, lush pasture, particularly clovers, alfalfa. Antibiotic induced diarrhea.	Altered fermentation rates directly or indirectly affect fluid shifts, secretion and fluid absorption. Irritatory type diarrhea due to high water content of pasture. Antibiotic induced clostridial overgrowth may be main cause of diarrhea.	Make all changes to feeds slowly. With fresh green feed or pasture, ensure access to natural grass and quality hay to balance moisture content of feed. Avoid excessive or long-term use of anti-microbial agents - do not feed antibiotic added feeds to horses - consult your vet for advice.
INTESTINAL INFLAMMATORY DISEASE	Rapid ingestion of processed low bulk feeds such as pellets.	Malabsorption of feed - protein loss and diarrhea due to changes in fluid compartmentation and intestinal motility.	Dilute pellete 50:50 with crumbled cubes or adequate hay and dampen prior to feeding. Some horses are sensitive to feeds - avoid consumption.

COLICS RELATED TO FEEDING

Type of colic	Predisposing Cause	Underlying Causes	Dietary Prevention
IMPACTION COLIC	**Stomach** Overeating grain, grain engorgement, small intestinal blockage. **Small Intestine** Muscular hyperatrophy or altered motility, often associated with eating pudgy or finely milled feed. **Large Intestine** Most common form of colic - 30% of all cases.Overeating grain and overfeeding in single meals, causes motility changes and fluid shifts to dry out ingesta - reduces microfloral fermentation.	Ingestion of concentrated meal causes rapid compartmental fluid shifts, changes in gastro-intestinal motility patterns, alterations of microflora and micro-environment of the intestinal tract. Alteration of microflora affects the mucosal barrier and increases absorption of intraluminal toxins. Large meals may accelerate passage to cecum, increasing colon fermentation - increasing fluid shifts into colon, with compensatory net fluid absorption and reduced motility leads to compaction of food mass.	Management to ensure a more continuous feeding pattern, providing good quality roughage and multiple small meals of concentrates during the day.
DILATION COLIC	**Stomach** Grain overload and feeding finely milled feed. Rapid ingestion of feed in "feed bolters".	Finely milled food increases rate of gastric fermentation.	Avoid feeding finely milled feeds or high grain rations to hungry horses. Feed small amount of roughage before main meal in "feed bolters".
FLATULENT/ GAS COLIC	**Large Intestine** Lush green feed secondary to impaction colic following rapid intake of highly fermentable feeds and grain engorgement, ingestion of grass clippings.	Highly fermentable feed rapidly increases microflora populations which ferment to produce gas, with secondary impaction of mass due to fluid shifts and reduced motility.	Avoid suddenly introducing horses to fresh clovers and legumes in pasture. Do not feed grass clippings.
SPASMODIC COLIC	Intake of very cold water by hot horse after exercise. May be associated with diarrhea.	Possible shock syndrome with altered blood flow and other unknown changes - can precipitate laminitis (founder).	Feed dampened hay for 30 minutes after hard exercise, or access to 2 pints of water every 10 minutes with chill taken off by adding hot water.
SAND COLIC	**Large Intestine** At pelvic and sternal flexures - type of impaction colic.	Impaction by settling out of certain types of sand - devitalization of intestinal lining and reduced motility, exacerbated by large numbers of encysted Small Strongyle worms.	Supplement horses with hay when grazing sandy areas in drought. Worm out regularly for small Redworms. Provide feed tubs and hay racks. (See also page 144.)
DISPLACEMENT/ TORSION COLIC	High grain - low roughage diets. Most common colic requiring surgical correction by your vet.	Similar primary cause as impaction colic - microflora increase and toxins absorbed affect motility.	Avoid feeding low roughage diets - provide adequate hay, particularly with high grain/pellet diets - not less than 50:50 roughage to concentrate by weight.

COLICS RELATED TO FEEDING

Type of colic	Predisposing Cause	Underlying Causes	Dietary Prevention
GASTRO-DUODENAL ULCERATION (Colic)	<u>Suckling foals</u> - deprived of feed due to injury, separation, transport or hospitalization. <u>Older foals</u> - too much milk/feed, very hot weather. <u>Weaning</u> - stress related. <u>Adults</u> - highly concentrated rations, minimum bulk.	Interruption of muco-phospholipid layer allowing gastic acid and pepsin to autodigest mucosa - associated with campylobacter infection <u>Symptoms:</u> Foals, grinding of teeth, lying on back - only occurs when foals have ulcers. Consult your vet for advice.	Ensure suckling foals are adequately nursing during sickness, injury, transport, or hospitalization. Avoid stress such as overcrowding, excessive handling, overfeeding and overmedication. Delay weaning if foals are stressed. Avoid highly concentrated rations.
CHOKE (Obstruction) (Colic)	<u>Esophagus</u> Bolting feed, dry feed, inflamed osophagus, nervous dysfunction, stricture or narrowing.	Physical obstruction of large food bolus, or inadequate muscle due to dry food, nervous dysfunction or inflammation.	Do not feed carrots/apples/potatoes to "feed bolters". Dampen all feed in "feed bolters". Slow down feed intake - stones in feeder. (See page 142.)
COLON OBSTRUCTIONS Enteroliths Fecoliths/ Constipation (Colic)	<u>Right dorsal small colon</u> <u>Enteroliths</u> Mineralized formation around core of pebbles,, metal, or silicon dioxide. Often mutliple enteroliths formed.	Mostly comprised of ammonium magnesium phosphate, possibly from high mineral content of soil, plants, water. Does not cause dysfunction during formation, eventually causes physical blackage of bowel.	If incidence is high - consider change of location or de-ionization of water supply. Avoid excessive magnesium supplementation. Surgical removal of enteroliths is necessary - see your vet.
INTESTINAL INFLAMMATORY DISEASE (Colic)	Rapid ingestion of processed low bulk feeds, such as pellets.	Malabsorption of feed - protein loss and diarrhea - changes in fluid compartmentation and intestinal motility.	Dilute pellets 50:50 with crumbled cubes and dampen prior to feeding. Some horses are sensitive to feeds - avoid consumption.
MONENSIN POISONING (Ionophorus antibiotics - growth promotants) (Colic)	Horses consume feeds containing monensin intended for poultry and cattle. Stomach content samples should be taken for identification. See your vet.	Toxicity results from increased transmembrane flux of electrolyte cations, particularly sodium and potassium, hence toxicity is worsened by exercise and sweat loss.	Ensure feeds containing monensin are not fed to horses - check feed bag labels. No specific antidote exists. Management includes limiting exercise for up to 8 weeks after ingestion, feeding high potassium supplements, and Vitamin E/selenium. Use laxatives to eliminate accidental dosage within first 24-36 hours.

COLICS RELATED TO FEEDING

Type of colic	Predisposing Cause	Underlying Causes	Dietary Prevention
BOTULISM POISONING (Colic)	Ingestion of preformed toxin in feedstuffs such as silage, haylage or poorly cured hay. Causes excessive salivation, inability to retract or move tongue, tail. Cause of Shaker foal disease in foals.	Neurotoxin - causes paralytic effect on the neuromuscular junction. Death occurs due to respiratory paralysis.	Outbreaks often associated with big bale hay, contaminated with dead animal carcases. Also poorly cured silage and moist haylage cured in plastic bags. Hay and silages stored in plastic bags should be avoided, if seals damaged - use haylage within 3 days after opening.
MOLDY FEED	Ingestion of moldy, spoiled corn, or "black patch" disease on clover, sweet clover molds.	Neurotoxins and irritant compounds produced by fungal or other organisms contaminating poorly stored feeds, or during certain seasonal growth conditions.	Weathered sweet clover can cause bleeding in horses. Avoid feeding any feed that has been poorly stored. Consult vet for advice if necessary.
BLISTER BEETLES	Blister beetles crushed during baling of alfalfa hay in mid to late summer. Only 2-5 crushed beetles can cause colic.	Release of cantharidin - causes depression, loss of appetite, colic, shock and death.	Inspect alfalfa fields, particularly field margins, prior to cutting, for blister beetles if swarming in warm weather. Do not cut hay from any small areas containing beetles. Inspect hay for beetles prior to feeding.
POISONOUS PLANTS	Ingestion of poisonous plants due to inquisitive nature in young or new horses, lack of feed, or during drought conditions.	Various plant toxins cause gastro-intestinal changes, with diarrhea and signs of colic.	Prevent access to waste lands, railroad areas or pastures known to contain poisonous plants. See tables on pages 155-161 for potentially toxic plants. Provide supplementary hay to horses during periods of poor pasture. Supply after snow falls or drought.

PLANTS POISONOUS TO HORSES

Many common weeds or garden plants can be poisonous to horses, but a little care can prevent serious illness.

Poisonous plants are generally not palatable, and horses - being careful and selective feeders - will only eat them when there is little else to graze, where pasture is overstocked, or dry and less palatable. Cases of plant poisoning are more common in drought seasons because many native local plants have adapted to survive and cultivated grazing pastures die out. Hungry horses may eat plants normally avoided, and newly introduced or young horses inquisitive for new tastes are at risk from plant poisoning. Although a dietary deficiency in certain minerals is often claimed as a reason for horses being tempted to eat poisonous plants, this is very unlikely.

Some plants are only toxic when eaten as green forage and risk of poisoning is confined to the areas in which these plants grow. However, other plants retain toxicity when dried or as seeds, and this can cause poisoning over a wide area if mixed into hay or grain.

HINT *The toxic substances are in low concentrations in most plants. Horses normally have to consume from one to three percent of their bodyweight before developing signs of poisoning.*

However, there are some exceptions. For example, Oleander and Yew can cause sudden death if amounts of 4oz (114g) or 0.025% bodyweight is consumed. Horses must be prevented from access to these plants at all times to avoid poisonings. Other plants such as Locoweed and Yellow Star Thistle contain cumulative poisons, requiring intakes of 30-200% of bodyweight over a period of a month or several weeks to cause toxic signs.

Unfortunately, many garden and ornamental plants can be extremely poisonous to horses, particularly if planted around stables. In cases of blister beetle poisoning in contaminated alfalfa hay, only two to five beetles need to be ingested to cause colicky signs. In hand fed horses, a common cause of poisoning is allowing the horse to feed on garden plant or lawn clippings as a greenfeed treat by well meaning, but unsuspecting gardeners.

Horses that are allowed to graze on areas such as infrequently used or abandoned railroad or roadway areas, are also likely to ingest poisonous plants. These areas are usually not as well controlled for weeds. Weed seeds are dropped and spread during transport of other animals or fodder, or by wind and water.

And lastly, even bedding, such as wood shavings, can contain toxic plant materials. Horses ingesting shavings of American Redwood have developed gastrointestinal signs. When horses lie down on bedding, contact with fresh Black Walnut shavings can cause soft swelling in the legs, lethargy and founder.

When plants are Poisonous

Some plants are particularly dangerous at all times, but most which cause toxicity are either seasonal growers, are only poisonous at a certain stage of growth or when wet, when frost causes leaf fall, after treatment with herbicides, or when eaten by horses under stress.

HINT *The range of symptoms caused by plant ingestion is related to the toxic compound(s) contained in the plant, and their relative concentrations, the age of the animal and relative stress, and the amount consumed.*

Some plants are believed to contain addictive drugs, and once introduced, horses will seek them out and graze them, even if there is an abundance of good quality pasture. Over the years, Locoweed has gained a reputation as being an addictive plant, but it is unclear whether this is so. Animals introduced to areas containing Locoweed are more likely to be poisoned than horses raised on areas where the plant is common.

Signs of Plant Poisoning

Symptoms such as colic, diarrhea, nervous signs, staggers, skin reactions or blindness may be the first signs of plant poisoning. Horses may also be found dead. Cumulative poisons may produce signs of poor health, loss of condition and nervous signs once the body systems begin to deteriorate. Definite symptoms often do not appear until severe kidney, liver, or nervous system damage has been done.

HINT *Death or abnormal behavior in a single horse often requires careful examination and an accurate grazing history before a diagnosis of plant poisoning can be made. Plant poisoning is usually suspected when a group of horses together exhibit similar signs without symptoms of common diseases.*

Laboratory tests or post mortem findings may help your veterinarian confirm a particular plant poisoning.

Action in the Event of Suspected Poisoning

Quick action may save a horse's life, or prevent others from being poisoned. Seek advice immediately from a veterinarian or local County Agricultural Agent. Give clear descriptions of the symptoms and how long the horses have been exhibiting them. Provide the history of previous disease or suspected poisoning, the routine feeding method, any changes in diet or grazing location, and the source and availability of water.

*   If a number of other horses could be at risk, shift them to another area, or confine them to a dry lot or corral and feed hay. However, if the affected horses are being hand fed, do not feed them until your veterinarian has examined a sample of feed or hay.

    Check grain and a hay for presence of contaminating leaves or seeds, blister beetles in alfalfa hay, or sample of corn that could be moldy, that could be potentially toxic. Collect a sample of bedding in case the horse has eaten or lain on toxic shavings.

*   Thoroughly search the pasture for unidentified plants that show recent signs of being eaten by horses, such as the flower heads missing. If necessary, contact the local County Weeds Officer, or take a fresh sample (preferably with flowers or fruits attached and wrapped in moist newspaper), or a sample of suspect hay or grain, to the County Agent's Office or University Clinic for identification.

If a horse dies or is found dead, then a post mortem may help identify the cause and save the lives of other horses.

Prevention of Plant Poisoning

Simple precautions will decrease the risks and effects of plant poisoning in horses.

* Don't turn horses, especially hungry ones, into strange or new pastures without first checking for poisonous plants.

* Keep a look-out for plants that may be poisonous. Regularly check fence lines, ditches, around tanks, springs, troughs and buildings, or under trees for poisonous plants. Remove the plants, and burn or mulch them in a safe place.

* If necessary, seek advice on seasonal control of poisonous weeds using selective herbicides from your local County Agent. Shift horses when spraying and obtain advice on a safe time for return of stock.

* Ensure that fences are sound to prevent horses wandering onto strange territories like home gardens, wasteland, open ranges, and abandoned railroad areas.

* Never feed garden or lawn clippings as they may cause colic and contain toxic plant leaves. Check new sources of alfalfa for blister beetle contamination, and grain for foreign seeds.

* Remove horses from pasture containing plants at the time when they may be toxic, for example, lush clover pastures that may cause founder (laminitis) or photosensitization in ponies in early spring.

* Trim garden plants which hang over into areas where horses graze. If plants such as Oleander, yew or poinsettia are growing within reach of horses, it would be safest to completely remove them. Make sure water supplies are suitable for horses, and leaves from potentially toxic plants do not contaminate dams, tanks or troughs.

* Contact your local County Weed Officer or Department of Agriculture Adviser and arrange a visit to your property to identify weeds or shrubs that are unknown to you. Alternatively, arrange for specimens of plants to be sent for identification and advice on control.

* In times of drought or unavoidable high stocking rates, provide adequate supplementary feed to reduce the need for horses to eat potentially toxic weeks or poisonous plants. (See page 61.)

Some Plants Poisonous to Horses

The plants described below are common garden shrubs, trees, weeds or pasture plants found in the United States, that have been reported to be poisonous to horses. It is by no means a complete list.

GARDEN PLANTS/ORNAMENTAL SHRUBS AND TREES POISONOUS TO HORSES

Common Name	Botanical Name	Locality	Toxic Compound	Poisonous Part	Amount	Onset of Poisoning	Symptoms
Azalea or Laurels	Rhododendron spp.	Common house plants. Ornamental plant in South	Cardiac glycosides	Leaves	Plant trimmings	Sudden death	Horse found dead after heart attack, nervous signs.
Castor Oil Plant	Ricinus Communis	Gardens	Phytotoxin Pyridine alkaloid	Seeds	25g (1oz) fatal	6-48 hours	Nervous signs, diarrhea, colic, liver damage, kidney damage.
Cestrum	Cestrum sp.	Gardens	Alkaloids (Solanine)	All parts, Clippings	-	6-24 hours	Diarrhea, nervous signs
Daphne	Daphne odora	Gardens	Coumarin	Leaves, berries	Plant trimmings	Fatal 24-36 hours	Prevents blood clotting, internal bleeding, death.
Delphiniums	Delphinum sp.	Gardens	Alkaloid	All parts	Old plants in green garden refuse	Depends on amount eaten	Salivation, convulsions, death.
Foxglove	Digitalis parpurea	Gardens ornamental	Cardiac glycosides	All parts, especially seeds	Plant trimmings	Sudden death	Heart attacks, nervous signs, found dead.
Hemlock	Conium maculatum	Gardens - general weed, early Spring	Pyridine alkaloid (Conine)	Green parts - hay is safe	4-5lb fresh leaves	2 hours - 2 days	Nervous signs, paralysis, convulsions, colic, death.
Ivy Snake Vine	Tinlospora imilacina	Gardens, creeper on walls	Unknown	All parts - wilted clippings	Clippings in refuse	Depends on amount eaten	Photosensitivity- sunburn type skin, sudden death.

GARDEN PLANTS/ORNAMENTAL SHRUBS AND TREES POISONOUS TO HORSES

Common Name	Botanical Name	Locality	Toxic Compound	Poisonous Part	Amount	Onset of Poisoning	Symptoms
Lantana	Lantana camara	Ornamental Southern States	Rehmannica cid	Plants, especially dark flowers	Variable	Depends on amount eaten. Animals stand in shade.	Photosensitivity and sunburn, diarrhea, liver damage.
Monk's Hood	Aconitum napellus	Gardens	Diterpenoid alkaloid	All parts	Clippings in refuse	Sudden death	Salivation, convulsions, death.
Oleander	Nerium oleander	Across Southern States, Ornamental around stables	Potent Cardiac glycoside (Oleandrin)	All parts, flowers	Wilted leaves less bitter, ½-1oz toxic, 30-40 leaves	12 hours fatal	Heart attacks, digestive upsets, sudden death.
Parsley	Petroselinum sativum	Gardens	Furocoum-arins	Leaves	Horses like taste	12-24 hours	Photosensitivity - sunburn type lesions.
Poinsettia	Euphorbia palcherrima	Garden ornamental	Irritant latex sap	Leaves and sap	Plant trimmings		Diarrhea, convulsions, death. Irritant sap, blisters on nose.
Poppy	Papaver sp.	Gardens	Isoquinoline alkaloids	Roots/leaves	Plant in refuse	12 hours	Dermatitis, blurred vision, nervous signs.
Potato	Solanum tuberosum	Garden and vegetable	Solanine	Green tubers whole potatoes	Unknown	Unknown	Nervous signs, colic, choke on whole potato.
Privet Hedge Plant	Ligustrum spp	Temperate regions. Abandoned home sites, gardens, hedges and shrubs	Ligustrin and other gut irritants	Leaves and fruits	Unknown	1-2 hours after ingestion.	Gut irritants - diarrhea, colic, incoodination, weakness, convulsions, death.
Rhubarb	Rheum rhaponticum	Garden vegetable	Chryso-'phanic acid, Oxalates	Leaves	1-2lbs leaves	Few hours	Red colored urine, salivation, colic, diarrhea, staggers
Soursob	Oxalis prescaprae	Gardens, wasteland, grazing land in Fall	Oxalate	All parts wilted after spraying	Unknown	2-4 weeks	Calcium imbalance, kidney damage.
Wisteria	Wisteria sinense	Gardens, wall creeper	Irritant juice	Seeds, pods, clippings	Garden refuse	6-24 hours	Colic and diarrhea.
Yellow Oleander	Thevetia peruviana	Garden ornamental	Cardiac glycosides (thevetin)	Leaves, clippings	Small amount	Sudden death	Heart attacks, digestive upsets, sudden death.
Yew Tree Japanese Yew Ground Hemlock	Taxus buccata Taxus caspictata	Widespread garden ornamental	Alkaloid-faxine	Eating shade tree, trimmings in refuse, green or dry	0.1-0.5% bodyweight readily consumed	Sudden death 5 minutes	Usually found dead next to source. Trembling, inco-ordination, heart attacks, diarrhea.

FODDER CROPS POTENTIALLY POISONOUS TO HORSES

Common Name	Botanical Name	Locality	Toxic Compound	Poisonous Part	Amount	Onset of Poisoning	Symptoms
Alfalfa (Blister beetle Intoxication)	Medicago sativa	Great Plains States and North. Blister beetles baled into hay mid to late summer	Cantharidin	Beetles crushed into hay	2-5 beetles produce colic	Stored hay can remain toxic for years. Onset time depends on dose.	Depression, loss of appetite, colic, shock, death.
Clovers Medics	Trifolium sp Medicap sp	Pasture legumes Widespread	UV sensitive pigments, Estrogens	Plant/flowers	Grazing Spring flush	1-3 days	Photosensitivity-sunburn type lesions, partial blindness, runny eyes. Infertility in mares.
Corn	Zea mays	Widespread	Mold, Fusarium moniliforme	Moldy grain, wet harvest.	10ppm 80-100% corn contaminated	1-6 weeks	Incoordination, wandering, brain damage, liver failure. Fatal in 24 hours.
Ergot of Paspalum	Paspalum sp.	Grain	Ergot fungus (Claviceps paspali)	Seed heads, sticky black seeds	Mixed into feed		Hypersensitivity, muscle tremors, staggers, drooling, abortion?
Ergot of Rye	Secale cereale	Grain	as above	Grain	Mixed into feed		Colics, abortions.
Kleingrass	Panicum coloratum	Pasture grass, South Western States	Liver damaging Saponins	Rapid growth pasture. Hay	1-3% body-weight	Relative to amount ingested	Depression, poor performance, liver failure, jaundice.
Panic (Blue Panic) Setaria Buffel Grass Argentine grass Dallas grass	Panicum spp. Setaria sphacelata (Cenchrus ciliaris)]] Paspalum spp.]	Sub tropical areas pasture	Oxalates	Rapidly growing, fertilized pasture	Continuous ingestion	Relative to grazing mix and season	Oxalates bind up calcium - Nutritional secondary hyperparathyroidism (NSH). Malabsorption causes skeletal deformities, Big head.
Phalaris	Phalaris sp.	Pasture grazing	Alkaloid	Rapidly growing young shoots after fire or drought.	1-3% body-weight	12-24 hours	Staggers, death
Singletary Pea Wild winter pea Caly Pea	Lathyrus hirsutus	Widespread forage and natural pasture	Unknown	Seeds in hay. (Harvest pea before seed heads appear)	Seed pods in hay	Few weeks to months	Stand with hind and front feet forward. Hind paralysis-Stringhalt movement.
Sorghum Milo Sudan grass Johnson grass	Sorghum sp.	Southwest and Eastern States	Cyanogenic glycoside (low glycoside varieties now available)	Hay/green feed	1-3% bwt	Depends on intake	Hind limb staggers, bladder inflammation and dribbling urine, scalding of skin, diarrhea, labored breathing, abortion.
Tall Fescue	Festuca arundinacea	Southwest States	Claviceps mold toxin	Pasture and hay	15% of pregnant mares affected	Toxic during last 60 days of pregnancy	Extended pregnancy, lack of milk, still-births, acute lameness, skin rot at fetlock.

WEEDS AND NATIVE PLANTS POISONOUS TO HORSES

Common Name	Botanical Name	Locality	Toxic Compound	Poisonous Part	Amount	Onset of Poisoning	Symptoms
Black Locust	Robina pseudoacacia	Eastern states	Phytotoxin	Chewing bark	Very toxic	Soon after ingestion	Weakness and depression, hind paralysis, loss of appetite, colic and diarrhea.
Black Nightshade	Solanum nigrum	East of the Rockies	Alkaloid Salanine	All parts especially green berries, sparse pastures	1-10lb.	Soon after ingestion.	Depression and weakness, diarrhea and colic.
Black Walnut (tree)	Juglans nigra	Widely distributed	Jugulone	Fresh furniture shavings as bedding, eating bedding	Black shavings 25%	12-24 hours	Increased heart rate. Swelling in legs (edema), lethargy and laminitis (founder).
Bracken Fern	Pteridium aquilinum	Northwest to upper Mid West	Thiaminase destroys Vitamin B1 (Responsive to Vitamin B1) therapy	Entire plant, green parts, especially new fronds in late summer. Leaves in sun-dried hay.	Unknown	Cumulative 30-60 days	Initial weight loss inco-ordination, front legs crossed, hind legs wide apart. Increased heart rate, staggering, trembling, head jerking. Arching of back, collapse.
Castor Bean Castor Oil Plant	Ricinus communis	Southwest and Southeast	Phytotoxins Pyridine alkaloid (ricinine)	Seeds or bean byproducts in feed	25g (about 1oz) of castor beans are fatal	6-48 hours	Nervous signs, depression, sweating, muscular spasms, pounding heart, rapid breathing, colic, diarrhea.
Choke Cherry Wild Black Cherry	Prunus virginiana	Fairly widespread	Cyanogenic glycosides	Leaves and fruit, drought, frost, wilting or rapidly growing plants.	Very toxic	Death: few minutes to 60 minutes. Can be treated if recognised early.	Symptoms due to cynanide poisoning. Trembling, collapse, respiratory arrest. Common Source: Branches and fruit blown down and wilted after summer storms.
Coffeeweed Coffee senna Wild Coffee	Cassia occidentalis	Roadsides, waste areas. Eastern states.	Alkaloids	Seeds most toxic.	Unknown	Hours to several days.	Gastric upset and muscle damage, diarrhea and staggers. Death due to heart failure.
Death Camas	Zigadenus nutallii	West of Mississippi on sandy plains, foothills of Rockies	Steroidal glycosidal alkaloid	Grazing plant in sparse pasture in Spring	10lb fatal	hours to several days	Signs within several hours - depression, staggering, salivation, lower heart and resp. rates. Death in several days.
Fiddleneck Yellow burr weed	Amsinckia spp	Pacific coast	Pyrrolizidine alkaloids	Grazing or in hay	50-150lbs	Cumulative over several weeks.	Weight loss, coli, loss of appetite, "poor doers", drowiness staggers, circling aimless walking. Liver damage, jaundice, sweating, death.
Hoary Alyssum	Berteroa incana	Northern States	Unknown	Green forage in dry pasture, baled in hay	Unknown	2-3 days after eating contaminatedh ay	Soft swellings in limb (edema). Symptoms subside in 2-4 days after withdrawal of hay.

WEEDS AND NATIVE PLANTS POISONOUS TO HORSES

Common Name	Botanical Name	Locality	Toxic Compound	Poisonous Part	Amount	Onset of Poisoning	Symptoms
Horse tail, Mares tail Scouring Rush	Equisetum arvense	Widely over Northwest, Northern, mid-west states, wet and cold areas	Thiaminase as for Bracken fern	Plant in dried hay	Unknown	Cumulative	Initial weight loss inco-ordination, front legs crossed, hind legs wide apart. Increased heart rate, staggering, trembling, head jerking. Arching of back, collapse.
Hounds Tongue	Cynoglossum officinale	Scattered	Pyrrolizidine alkaloids	Leaves	Unknown	Cumulative: several weeks to months	Poor doers, weight loss, drowsiness, staggers, aimless walking. Jaundice, liver damage.
Locoweed Vetch	Astragalus sp (Oxytropis sp.)	Astragulus sp.-Western States Oxytropis sp. - Central States	Alkaloid locoine (Astragulus can accumulate selenium)	Whole plant throughout year.	30% bwt	6 weeks	Early stages - inco-ordination & visual disturbances - dangerous to ride. Rearing and falling back on haunches, circling, wild behavior if excited, convulsions and death.
Milkweed	Asclepias spp.	Widespread in pastures	Cardiac glycosides	Plants only grazed in drought or over-stocking	0.5-2.0% body-weight	Rapid death	Horses found dead due to heart block.
Poison Hemlock	Conium maculatum	Widespread	Alkaloids	Green leaves or roots. Safe when dried in hay.	4-5lb fresh leaves fatal.	2 hours - 2 days. Fatal in 5-10 hours	Excitement then depression, lack of awareness, trembling, collapse.
Pokeweed Poke	Phytolacca americana	Rich soils, new pastures. Eastern states.	Oxalic acid, alkaloids.	All parts, roots most toxic.	Unknown	2-3 hours	Gastric irritation, colic, bloody diarrhea, difficult breathing, convulsions, death.
Ragwort Stinking Willie Common Groundsel Bitterweed	Senecio spp. Senecio jacobaea Senecio vulgaris Senecio spp.	South Pacific N/West New England	Pyrrolizidine alkaloids	All parts (can contaminate hay)	50-150lbs	Cumulative several weeks	Weight loss, colic, loss of appetite, "poor doers", drowsiness staggers, circling, aimless walking. Liver damage, jaundice, sweating, death.
Rattleweed Rattle box	Crotalaria spp.	South & West to Texas	Pyrrolizidine alkaloids	Leaves (can contaminate hay)	Unknown	Cumulative several weeks	Weight loss, colic, loss of appetite, poor doers, compulsive wandering, staggering, yawning. Lung and liver damage, jaundice, death.
Rayless Goldenrod (Jimmy or burrow weed)	Isocoma wrightic	Southwest in open grazing	Tremetone toxin	Whole fresh plant or baled in hay	0.5%-2.0% bwt lethal	Depends on dose, sudden death	Stiffness in gait, inco-ordination, sluggishness, sweating, throat paralysis or sudden death.

WEEDS AND NATIVE PLANTS POISONOUS TO HORSES

Common Name	Botanical Name	Locality	Toxic Compound	Poisonous Part	Amount	Onset of Poisoning	Symptoms
Red Maple	Acer rubrum	Eastern States but also Texas and Rockies	Unknown, possible oxidant. Summer & Fall	Wilted red maple leaves in Fall, or trimmed branches	1.5g/kg bwt	Few hours to 5 days	Loss of appetite, depression, weakness, anemia, jaundice & respiratory distress, coma prior to death.
Russian Knapweed	Centaurea ripens Centaurea picris	Pacific Coast to Colorado	Alkaloid	Green or dried plant	86-200% body-weight	Cumulative 30 days	Brain damage - Inability to hold or chew food or drink. Wandering, swelling in face. Death by starvation or inhaling food or water.
Salvation Jane Paterson's Curse	Echium lycopsis	California localised areas (purple flower - Rosette young plant)	Pyrrolizidine alkaloids	All parts. Dominant plant which spreads to become sole source of green pick in Spring-Summer. Leaves in hay.	Unknown	Cumulative, several weeks to 2-3 years exposure	Weight loss, colic, loss of appetite, poor doers, compulsive wandering, staggering, yawning. Lung and liver damage, jaundice, death.
Sleepy Grass	Stipa sp.	New Mexico	Mechanical damage to mouth	Rough plant	-	Lacerates mouth	Mouth lesions - loss of appetite, drowsiness.
St.Johns Wort	Hypericum perforatum	Pacific and Atlantic Coast Southeast.	Photo-sensitizing agent	Leaves and flowers, lush green plants	Large amounts	24 hours to 5 days	Sunburn type lesions. Horses with white areas of skin most affected - skin peels or rots off.
Vetch (Locoweed) Woody Aster Goldenweed Prince's Plume	Astragalus sp. Xylorhiza sp. Oonopsis sp. Stanleya sp.	Mississippi to western slope of Rockies	Accumulate selenium	Fresh plants. Dry plants in hay.	Depends on selenium level.	Addictive Acute: 6 -24 hrs Subacute: days to several weeks Chronic: Weeks to months	**Acute:** fatal, depression, diarrhea, respiratory failure. **Subacute:** Blind staggers, blindness, weakness, paralysis. **Chronic:** alkali disease, weight loss, poor appetite, loss of hair from mane & tail. Coronary separation, cracked and broken away hooves - lameness.
Water Hemlock Cowbane	Cicuta sp.	Wet areas, ditches - Upper Midwest to Pacific	Cicutoxin resin	Leaves in Spring. Dried leaves in hay less toxic. Roots extremely toxic	8oz of roots are fatal	10-60 minutes	Nervous stimulation, muscle tremors in neck, fear. Inco-ordination, labored breathing, collapse, convulsions, death.
White Snakeroot (Snakeroot or Richweed)	Eupatorium rugosum	Midwest South Eastern States in wooded pastures - Late Summer	Tremetol toxin	Grazing fresh stalks above snow, or baled in hay	2-10lb 0.5-2.0% bwt lethal	Depends on dose - sudden death	Trembling, sluggishness, stiffness in gait, inco-ordination, sweating, throat paralysis or death.

WEEDS AND NATIVE PLANTS POISONOUS TO HORSES

Common Name	Botanical Name	Locality	Toxic Compound	Poisonous Part	Amount	Onset of Poisoning	Symptoms
Wild Jasmine	Cestrum diurnum	Wasteland, Texas and Florida	Steroidal Vitamin D-like compound	Toxic all year round	Unknown	2 to 6 months	Weight loss, lameness increases humped up in back and short steps. Lies down frequently.
Yellow Star Thistle	Centaurea solstitialis	California	Alkaloid	Green or dried plant particularly if on green forage.	59%-71% body-weight	Cumulative 54 days.	Brain damage - Inability to hold or chew food or drink. Swelling in face. Death by starvation or inhaling food or water.

SECTION NINE

ESTIMATING BODYWEIGHT AND CONDITION SCORING

Many newer horse owners find it difficult to estimate the bodyweight of their horses to ensure correct feeding rates of concentrate feeds, and dose rates of worming pastes, or other medications. Most of the commercial sweet and custom feeds for working horses are recommended on a bodyweight basis, and underestimation of a horse's weight can lead to oversupply of energy, and related handling and behavioral problems. Often the feed itself is blamed for being "too hot", when it may be due to overfeeding in proporation to bodyweight and exercise level. Monitoring the bodyweight on a regular basis is useful as an early indicator of health problems. Regular weighing of growing horses on larger breeding farms can monitor growth rates, and if necessary, feeding changes can be made to prevent overgrowth and risk of future unsoundness.

Condition scoring is a practical system of monitoring the optimum condition and fat distribution for show, working and breeding horses. It provides a target range of condition in which the animal should be for its well being, health, performance and breeding efficiency. Condition scoring provides a standardized, repeatable method of assessing variation in condition in breeding horses from season to season.

BODYWEIGHT

An accurate estimate of a horse's bodyweight is important when formulating or making adjustments to its ration to meet specific needs. Ideally, feeds should be weighed, and the ration calculated according to a horse's bodyweight, as the total dry matter a horse can consume to meet maintenance, exercise and reproduction needs is proportional to its bodyweight. (See page 171.)

HINT

As a guideline, most horses will consume about 2% of their bodyweight to meet needs for light work. As workload increases, more feed is required, but bulk of the ration may be limited by appetite, type of horse and exercise to between 2.5-3.0% of bodyweight.

Surveys have shown that most horse owners and veterinarians alike, tend to underestimate a horse's bodyweight about 80% of the time. Visual appraisal of bodyweight from the build, type and condition of the horse can be up to 150lb (70kg) underweight. Wider variations occur in horses above 1100lb (500kg) bodyweight, as appraisal of condition and proportion is more difficult. However, with experience, many horse owners can make very accurate appraisals, within ±5%.

As most medications, and particularly worming pastes are administered on a bodyweight basis, underdosing can lead to reduced effectiveness, and in the case of wormers risk of resistance build-up against the chemical, or side-resistance to the class of compounds.

HINT

Bodyweight is proportional to girth diameter, height, and length of the body. It is influenced by type, build and breed of the individual horse, and its relative condition. High fiber content in a ration increases gut distension and water retention in the large bowel, acting to increase bodyweight relative to size by up to 3%.

There are several methods that can be used to measure or estimate the bodyweight of a horse.

A. *Weighing Scales - 100% Accurate*

Horse weighing scales, either in a chute, or as an electronic weight sensitive mat, are becoming more widely used in training stables to monitor the weight of performance horses on a weekly basis. A record of the horse's bodyweight when conditioned and fit for racing or competition, can be kept and related to performance.

HINT

Surveys indicate that racing horses perform more consistently when maintained within ± 20lb (about 10kg) of their last winning race weight, with weight handicaps taken into account. However, the relative recovery rate, condition and response to training must be taken into consideration when assessing a horse's potential to perform on a repeated basis when the bodyweight is maintained within these limits.

HINT

If scales are not available, haul your horse to the local feed store, or to a weighbridge for trucks.

Avoid weight horses just after feeding or drinking as gut fill can add up to 20lb (about 10kg) onto a horse's average weight.

B. *Body Proportions Relative to Girth² and Length -90-95% Accurate*

The relative body proportions change with age, condition score, breed and type of horse. Measurement of the chest circumference or heart girth, combined with barrel length, using a mathematical calculation will give a reasonably accurate estimation of bodyweight. This method is accurate enough to calculate bodyweight for a worming dose.

The equations for calculating bodyweight based on heart girth and length are as follows:

Bodyweight (Pounds) =

$$\frac{\text{Heart girth (in)}^2 \times \text{length (in)}}{241}$$

Bodyweight (Kilograms) =

$$\frac{\text{Heart girth (cm)}^2 \times \text{length (cm)}}{8717}$$

> **HINT**
>
> **Heart girth -** *make sure the horse is breathing out when you take the girth measurement. Watch the nostrils or flanks. Take girth circumference just behind the point of the elbow and slope the tape back to immediately behind the withers area. (Height is measured to central area of the withers.)*
>
> **Length Measurement -** *Measure from point of shoulder, inclining tape upwards in a straight line*

to the point of the pelvis or buttock just to the side and below the tail.

In racing horses, in lean, fit condition, these equations can overestimate bodyweight by up to 45lbs (20kg).

C. *Weight Belts or Tapes - 85-90% Accurate*

Girth tapes, calibrated with a reading of relative bodyweight for an adult horse in average condition, are available from feed stores or saddleries, and give a practical estimate of bodyweight. Accuracy of measurement is influenced by the elasticity of the tape, position around the chest area, and thickness of hair coat. Taught tapes are not very accurate in heavily pregnant mares, or thin fit race horses due to the variations in fluid, body fat and gut content. Encircle the tape around the girth just behind the wither, and read off the weight when the horse is breathing out. This method is not very accurate as the condition and length of the horse is not taken into account. However, it does give a very good indication of your horse's relative gains and losses if taken on a regular basis. Keep a chart on each horse's bodyweight using the same measuring technique each time at weekly intervals. The feed intake and work load may be adjusted accordingly to maintain a relatively constant bodyweight or desirable degree of condition.

D. *Experienced Guesstimates*

Some people have the experience and eye for making rough estimates of an individual horse's weight. However, these *guesstimates* are not reliable where accurate doses of medication are to be administered.

E. *Helpful Guidelines to Ages/Breeds*

HORSES IN AVERAGE CONDITION (Condition Score 4-5)		
Height	BODYWEIGHT	
(Hands)	Pounds	Kilograms
10-12	550-660	250-300
12-14	660-880	300-400
14-16	880-1100	400-500
16-17	1100-1200	500-550
17-18	1200-1320	550-600

CONDITION SCORING

In the early 1980's, the concept of condition scoring was developed by researchers at Texas A & M University, and this system has been adopted to grade the body condition of horses. This system scores relative condition from very poor and emaciated, to extremely fat in a 9 point score range. Another system was developed in Australia, with a score range of 1-5.

Condition scoring provides an objective assessment of body condition, and includes consideration of the body fat distribution as a standardized method of monitoring optimum condition in all horses. The system is relatively simple and quick to score, and repeatable scores can be made even by horse persons with no previous experience of assessment and scoring methods.

There has been little work to relate optimum body condition required for various classes of horses; hard working horses such as endurance, polo horses and eventers, are usually kept in lower body condition than racehorses, showjumpers and show horses.

Breeding mares should be kept at a condition score of 5 or higher to ensure best fertility and better overall milk production.

An optimum body condition score for various types of horses has been included as a practical guideline in Table 1 below. Adjustments to the ration and exercise program may be necessary to maintain condition within an optimum score range.

Body condition scores are also helpful to monitor the degree of obesity in ponies and horses that are likely to founder.

The warning signs of likely laminitis or founder on spring pastures in ponies include enlargement of the crest, high condition score and often long overgrown toes. Body weight by girth measurements, crest size and condition score should be monitored at least weekly, with twice weekly assessment during high risk periods. Other breeds of horses such as Quarter horses, Morgans, Saddlebreds, Standardbreds, and Thoroughbreds, particularly those individuals that are easy keepers or good doers, should be monitored regularly during high risk periods when grazing high risk pasture.

HINT

Map the animal's condition score on a weekly basis, assess size of crest, length of toe on the hoof, and check pasture growth at least twice weekly during early Spring or periods of rapid growth. If the crest development and condition score increase to an obese score, then reduce the animal's intake of feed by fitting a mesh muzzle allowing only restricted grazing time, and increase the amount of exercise as a weight reduction measure.

Also, have the toes trimmed to reduce the rotation forces on the pedal bone by ensuring normal hoof shape and toe angles. However, do not exercise an animal that is already exhibiting clinical signs of founder like lameness. Founder is an emergency situation - Consult your vet for advice immediately.

TABLE 1

OPTIMUM CONDITION SCORE for
various Classes of Horse

Class of Horse	Condition Score
Dressage Horses	6 - 8
Endurance Horses	4 - 5
Eventing	4 - 5
Hunters	5 - 7
Open Mares	4 - 6
Polo and Polocrosse	4 - 5
Ponies on Spring Pasture	7 - 8
Pregnant Mares	7 - 8
Quarter Horses	6 - 8
Ranch Horses	4 - 5
Show Hacks	6 - 8
Showjumpers	5 - 7
Stallions (Breeding)	5 - 7
Stallions (Off season)	4 - 6
Standardbred Racing Horses	4 - 6
Thoroughbred Racehorses	5 - 7
Refer to Table 2 for method.	

TABLE 2
STANDARD U.S. BODY CONDITION SCORING SYSTEM FOR HORSES *

SCORING METHOD: Each area should be assessed individually, the scores totalled, then averaged to give the Condition Score.
* Adapted from Henneke et al (1983) Equine Vet. J.15: 371-372

HINT: Score the neck first visually and then feel for fat; repeat for the withers, loin, tailhead, ribs, and finally shoulder. Add scores, divide by 6 to give Condition Score.

Condition Score	General Condition	Neck	Withers	Loin	Tailhead	Ribs	Shoulder
1	**Very Poor**	Individual bone structure visible	Bones easily visible. No fat.	Spine bones visible. Ends feel pointed.	Tailhead and hip bones very visible.	Ribs very visible and skin furrows between ribs.	Bone structure very visible.
		Animal extremely emaciated; no fatty tissue can be felt.					
2	**Very Thin**	Bones just visible. Animal emaciated.	Withers obvious, very minimal fat covering.	Slight fat covering over vertical and flat spin projections. Ends feel rounded.	Tailhead, hip bones obvious.	Ribs prominent, slight depression between ribs.	Bone structure can be outlined.
3	**Thin**	Thin, flat muscle covering.	Withers accentuated with some fat cover.	Fat build-up halfway on vertical spines, but easily discernible. Flat spinal bones not felt.	Tailhead prominent. Hip bones appear rounded, but visible. Pin bones covered.	Slight fat cover over ribs. Rib outline obvious.	Shoulder accentuated, some fat.
4	**Moderately Thin**	Neck some fat, not obviously thin.	Withers not obviously thin, smooth edges.	Slight ridge along back.	Fat can be felt.	Faint outline visible.	Shoulder not obviously thin.
5	**Moderate**	Neck blends smoothly into body.	Withers rounded over top.	Back level.	Fat around tailhead beginning to feel spongy.	Ribs cannot be seen but can be easily felt.	Shoulder blends smoothly into body.
6	**Moderately Fleshy**	Fat can be felt.	Fat can be felt	May have slight inward crease.	Fat around tailhead feels soft.	Fat over ribs feels spongy.	Fat layer can be felt.
7	**Fleshy**	Visible fat deposits along neck.	Fat covering withers is firm.	May have slight inward crease down back.	Fat around tailhead is soft and rounded off.	Individual ribs can still be felt.	Fat build-up behind shoulder.
8	**Fat**	Noticeable thickening of neck.	Area along withers filled with fat.	Crease down back evident.	Tailhead fat very soft and flabby.	Difficult to feel ribs.	Area behind shoulder filled in flush with body.
		Fat deposited along inner buttocks					
9	**Extremely Fat**	Bulging fat.	Bulging fat.	Obvious deep crease down back.	Building fat around tailhead	Patchy fat over ribs.	Bulging fat.
		Fat along inner buttocks may rub together. Flank filled in flush.					

FORMULATING OR CHECKING YOUR HORSE'S RATION

This handbook provides practical ration guidelines for various classes of working and performance horses based on NRC (1989) recommendations and my own practical experience of feeding horses.

Generally, if a horse finds a ration palatable, maintains bodyweight and vitality and performs well, then the basic diet is adequate. Additional supplements of vitamins, minerals and electrolytes will help ensure the balance of nutrients within the ration and compensate for exercise demands and variables such as climatic conditions.

As horse owners, you may wish to check your home mixed diets based on a blend of locally available feeds to make sure these adequately meet your horse's requirements. You may also wish to change ingredients to a least cost ration formulation, using the step-by-step "user friendly" system provided.

HINT	*Rations need not be complicated mixtures or concentrate muesli.*

For basic rations, one or two sources of energy (eg oats and corn, or barley), one source of protein for working and growing horses (eg soybean meal or sunflower seeds), one source of fiber (eg alfalfa or mixed hay) will be adequate.

EASY CHECK CALCULATIONS

You can either commence with a specific type of working or performance horse to feed, or alternatively check if the ration you are currently feeding is adequate.

NOTE: All feed weights and calculations are based on pounds and grams. Conversion to metric units (kg and grams) are given at the bottom of the tables.

Step 1: Determine Daily Requirements

1.1   Estimate the bodyweight of your horse using the methods outlined on page 163 - Estimating Bodyweight and Condition Scoring.

The horse's estimated bodyweight is

[_____ lb]

HINT	*In very hard working horses such as Endurance horses, add **half** your own bodyweight to obtain the total mass and use this as a bodyweight for your horse in full training.*

1.2   Refer to Table 3 on page 171 to match the type of work your horse is performing regularly to estimate the daily nutrient requirement for your horse's bodyweight.

1.3   The estimated daily nutrient needs for _____work intensity are:

Digestible Energy   _____ Mcal
Crude Protein   _____ grams
Calcium   _____ grams
Phosphorus _____ grams

Step 2: Determine the Amount of Feed Required

Refer to Table 4 on page 172 to calculate the approximate total daily weight of concentrate and hay required on a bodyweight basis for the type of work your horse is regularly performing.

Type of work _____

Approx weight of feed required each day = _____ lb.

NOTE: This is an **approximate** requirement. It is most important to have the energy requirement met, not exceeded by more than 5% which may mean the total weight of feed may be ± 10% of this approximation.

Step 3: The Roughage Base

3.1 Refer to Table 5 on page 172 to calculate the amount of hay or roughage (by weight) required each day from the total weight of feed estimated in Step 2.

> **HINT**
>
> *If you are checking your present ration, always consider the roughage base in the ration first. Weigh the hay or cubes and calculate the energy, protein, calcium and phosphorus contributed.*

The amount of hay or roughage required each day is _____lb.

3.2 The available roughages are usually alfalfa hay or cubes, mixed hay, grass hay.

Select the type of hay that is readily available.

> **HINT**
>
> *In most cases, alfalfa hay will provide excess protein relative to needs, and grass may be too low in protein for hard working horses. Mixed hay, or a blend of alfalfa (40% fed in morning) and grass hay (60% fed at night) is generally more suitable.*

> **HINT**
>
> *There is at least a 10% wastage factor in long grass hay, so add an extra 10% to total amount of grass hay required, but calculate on the recommended amounts in table 5.*

3.3 Using Table 5 on page 173, calculate the nutrient content of the roughage base. _____lb of roughage provides

Energy	_____	Mcal
Protein	_____	grams
Calcium	_____	grams
Phosphorus	_____	grams

3.4 Refer back to Step 1.2 to calculate the shortfall of nutrients. (Daily requirements minus those nutrients provided by the roughage base.)

If molasses syrup is to be added as a sweetener in a dampened ration at night, then add 4oz (3/4 teacup) for ponies, and 8oz (or 1½ teacups) for adult horses. Mix this volume with an equal volume of hot water, and mix well into the feed. Generally, this provides 0.3Mcal (3/4 teacup) to 0.6Mcal (1½ teacups) of energy to the daily ration. (See Table 6 for other nutrient values.) Add this to the total energy contribution of the roughage base.

	Total Required		Provided by Roughage		Provided by Molasses		Shortfall*
Energy (Mcal)		minus		minus		=	
Protein (grams)		minus		minus		=	
Calcium (grams)		minus		minus		=	
Phosphorus (grams)		minus		minus		=	
*This shortfall is to be made up by the concentrate portion of the ration.							

Step 4: The Concentrate Portion

4.1 The majority of shortfall of energy and other nutrients is made up by the concentrate portion of the ration. In Step 3.1, a relative weight percentage of roughage and concentrate was outlined as a guide.

The nutrient shortfall is to be made up by grain, protein meal, and fat (as oil or tallow). It is essential that the energy content of the ration be satisfied initially by selecting one or two sources of grain, such as oats and corn, (and fat if you wish), depending on availability, type of horse and its use, relative cost or limit on the total bulk of the ration required.

> **HINT**
>
> *A practical ratio between oats and corn (or barley) for working horses to limit bulk of ration by weight is given on page 169.*

4.2 The total energy shortfall (3.4) is _____Mcal.

Using the above guidelines for ratios of oats to corn, other grain or fat, and referring to the values in Table 6 on page 173, calculate the weight of oats and corn required to meet daily energy needs.

_____lb Oats provides _____ Mcal Energy
_____lb Corn provides _____ Mcal Energy
_____lb Fat provides _____ Mcal Energy

Total _____ Mcal Energy (to meet requirements from Step 1)

4.3 Calculate the protein, calcium and phosphorus contributions from these grains, using the values in Table 6 on page 173.

		Oats	Corn (or Barley)
Light work		70%	30%
Medium work		60%	40%
Intense work		40%	60%
Endurance		30%	65% 5% Fat
Nervy Horses		-	65% Barley 30% Corn 5% Fat

		Energy (Mcal)	Protein (g)	Calcium (g)	Phosphorus (g)
Oats	lb				
Corn	lb				
Fat	lb		---	---	---
TOTALS					

Step 5: Match Requirements to Supply

Check if the estimated requirements from 1.2 are provided by the roughage and concentrate mix that you have formulated.

		Energy (Mcal)	Protein (g)	Calcium (g)	Phosphorus (g)
Roughage	**from Step 3.3**				
Molassses	**from Step 3.5**				
Concentrate	**from Step 4.4**				
TOTAL					
Daily Requirements **Step 1.2**					
SHORTFALL/EXCESS					
		(Should be satisfied. Do not exceed by more than 5%)	(May be high if alfalfa used, low if grass hay used. Do not exceed requirement by more than 15%)	(Usually low except if alfalfa used)	(Usually low)

Step 6: Energy and Protein Balance

6.1   This is the tricky part. The energy content should meet requirements or not be more than 5% over under comfortable weather conditions (70-85°F [20-30°C]). Protein, calcium and phosphorus may be more or less than is required.

HINT

In most rations based on alfalfa or mixed hay, the total protein supplied will normally exceed the daily requirement. In this case, part substitution with grass hay may help to reduce protein to about the requirement. You will then need to recalculate the energy content relative to the need. The protein should at least meet requirements, and in practice, be no more than 15% over this amount.

HINT

If total protein supplied in a grass hay based ration is below requirements, select a protein source readily available in your area (eg soybean or linseed meal). Using the data in Table 6 page 173, calculate the weight of protein meal required to make up the shortfall in crude protein.

Obviously, the energy supplied by the extra protein meal will exceed requirements, so a slight reduction in the grain content is required. Protein meals contain roughly the same energy content as common grains, but the protein content is usually 3 to 4 times as much, so only small amounts are required.

Amount of extra protein meal _____gram. Recalculate the total nutrients supplied in the grain, protein meal and hay combination:

Energy (Mcal)	_____
Protein (g)	_____
Calcium (g)	_____
Phosphorus (g)	_____

To maintain similar energy levels in the new grain and protein mix, add 25% to the calculated amount of protein required. Reduce the weight of grain originally calculated by the same amount. For example, you calculate to need 100g protein meal. Add 25% extra, which now requires 125g protein meal. Reduce the grain mix by about 4½oz (about 125g); this will maintain similar energy levels, and replace the protein lost by removal of the grain.

Although the NRC (1989) level of protein will be satisfied in this way, the crude protein percentage of the total ration calculated as feed intake related to bodyweight will be less than 10%. A little extra protein to not less than 10% may be added if required for horses in early training or subjected to regular hard work.

6.2 Fat boosted rations

If corn oil or fat is substituted for grain as an energy source in the diet to increase energy density for a hard working horse, then extra protein, vitamin E, and dicalcium phosphate should be added (see page 26).

6.2.1 Protein Meal (eg Soybean meal)

eg 8oz (2 teacups) of corn oil	- no extra protein
12oz (3 teacups) of corn oil	- 1 teacup extra protein
16oz (4 teacups) of corn oil	- 2 teacups extra protein

6.2.2 Vitamin E

4oz (1 teacup) of corn oil	- 1000iu Vitamin E
8oz (2 teacups) of corn oil	- 1200iu Vitamin E
12oz (3 teacups) of corn oil	- 1400iu Vitamin E
16oz (4 teacups) of corn oil	- 1600iu Vitamin E

6.2.3 Dicalcium phosphate (DCP)

For each 8oz (2 teacups) of corn oil, add extra ½oz (15g, or 1 tablespoon) DCP.

Step 7: Calcium and Phosphorus Balance

The shortfall of calcium and phosphorus can then be corrected using the values in Table 6 on page 173, by adding dicalcium phosphate for calcium (Ca) and phosphorus (P). It is important to add sufficient to meet phosphorus requirements.

Example: Each ounce of DCP contains 5.1g phosphorus, and 6.5g calcium.
If the shortfall of phosphorus needed is 5g, then 1oz of DCP is needed.

In most cases an alfalfa or mixed hay roughage base will meet calcium requirements, but may not provide sufficient phosphorus.

Although in this case, a straight phosphorus supplement can be added, such as sodium phosphate, or even wheat bran, usually dicalcium phosphate is cheaper and more readily available. Provided phosphorus requirements are met, then excess calcium in normal feeds up to a ratio of 4.0 Ca : 1.0 P can be tolerated by adult working horses.

If calcium is lacking in grass hay based diets, then add a cheap source of calcium, such as limestone, using the values in Table 6 on page 173.

It is best to add the calcium and phorphorus supplement to the evening feed. Mix well into feed.

Step 8: Divide the Ration Between Feed Times

In stabled horses, or those confined to yards with little grazing, divide the ration into at least two feeds. Feed about 60% of the total grain and 40% of the roughage in the morning feed. Feed the remaining feed in the evening, which provides the major proportion of the roughage overnight to reduce the risk of boredom and related vices such as wood chewing.

In full-time stabled horses, provide at least three feeds daily. To make up a midday or early afternoon feed, take 10% by weight off each of the morning and evening feeds and combine to make up this meal.

Hand grazing for 20-30 minutes, or 3-4lb of green feed in mid afternoon will help to relieve boredom and sharpen the appetite.

Step 9: Adding Minerals and Electrolytes

Although sophisticated calculations can be made to determine the need for additional minerals, salt and electrolytes for working horses, the addition of a recommended amount of supplements will provide sufficient to meet daily requirements and overcome low levels or imbalances in the ration.

Feed the supplements according to the manufacturer's dose rate to match your horse's exercise level, age or use.

Add the Vitamin E (such as White-E) to the morning meal, and general mineral supplements containing iron or copper (such as Feramo-H and Ironcyclen) to the evening meal. Iron and vitamin E should be given in separate feeds to avoid loss of Vitamin E potency due to interaction with iron in damp feeds. Divide the dose of electrolytes (such as Humidimix) into two equal parts, and give half the dose in the morning feed and the remainder in the evening feed. An extra supplement of B-Complex vitamins, (such as in Pulse-8), can be given as required to picky eaters or horses that lose their appetite following hard exercise. An alkaline buffer (such as Neutradex) may be given over the tongue can be after fast work, and an electrolyte drink (such as Recharge) or concentrate over the tongue, can be provided after travelling or heavy sweat exercise. The calcium or phosphorus supplement, if required, should be mixed well into the evening feed.

Step 10: Practical Adjustments

Assess the acceptance of the ration, and the relative appetite of the horse in relation to its temperament and workload. Using the following guidelines:

*   *If a horse consistently leaves feed when subjected to hard exercise, then reduce the bulk of the ration by reducing hay by 10% and adding an extra 5% of grain by weight such as corn and barley to meet energy demands.*

*   *If a horse cleans up well and appears hungry, then increase the bulk by adding 10% extra roughage by weight, such as hay, and reducing the grain by 5%.*

*   *Reduce grain on rest or light work days to half levels, preferably starting the evening before. Return to full grain in a stepwise manner over two days once exercise resumes.*

*   *In a hard working horse that becomes playful and hard to handle on a grain based ration, substitute up to 8oz (2 teacups) of corn oil for 1½lb oats, or 1¼lb corn. (See Table 6 for substitution rates, and Step 6.2 for other ration adjustments.)*

*   *Monitor the bodyweight and condition score of the horse to ensure it maintains weight, overall performance and a desirable temperament. Minor adjustments to the ration from time to time may be needed to maintain these standards.*

*   *Refer to specific sections in the ration guidelines for additional practical hints for your class of horse.*

The horse's own ability to utilize feed also influences the ration formulation. Hard keepers or poor doers may require more than the recommended NRC (1989) level of energy to maintain stamina and vitality. Conversely, easy keepers or good doers may need their rations reduced to prevent them gaining excessive condition.

TABLE 3						
REQUIREMENTS FOR WORKING HORSES - Adapted from NRC (1989)						
	Weight	**Activity**	**Digestable Energy (Mcal)**	**Crude Protein (g)**	**Calcium* (g)**	**Phosphorus * (g)**
PONIES	450lbs (Approx 200kg)	Rest/maintenance Work { light { moderate { intense	7 9 11 15	296 370 444 592	8 11 14 18	6 8 10 13
	650lb (Approx 300kg)	Rest/maintenance Work { light { moderate { intense	10.4 13 16 21	416 520 640 840	12 16 20 26	8.5 11.5 14 18.5
HORSES	900lb (Approx 400kg)	Rest/maintenance Work { light { moderate { intense	13 17 20 27	536 670 804 1072	16 20 25 33	11 15 17 23
	1000lb (Approx 450kg)	Rest/maintenance Work { light { moderate { intense	14.5 19 22.5 30	600 750 900 1200	18 23 28 36	13 17 19 26
	1100lb (Approx 500kg)	Rest/maintenance Work { light { moderate { intense	16 21 25 33	656 820 984 1312	20 25 30 40	14 18 21 29
	1200lb (Approx 550kg)	Rest/maintenance Work { light { moderate { intense	17.5 22.5 27 36	720 900 1070 1430	22 28 33 44	16 20 23 32
	1300lb (Approx 600kg)	Rest/maintenance Work { light { moderate { intense	19 24 29 39	776 970 1164 1552	24 30 36 47	17 21 25 34

MAINTENANCE = Resting, walking in yards daily.
LIGHT WORK = Pleasure, dressage, showing; 30-60 minutes daily walk and trotting exercise.
MODERATE WORK = Ranch work, roping, cutting, jumping; 60-120 minutes daily trotting, cantering, some galloping.
INTENSE WORK = Racing, eventing, polo, endurance, race trotting and galloping; 30-60 minutes canter and gallop, 3-4 hours or more endurance competition.

* The values for <u>elemental</u> calcium and phosphorus required each day have been calculated assuming a 50% absorption efficiency for calcium, and a 35% absorption efficiency for phosphorus in resting and working horses, as recommended by NRC (1989) guidelines.

TABLE 4

APPROXIMATE DRY FEED INTAKE PER DAY
IN WORKING HORSES

Note: The feed intake related to bodyweight is a guide only. The ration should be formulated on a roughage base (see Table 5). The remaining energy shortfall should be made up by the concentrate portion. The final weight of the ration fed may be less than the guidelines provided below if energy dense grains such as corn, or barley, or oils, are used as energy sources. Horses in hard or intense work may not be able to consume 3% bodyweight, so 2.5% bodyweight as for moderate work may meet their needs if energy dense concentrates are used.

	450lb (200kg)	900lb (400kg)	1000lb (450kg)	1100lb (500kg)	1200lb (550kg)	1300lb (600kg)
Maintenance (1.5% bodyweight (Resting)	7lb (3kg)	13½lb (6.1kg)	15lb (6.8kg)	16½lb (7.5kg	18lb (8.2kg)	19½lb (9kg)
Light work (2% bodyweight)	9lb (4.1kg)	18lb (8.2kg)	20lb (9.1kg)	22lb (10kg)	24lb (11kg)	26lb (12kg)
Moderate work (2.5% bodyweight)	11¼lb (5.1kg)	22½lb (10.2kg)	25lb (11.4kg)	27½lb (12.5kg)	30lb (13.6kg)	32½lb (14.8kg)
Intense work (2.5-3% bodyweight)	13½lb (6.2kg)	27lb (12.3kg)	30lb (13.6kg)	33lb (15kg)	36lb (16.4kg)	39lb (17.7kg)

TABLE 5

APPROXIMATE ROUGHAGE BASE RATIOS BY WEIGHT
IN WORKING HORSES

	Hay %	**Grain/Concentrate %**
Maintenance (Resting)	90-100%	0-10% maximum
Light work	Average 70%	Average 30%
Moderate work	Average 60%	Average 40%
Intense work*	Average 40-50%	Average 50-60%
Endurance work+	Average 50%	Average 45% grain 5% fat

*   Horses subjected to intense exercise or long duration type exercise may require a more concentrated diet to ensure they can consume the weight of ration provided.

Although it is universally recommended to not exceed 50:50 roughage to concentrate ratio by weight, the greater the physical activity, the less forage or bulk can be consumed relative to concentrates.

The concentrate level may be increased by up to 10% by weight during periods of regular hard training and competitive exercise, but the concentrates should be reduced to one third on the evening prior to light work or rest days with the weight made up by good quality hay and fed at this rate during rest days or downtime from training.

The concentrates should then be increased to 60% of full ration for the first day on return to full work, and reinstated fully on the second day of regular training. These guidelines will help reduce the risk of digestive upsets such as colic and diarrhea, or metabolic conditions such as tying-up and even founder.

+   Endurance horses should be provided with enough roughage to ensure adequate water retention in the large bowel to combat sweat loss in long distance training. The use of large amounts of energy dense feeds such as corn, or corn oil during training will reduce the volume of feed that needs to be consumed. However, reduction of grains and substitution with roughage as hay or grazing must be carried out on light work or rest days, as outlined above.

TABLE 6 — NUTRIENT CONTENT OF FEEDS (VALUES AS FED)

	Digestible Energy Mcal/lb	Crude Protein g/lb	Fiber %	Fat %	Lysine g/lb	Methionine g/lb	Calcium g/lb	Phosphorus g/lb
GRAINS								
Oats	1.30	54	10.7	4.6	1.7	0.77	0.36	1.55
Barley	1.49	53	4.9	1.8	1.8	0.8	0.23	1.55
Corn (Dent, yellow)	1.54	41	2.2	3.6	1.1	0.8	0.23	1.23
Sorghum (Milo)	1.46	52	2.6	2.7	1.2	0.45	0.18	1.54
Rice Grain (ground)	1.54	34	8.6	1.6	1.1	0.64	0.32	1.54
PROTEIN								
Soybean meal (Whole seed meal)	1.43	202	6.2	1.4	13	2.7	1.6	2.86
Whole Linseed seed (boiled)	2.0	100	7.6	31.6	3.5	1.4	1.1	2.36
Linseed meal	1.25	165	9.1	1.4	5.27	2.2	1.77	3.64
Cottonseed meal	1.25	188	12.2	1.5	7.6	2.3	0.77	5.05
Sunflower meal (without hulls)	1.17	205	11.7	2.7	7.64	7.3	1.91	4.27
Sunflower seeds	1.82	105	29.0	26	4.32	4.1	1.0	2.1
Milk powder - skimmed	1.73	152	0.2	1.0	11.5	4.5	5.82	4.64
Peas	1.4	106	5.6	1.0	7.5	0.91	0.55	1.86
Peanut meal (no coats)	1.36	222	7.7	2.1	6.6	1.9	1.32	2.77
Canola seed meal	1.28	169	11.0	2.8	9.45	3.2	2.86	5.36
ROUGHAGES								
Alfalfa fresh green (part bloom)	0.27	21	6.5	0.6	1.22	0.18	1.63	0.27
Alfalfa hay (early bloom)	1.02	82	20.8	2.8	3.68	0.82	5.82	0.86
Alfalfa meal (dehydrated)	0.98	71	24	2.8	3.86	1.27	6.27	1.05
Mixed hay (early bloom) - average	0.88	55	27	2.4	1.91	NA	2.82	0.91
Kentucky Bluegrass hay	0.72	82	29.9	3.0	NA	NA	1.09	1.13
Timothy Hay (early bloom)	0.83	96	3	2.5	NA	NA	2.05	1.14
Oat Hay	0.79	86	29.1	2.2	NA	NA	1.32	1.05
Grass Hay (early bloom) - average	0.8	39	30	2.3	1.13	NA	1.9	1.0
Sunflower hulls	0.82	45	38	1.9	1.2	0.5	2.0	0.73
Oat hulls	0.73	17	30.6	1.4	0.82	0.45	0.73	0.64
Bran (wheat)	1.33	70	10	3.8	2.5	0.73	0.64	5.14
MISCELLANEOUS FEEDS								
Molasses (Blackstrap)	1.18	19	0.4	0.2	-	-	3.36	0.36
Molasses Beet	1.20	66	-	0.2	-	-	0.55	0.1
Yeast (Brewers)	1.4	197	3.2	1.0	14.7	3.18	0.64	6.2
Fats (Tallow)	3.61	-	-	98.4	-	-	-	-
Mill run (wheat)	1.42	71	8.2	4.1	2.6	0.55	0.45	4.64
Polyunsat Veg Oils (eg Corn Oil)	4.08	-	-	99.7	-	-	-	-
Calcium carbonate (Limestone)	-	-	-	-	-	-	166 (10.4g/oz)	82 (5.1g/oz)
Dicalcium phosphate (DCP)	-	-	-	-	-	-	104 (6.5g/oz)	100 (6.3g/oz)
Sodium phosphate (Dibasic)	-	-	-	-	-	-	-	-
Steamed bone flour	-	-	-	-	-	-	145 (9.1g/oz)	60 (3.8g/oz)

NOTE: Calcium and phosphorus values given are elemental mineral content for average feed in grams per pound.
To calculate Mcal/kg, multiply Mcal/lb by 2.2. To calculate MJ/kg, multiply Mcal/lb by 2.2, then 4.184.
To calculate g/kg, multiply g/lb by 2.2. To calculate g/oz, divide g/lb by 16.
For a complete guide to all feed values, refer to NRC (1989).

NA = Value not available
- = No content

THE GRAINS

Cereal grains provide extra energy for growing, working and performance horses. Energy is the fuel for the body processes, including maintaing body function, temperature and tissue repair, as well as growth and work. Horses doing only light work require little or no grain. Match grain intake to level of work. Always measure grain by weight rather than volume as variations in quality from season to season, or bag to bag, can be more accurately adjusted. Cut grain level to one third on idle days to prevent risk of "tying up" in performance horses. Re-introduce to full grain over two days once full work is resumed.

RELATIVE NUTRIENT CONTENT AS FED

	USE	ENERGY Mcal/lb+	CRUDE PROTEIN g/lb	FIBER %	CALCIUM g/lb	PHOSPHORUS g/lb	SUBSTITUTION RATIO FOR ENERGY ON A 1lb OATS BASIS++	ADVANTAGES	DISADVANTAGES	SELECTION	METHOD OF FEEDING
OATS*	Energy Fiber	Medium 1.3	Low 54	Medium 10.7	Low 0.36	Medium 1.55	1lb	Palatable. Easily digested. Safe. Good maintenance grain.	Low in B complex vitamins. Low in Vitamin A (Carotene). Deficient in essential amino acids.	Plump, clean, free from dust. Bushel weight above 32lb.	Best fed whole. Crimping and crushing improves digestion in young and old horses.
CORN (Maize)	Energy	Very High 1.54	Very Low 41	Very Low 2.2	Low 0.23	Low 1.23	13½oz	High energy grain for performance horses. Palatable, digestible. Source of Vitamin A, Vitamin E.	Low in essential amino acids, particularly lysine. Cannot be fed alone. Cut out on rest days.	Plump, clean. Cracked corn - use within 3 weeks seal bags after each days use.	Best fed cracked - but deteriorates on storage. Do not grind too finely. Introduce gradually to horse's ration.
BARLEY	Energy	High 1.49	Low 53	Low 4.9	Low 0.23	Medium 1.55	14oz	Higher energy than oats. Boiled barley palatable and appetising.	Low palatability when whole. Low in B complex vitamins. Deficient in essential amino acids.	Plump, clean, free from dust.	Crushed or boiled. Boiling destroys vitamin content. Steam rolling increases palatability.
SORGHUM (Milo)	Energy	High 1.46	Low 52	Very Low 2.6	Very Low 0.18	Medium 1.54	14¼oz	Where available - can substitute for corn. Palatable when cracked.	Low in all vitamins, minerals and essential amino acids. Large amounts can cause constipation.	Round, plump, yellowish grain. Free from dust.	Cracked or coarsely ground. Soak whole grain before feeding or mix into damp feeds.
WHEAT	Energy	Very High 1.55	Low 52	Very Low 2.4	Very Low 0.18	Medium 1.7	13½oz	High energy substitute for corn. Source of Vitamin E.	Expensive. Low in B vitamins and essential amino acid. Cannot be fed alone - max 10% of ration.	Plump, clean, free from dust.	Whole or cracked. Do not grind. Soak whole grain before feeding or mix into damp feeds.
RYE	Energy	Very High 1.53	Low 55	Very Low (2.2-2.5)	Low 0.27	Medium 1.54	13½oz	High energy substitute for corn. Source of Vitamin E.	Low in B complex vitamins and essential amino acids.	Plump, clean, free from dust and mold.	Store for two months after harvest. Crushed or steam rolled.
RICE (ground)	Energy	Very High 1.54	Very Low 34	Low 8.6	Low 0.32	Medium 1.54	13½oz	Safe energy. Protein has some lysine.	Low palatability when whole. Not widely available.	Well filled grain, clean and dry.	Coarse ground, soaked.

* Oats, being the most common grain used as an energy source, is used as the standard.
+ To convert Mcal/lb to Mcal/kg, multiply by 2.2. For conversion to MJ/kg multiply by 4.184.
++ For conversion to grams, multiply by 28.5.

THE PROTEINS

Horses require adequate amounts of protein for growth, work and during pregnancy and lactation. Proteins in feed are digested to supply essential amino acids, which provide the building blocks for the synthesis of proteins of blood, bone, muscle and other tissue. Proteins vary in quality due to amino acid content. All essential amino acids must be available, particularly adequate quantities of lysine, methionine and cystine, for growth in young horses. Extra protein should be given when anabolic steroids are being administered.

RELATIVE NUTRIENT CONTENT AS FED

	USE	ENERGY Mcal/lb+	CRUDE PROTEIN g/lb	FIBER %	CALCIUM g/lb	PHOSPHORUS g/lb	SUBSTITUTION RATIO FOR PROTEIN ON A 1lb SOYBEAN MEAL BASIS++	ADVANTAGES	DISADVANTAGES	SELECTION	METHOD OF FEEDING
SOYBEAN MEAL	Protein	Medium 1.43	High 202	Low 6.2	Low-Medium 1.6	Medium 2.86	1lb	Very high quality protein for horses. Digestible. Oil content helps condition coat.	Less palatable to some horses. Low in B complex vitamins.	Free flowing. Not rancid. Toasted or roasted Soybean meal. Commercial processed forms available.	Whole beans should be crushed and boiled before use to destroy anemia/diarrhea toxin. Introduce slowly to rations.
LINSEED MEAL	Protein	Medium 1.24	Medium 165	Medium 9.1	Low-Medium 1.77	Medium 3.64	19½oz	Palatable to most horses. Slightly laxative. Good coat conditioner. Higher B vitamin than Soybean meal.	Lower quality protein. Often more costly than Soybean meal. Toxic factor in seeds must be boiled.	Seed uniform in size. meal - free flowing, no rancid odor.	Seeds and untreated meal must be boiled before use to destroy toxic factor. Heat treated meal or solvent extracted meal.
LINSEED SEED (Boiled)	Protein	High 2.0	Low 100	Low 7.6	Low 1.1	Medium 2.36	2lb				
COTTONSEED MEAL	Protein	Medium 1.25	High 188	Medium 12.2	Low 0.77	High 5.05	17oz	Better quality protein than linseed meal. Palatable, particularly when boiled.	Low levels of all vitamins. Low lysine content. Contains toxic factor if not heat treated. Contains vitamin E antagonist.	Finely ground. free from lint and sour odors.	Meal - introduce slowly. Better accepted when fed boiled.
SUNFLOWER MEAL	Protein	Medium 1.17	Very High 205	Medium 11.7	Low-Medium 1.91	High 4.27	1lb	Palatable. Horses like seeds. Good coat conditioner. Adds variety.	Low in most vitamins.	Meal - free flowing. Seeds - plump, clean, free from dust.	Meal - introduce slowly. Seeds - whole. Cracked, soaked in water for older horses.
SUNFLOWER SEED		High 1.82	Low 105	High 29	Low 1.0	Very Low 2.1	2lb				
MILK POWDER (Skimmed)	Energy Protein	High 1.73	Medium 152	Very Low 0.2	High Balanced Ratio 5.82	High 4.64	21oz	Palatable. High lysine. Well balanced animal protein for growth. High levels B group vitamins.	Energy not highly available to weaned horses. Low in Vitamins A, D, E. Low in iron and copper. Expensive.	Spray dried is more digestible. Dry, free from moisture.	Mixed well into feed. Expensive. Lysine more available to young horses.
PEANUT MEAL (no coats)	Protein	Medium 1.36	Very High 222	Low 7.7	Low 1.32	Medium 2.77	14¾oz	Some energy. Good quality meal high in protein. Palatable. Oil content helps coat condition.	Low in lysine, methionine and cystine. Low calcium and most vitamins. Do not store for longer than two months.	Free flowing. Free from hulls. Nutty taste. Free from rancid odor.	Introduce slowly and mix in well. Select only good quality meal. Do not store damp feed - mold.
CANOLA MEAL	Protein	Medium 1.28	Medium 169	Medium 11.0	Medium 2.86	High 5.36	19oz	Good palatability. Higher in lysine than other common meals except Soybean.	Not widely available. More research required for horses.	Free flowing, mold free and low odor. Lower in toxic compounds than rapeseed meal.	Introduce slowly and mix in well. High in choline and some B Complex Vitamins.

*   SOYBEAN MEAL, being the most commonly used source of protein, is used as the standard.
+   For conversion of Mcal/lb to Mcal/kg, multiply by 2.2. For conversion to MJ/kg multiply by 2.2, then multiply by 4.184.
++ For conversion to grams, multiply by 28.5.

THE ROUGHAGES

Horses require an adequate amount of fiber to increase bulk of ration, and dilute highly concentrated energy and protein feeds. Fiber opens up the digestive mass and allows better bacterial fermentation in the large bowel. Up to 90% of the ration by weight should consist of hay for a horse at rest, a minimum of 50% by weight of the ration in working horses.

RELATIVE NUTRIENT CONTENT AS FED

	USE	ENERGY Mcal/lb+	CRUDE PROTEIN g/lb	FIBER %	CALCIUM g/lb	PHOSPHORUS g/lb	SUBSTITUTION RATIO FOR FIBER ON A 1lb ALFALFA BASIS**	ADVANTAGES	DISADVANTAGES	SELECTION	METHOD OF FEEDING
ALFALFA HAY*/ PELLETS/ CUBES	Fiber Protein	Medium 0.98-1.1	Medium 75-82	Medium/ High 24	High 5.82	Low 0.86	1lb	Highly palatable. Good protein. High Vitamin D - sun cured. Good calcium. Pellet and cubes - high leaf content.	Hay - often dusty and dry. Contains Vitamin E antagonist.	Pellets/cubes - greenish, fed as supplement, sweet smell, free of dust. Hay - sun cured, leafy, no dust or mold. 15-17% CP for horses.	Hay - hay rack or in tub. Pellets/cubes - feed in tub.
GRASS HAY	Fiber	Low 0.8	Low 39	High 30	Low 1.9	Low 1.0	13oz	Palatable when mixed with grains. Provides roughage.	Often dusty. Large intakes cause "hay belly". Up to 12% wastage.	Hay - clean with some grain in head. Sweet smell, no dust.	Hay - put in hay rack to avoid wastage.
MIXED HAY	Fiber	Low 0.88	Low 55	High 27	Medium 2.82	Medium 0.91	14oz	Good supplementary roughage if good quality	Often dry and fibrous. Clover blend is more acceptable.	Leafy, no dust or weeds.	Feed as supplementary hay - not uniform enough for performance horses. Chopping improves acceptance.
CLOVER HAY (average)	Fiber Protein	Low 0.90	Medium 64	High 25	High 5.4	Medium 1.1	1lb	Suitable supplementary roughage.	High legume content may cause founder in ponies.	Leafy, no dust or weeds. Sweet smell. Not moldy.	Feed as supplementary hay - not uniform enough for stabled performance horses.
WHEAT BRAN	Fiber	Medium 1.33	Medium 70	Medium 10	Low 0.64	High 5.14	Max 10% of ration N/A	Palatable. Some B-complex vitamins. Increases palatability of supplements or additives.	High phosphorus. Low calcium. Expensive. Low Vitamin A & D. Not a good laxative as once claimed.	Clean and dry, free from caking, dust and odors.	No more than 10% of ration. Dry or wet. Avoid mixing calcium into pure bran mashes.
OAT HULLS/ RICE HUSKS	Fiber	Low 0.73	Very Low 17	High 30.6	Low 0.70	Low 0.64	12½oz	Palatable when mixed. Cheap form of fiber. Rice husks can be used as bedding.	Usually very dusty. Laceration of mouth and tongue. Low nutritional value. Not always available.	Low dust, free flowing. Not moldy or damp.	Mixed well into ration. Best fed damp to reduce dust. Discontinue if mouth problems develop.
CRUSHED CORN COBS	Fiber	Low 0.56	Very Low 11.4	High 31.9	Low 0.5	Very Low 0.18	12oz	Palatable. High in iron and other minerals.	Often dusty. Can cause choking. Not always available. May lacerate mouth.	Even sized portions. Avoid large lumps. Low dust.	Mix well into ration. Best fed damp if dusty. Pick out large pieces of cob to avoid choking. Do not feed alone.
SUN-FLOWER HULLS	Fiber	Very Low 0.82	Low 45	High 38	Medium 2.0	Low 0.73	10oz	Not very palatable. Cheap form of fiber.	Often dusty. Laceration of mouth and tongue. Not always available.	Low dust, free flowing. Some seed content if possible. If oily, avoid rancidity.	Mixed well into ration. Best fed dampened if dusty. Do not feed alone. Avoid feeding to young growing horses.

* Alfalfa hay, being a most common source of fiber, is used as the standard.
** Compare relative energy values when substituting in ration.

\+ For conversion to Mcals/kg multiply by 2.2. For conversion to MJ/kg multiply by 4.184, then by 2.2
\+\+ For conversion to grams, multiply by 28.5.

APPETIZERS/MISCELLANEOUS

Appetizing agents are often mixed with feed to make rations more acceptable. Only small amounts are acceptable. Compounded pellets, sweet feeds and custom mixes are convenient and time saving in mixing and feeding out. Read manufacturer's directions carefully. Choose type of pellet, sweet feed or custom mix to suit your horse's exercise demand.

RELATIVE NUTRIENT CONTENT AS FED

	USE	ENERGY Mcal/lb*	CRUDE PROTEIN g/lb	FIBER %	CALCIUM g/lb	PHOSPHORUS g/lb	MAX % OF RATION	ADVANTAGES	DISADVANTAGES	SELECTION	METHOD OF FEEDING
MOLASSES (Blackstrap)	Energy Palatability	Medium 1.18	Very Low 19	Very Low 0.4	High 3.36	Very Low 0.36	10%	Sweeten taste. Increases acceptance particularly in picky eaters. Palatable. Slightly laxative.	Low overall vitamin content. Sticky. Attracts flies. Beet source has lower calcium and phosphorus.	Powder - dry, free flowing. Liquid - sweet smell, no fermentation.	Mixed 50:50 with warm water - increases palatability of feed.
WHEAT - MILL RUN	Energy Palatability	Medium 1.42	Low–Medium 71	Low 8.2	Very Low 0.45	High 4.64	5%	Palatable. Useful for putting on body condition in starved horses.	Dusty. Too much can cause gut upset. Not suitable for performance horses.	Free flowing. No damp lumps.	Feed dampened - avoid dust which can lead to respiratory problems. Mix well into ration.
YEAST (Brewers)	Vitamins Palatability	Medium 1.4	High 197	Very Low 3.2	Low 0.64	High 6.2	0.5%-1.0%	Palatable. Supplies some B-complex.	Expensive. Large amounts required to provide adequate vitamins.	Brewers yeast more suitable, but expensive. Torula yeast less vitamins.	Mix with damp feed.
FAT - Tallow - Vegetable Oil	Energy Coat condition	Very High 3.61 (Tallow) 4.08 (Veg Oil)	-	-	-		0.5% (up to 5% as energy)	Veg oil - polyunsaturated fats for coat condition. Energy. Corn oil most palatable.	Develops rancidity if not stored in air-tight containers.	Blended cooking oils. Peanut or Safflower oil. Do not feed boiled linseed oil made for paint (contains lead).	Tallow - mix in warm. Helps reduce dust. Introduce slowly in a step-wise manner over 10-14 days.
PELLETS	Concentrate or Complete Feed	Compounded to provide concentrate base for specific classes of horses. Pelleted grain concentrate - feed with hay or pasture for roughage. Pelleted complete feed - roughage included.					Manufacturer's directions	Less wastage and dust. Complete feed. Easy storage. Economical. Convenient.	Quickly consumed. Adequate water must be available. May increase risk of chewing vices in stabled horses.	Low crumble. Content of nutrients. Dry and free flowing.	Feed as recommended. Can be boosted by grain or fat for energy.
SWEET FEEDS	Concentrate Feed	Compounded to provide concentrate base for specific classes of horses, with hay or pasture providing roughage balance.					Manufacturer's directions	Convenient to feed - time saving. Palatable to most horses.	Variable content and made to price. Loss of vitamins by deterioration and mineral contact in damp sweet mix during storage.	Check contents and form - sweet smell. No caking.	Usually fed with hay - can mix in extra grain. Add extra vitamins and minerals to ensure diet meets requirements.
CUSTOM MIXES	Complete Feed	Compounded to provide concentrate base for specific classes of horses, with hay or pasture providing roughage balance.					Manufacturer's directions	Convenient and often economic in time saving. Palatable. Contains set protein and fiber levels.	Variable content and quality of ingredients.	Check contents - free flowing, not spoilt. No caking.	Usually fed with hay. Can mix in extra grain. Dampen to avoid dust in dry forms.

* For conversion to Mcals/kg, multiply by 2.2. For conversion to MJ/kg, multiply by 2.2, then 4.184.

MINERALS

Fourteen minerals and trace elements are considered essential for skeletal development, body function and metabolism in the horse. The need for strong skeletal structure, efficient metabolism, and continuous tissue repair in the performance horse increases the demand for a balanced and adequate supply of these nutrients in the diet. However, soil deficiencies, natural imbalances, and poor availability of certain minerals reduce the certainty that stabled horses, in particular, will obtain sufficient levels from grains and hay. Therefore, it is almost mandatory to provide a balanced mineral intake in supplement form in the ration of growing, breeding and performance horses. Minerals are classified into major minerals, trace-elements and electrolytes. The following table outlines the function, requirements, deficiency symptoms, and benefit from supplementation of the essential minerals required by horses.

NUTRIENT	FUNCTION	DEFICIENCY SYMPTOMS	DAILY REQUIREMENT/ 1100lb (500kg) BODYWEIGHT	BENEFITS OF SUPPLEMENTATION
MINERALS, CALCIUM and PHOSPHORUS	Calcium and phosphorus, in conjunction with Vitamin D, are required for bone development and strength. **Calcium** - muscle contraction, metabolism, blood clotting, bone growth. **Phosphorus** - metabolism, bone growth.	**Calcium** deficiency or imbalance results in skeletal problems such as bone deformities and weakness, joint problems, epiphysitis, rickets, shifting lameness. Essential for lactation in mares. **Phosphorus** - poor appetite and infertility.	Amount dependent on diet, age, work, sweat output, bone stress, etc. See individual rations for amount. Adequate Vitamin D must be available. More calcium in horses grazing tropical pasture contain oxalates. Phosphorus low on high alfalfa diets.	Calcium 50% Phosphorus approx 35% available from feedstuffs. Avoid excess of both minerals. Optimum ratio 1.2-2.0:1.0. Calcium more likely to be deficient in high grain rations. Supplementation will help ensure development and maintenance of a strong musculo-skeletal system.
ELECTROLYTES SODIUM and	**Sodium:** Muscle contraction, nerve and cellular function.	Poor appetite, growth. Poor performance. Dehydration and risk of heat stress.	Amount dependent on work, temperature and humidity. Sodium and chloride as salt is approx salt 40-60g daily. Adequate water must be available.	Replacement of sweat loss of these salts is essential in hot weather or heavily sweating horses. Helps ensure adequate intake of water to help correct dehydration.
CHLORIDE	**Chloride:** Kidney function. Fluid & Acid/Base balance.	Dehydration, alkalosis of the blood with thickwindedness, nervousness and poor performance.		
POTASSIUM	**Potassium:** Inter-related to sodium in nerve and muscular function. Cellular metabolism. Fluid balance.	Reduced appetite. Poor growth rate. Poor performance. Dehydration. Stiffness of the muscles and joints in working horses.	Amount dependent on work, temperature and humidity 60mg/kg bwt or about 30g daily.	Increased amounts lost as sweat output increases. Essential to maintain performance and fluid balance in heavily sweating horses.
MAGNESIUM	Inter-related to calcium and phosphorus in development of bones. Metabolism.	Muscle and skeletal weakness. Poor growth and performance. Deficiency may predispose to "tying up" in performance horses. Nervousness, rapid breathing, muscle tremors.	15mg/kg bwt, or about 7.5g daily. Absorption decreased in presence of high calcium intake. Extra in lactating mares and heavily sweating horses.	Approximately 40-60% available from feed. Adequate amounts important to maintain metabolism and musculo-skeletal soundness. May help prevent "tying up" in heavily sweating horses.
TRACE ELEMENTS IRON and	**Iron:** Constituent of haemoglobin. Cell metabolism.	**Iron:** Anemia - resulting in lack of stamina, labored respiration and poor performance.	**Iron:** Performance horse requirement estimated from 800-1,000mg daily in hard working horses. Approx 24mg lost in each liter of sweat.	Iron is only 15-18% available from feedstuffs, so supplementation is considered necessary in performance horses. Essential to supply copper for efficient utilization of iron. Essential for production and maintenance of the blood count. Performance horses unable to synthesize and absorb Vit B12 as efficiently. Vitamin B12, Vitamin B6, Folic Acid, Vitamin C, and protein involved in blood cell and hemoglobin formation and maintenance in performance horses.
COPPER and	**Copper:** Trace amounts required to enable incorporation of iron into haemoglobin. Bone and cartilage formation.	Copper deficiency may cause bone weakness, and yellowing of coat in chronic cases.	**Copper** up to 70mg daily. Growing horses: from 25-50mg/kg feed for proper cartilage development on energy controlled diets and adequate exercise.	
COBALT	**Cobalt:** Constituent of Vit B12, which is synthesized by bacterial fermentation in large bowel.	**Cobalt:** Inadequate Vitamin B12 can cause poor energy utilization. Excess may actually cause anemia.	Cobalt 1-2mg daily.	

NUTRIENT	FUNCTION	DEFICIENCY SYMPTOMS	DAILY REQUIREMENT/ 1100lb (500kg) BODYWEIGHT	BENEFITS OF SUPPLEMENTATION
MANGANESE	Metabolism of carbohydrates, protein and fats. Calcium and phosphorus utilization. Bone development and formation. Reproduction in mares and fertility in stallions.	Symptoms not known in horses. May cause reduced fertility and bone weakness, knuckling over the joints. Excess may cause anemia.	Approximately 300mg daily. Absorption decreased in presence of high calcium intake.	About 47% available from feedstuffs. Adequate amounts important to maintain metabolism and musculo-skeletal soundness.
ZINC	Enzymes in metabolism. Cartilage, hoof formation. Health of skin.	Reduced appetite. Poor growth. Dry, thickened skin and skin lesions. Hair loss in severe induced deficiencies.	Approximately 400mg. Absorption decreased in presence of high calcium intake.	Supplementation may be necessary on diets with added calcium, or high content of phytic acid in grains. Toxicity causes anemia, epiphysitis and lameness.
SELENIUM	Inter-related with VITAMIN E. Contained in enzyme glutathione peroxidase which protects muscle membranes from superoxide induced damage.	Poor muscle development and weakness (white muscle disease) in foals. May predispose to tying up, and reduced performance. Selenium deficient soils in feed growing areas reduce content in feedstuffs. Marginal selenium deficiency seems to be widespread.	Approximately 1.0mg. Selenium excess is extremely toxic. Plants such as milk vetch, princes plume and goldenweed may accumulate toxic levels when growing on high selenium soils.	In conjunction with VITAMIN E, to prevent tying up in performance horses and white muscle disease in foals. Widespread response to selenium supplements indicated by improved performance.
IODINE	Constituent of thyroxine for thyroid function and control of metabolism. Growth and reproduction.	Goiter (enlarged Thyroid gland) and weakness in foals when deficiency occurs in pregnant mares. Reduced metabolism.	Iodine deficient soils reduce content in feedstuffs. Approximately 1-2mg daily. Excess may cause congenital goiter in foals of mares consuming high levels. Excessive supplements of kelp may cause iodine excess.	Important in iodine deficient areas, particularly for pregnant and lactating mares - better health and fertility.
SULFUR	Sulfur containing amino acids. Methionine and cystine.	Deficiency not known provided high quality protein is fed.	Adequate intake in protein.	Various supplementary sources available. Claimed useful in correcting leg problems, repelling ticks, hoof repair. Not proven.
MOLYBDENUM	Enzymes in metabolism.	Deficiency not known in horses, although is lacking in many soils and pastures.	Soil deficiencies may exist. Excess may interfere with copper uptake.	No need to supplement normal good quality rations.
FLUORINE	Important in bone and teeth development.	Deficiency is not a problem in horses. Excesses can lead to bone lesions and lameness due to softening and thickening of bone tissue.	Traces are present in most limestone based supplements. Horses can tolerate up to 500mg daily.	No proven benefit from supplementation.

VITAMINS

Vitamins are required in very small amounts as compared with other nutrients. Studies have shown that there are 16 vitamins that are involved in physiological and metabolic processes in the body. The requirements of vitamins are related to age, growth rate, reproductive status, and type of activity performed by the horse. Studies have shown that extra amounts of many vitamins are required during growth, pregnancy and lactation, or when horses are worked hard. Laboratory analysis indicates that many of the common feedstuffs fed to performance horses are deficient, or have imbalanced levels of many essential vitamins. Climatic conditions, harvesting, long-term storage and processing results in a further loss of natural vitamin content from feedstuffs.

Some vitamins are considered "essential" because they can only be obtained from food (Vitamin A, as carotene, Vitamin E and some Vitamin D), whereas other vitamins are synthesized during bacterial digestion in the large bowel (B Complex, Vitamin K) and liver (Vitamin C). Vitamin D is also synthesized in the skin by sunlight. A deficiency disease can develop if the intake of essential vitamins is inadequate due to feed deficiencies, or the synthesis of other vitamins is reduced, such as occurs in young horses, during severe diarrhea or when horses are under stress of hard work and racing. The need for supplementary vitamins has become more widely recognised, particularly when horses are stabled and perform on a repeated basis with little access to high quality pasture.

The following table summarizes the function, requirement, deficiency symptoms and benefits from supplementary vitamins in horses.

VITAMIN	OTHER NAMES	FUNCTION	DEFICIENCY SIGNS	DAILY REQUIREMENT ALLOWANCE PER 1100lb (500kg) BODYWEIGHT	BENEFIT OF SUPPLEMENTATION
VITAMIN A (as carotene in feedstuffs)	Retinol	Energy metabolism, vision, skin, mucous membranes, reproduction, growth, blood and bone formation.	Poor performance, weak bones. Incidence of tendon problems. Poor blood count, infertility and abortion, poor skin and hooves, poor growth, lack of appetite. Poor night vision.	Up to 50,000iu daily in performance horses as Retinol may help maintain tendon strength. Green pasture contains adequate for grazing horses.	Helps ensure red blood cell production, tendon strength, performance, skin health, fertility. Pre-cursor carotene in feeds rapidly destroyed in feedstuffs during curing and storage.
VITAMIN D3 (As D2 in suncured feedstuffs)	Cholecalciferol	Calcium and phosphorus utilization and bone formation. Synthesized by sunlight on skin of horses.	Increased incidence of joint and bone breakdown. Imbalanced calcium-phosphorus ratio. Rickets in young horses.	Up to 6000iu daily in performance horses (adequate calcium and phosphorus must be present in diet).	Stabled horses for strong musculo-skeletal system. Helps reduce incidence of bone and joint breakdown. Horses require up to 20 minutes of bright sunlight daily to provide Vitamin D from skin.
VITAMIN E	Natural source Vitamin E d-alpha tocopherol. Synthetic Vitamin E dl-alpha tocopherol	Anti-oxidant. Immune response, Vitamin E - selenium inter-relationship in muscle strength. Vitamin E - Vitamin A inter-relationship in reproduction. Vitamin E deficiency - EDM in growing horses.	Anemia. Increased incidence of tying up in selenium deficient horses. Reduced muscle strength. ("Wobbler" Syndrome in growing horses.) Supplementary Vitamin E destroyed by iron tonics in same feed.	From 600-1800iu daily for performance horses. Endurance horses 4000-4500iu may be beneficial. Growing horses: 1000-1500iu daily.	Improved stamina and performance. May aid muscle strength. May help reduce incidence of tying up. Wobbler Syndrome - growing horses on small lots (EDM).
VITAMIN K	Menadione	Blood clotting.	Internal hemorrhage and slow blood clotting.	Intestinal synthesis. Up to 20mg daily in feed.	May be beneficial prior to extensive surgery.
VITAMIN B1	Thiamine	General metabolism. Nerve and muscular function.	Poor appetite. Nervousness, poor fertility, poor performance. Bracken fern poisoning causes deficiency.	50-100mg daily. Also intestinal synthesis, but reduced under stress. 3000mg daily - may reduce nervous behaviour.	Utilization of high energy rations. Performance, maintain appetite.
VITAMIN B2	Riboflavine	Energy, metabolism.	Poor growth and performance. Decreased growth rate and poor feed utilization.	Up to 50mg daily. Also intestinal synthesis, but reduced under stress.	Utilization of high energy rations. Performance.

VITAMIN	OTHER NAMES	FUNCTION	DEFICIENCY SIGNS	DAILY REQUIREMENT ALLOWANCE PER 1100lb (500kg) BODYWEIGHT	BENEFIT OF SUPPLEMENTATION
VITAMIN B3	Niacin Nicotinamide Nicotinic Acid	General metabolism. B3, B2 and Folic Acid inter-relationship in energy production.	Poor performance. (Niacin in grains poorly available to horses.)	Up to 400mg daily. Also intestinal synthesis from amino acid tryptophan.	Utilization of high energy rations. Performance.
VITAMIN B5	Pantothenic Acid D-panthenol	General metabolism. Steroid synthesis?	Poor performance.	Up to 100mg daily. Also intestinal synthesis but reduced under stress.	Utilization of high energy rations. Performance.
VITAMIN B6	Pyridoxine	General metabolism. Hemoglobin formation. Amino acid utilization.	Poor performance. Anemia. Impaired immunity.	25-50mg daily. Also intestinal synthesis reduced under stress.	Blood cell production. Aids utilization of iron tonics. Performance.
VITAMIN B12	Cyanocobalamin	Hemoglobin formation. General metabolism.	Deficiency not common. Anemia, weight loss, poor growth. Reduced performance.	Up to 200mcg. Intestinal synthesis - cobalt supplement.	Helps maintain hemoglobin levels. Performance. Best given orally as injections rapidly excreted.
VITAMIN B15	Pangamic Acid DPDA	Blood oxygenation? Metabolism? Reduction of fatigue? Liver function? Cancer forming.	Poor performance? Poor recovery.	Unknown. Injections usually. Benefit not proven.	Aids performance? Reduces fatigue? Aids recovery from racing?
FOLIC ACID	Folacin Vitamin M	General metabolism. Hemoglobin and red cell formation.	Anemia. Poor performance (proven). Reduced growth rate.	Up to 15mg. Some intestinal synthesis. Daily oral supplementation beneficial on grain rations.	Performance. Helps maintain blood count. Utilized best by oral supplementation.
BIOTIN	Vitamin H	General metabolism. Nervous function. Reproductive function. Hoof and hair growth?	Poor hoof quality. Inter-related with B1, B6, B12, Vitamin C, folic acid.	Intestinal synthesis. Low availability in feeds.	15mg daily aids hoof strength and growth. Calcium and Biotin both required for hoof bonding.
INOSITOL	Myo-inositol	Metabolism of fats?	Poor growth and loss of hair?	Synthesized in body in adequate amounts.	Unknown.
CHOLINE		Metabolism of fats. Nervous function?	Unthrifty, poor fertility.	600mg. Liver synthesis. (Vitamin B12 required.)	Choline can be synthesized from amino acid methionine.
VITAMIN C	Ascorbic Acid	General metabolism. Iron absorption. Anti-stress hormones. Activation of folic acid. Blood cell formation. Tendon fiber strength?	Horses synthesize sufficient amounts in liver from glucose. Greenfeed provides adequate intake.	Intestinal synthesis. Requires 4.5g daily in feed to increase blood levels.	Does not prevent bleeding in racehorses. Aids in reducing stress? Prevention of virus flu. Performance? Between 5-20g daily used in racehorse rations.
PABA	Para-amino benzoic acid.	Part of the folic acid structure.	Unknown - maybe as for folic acid.	As for folic acid. Up to 100mg daily is safe.	Similar benefits to folic acid?

COMMON FEEDS - SELECTION

FEED	DESCRIPTION	WEIGHT	OTHER INFLUENCES	SIMPLE TESTS/HINTS
Oats	**Whole Oats:** Good quality or prime oats are plump, clean, free from dust, weeds or other foreign material. Fresh smelling. Occasionally oats can be contaminated in wet seasons by ERGOT fungus, with blackened grains resembling rat or mice droppings. Causes vascular problems - do not feed contaminated oats to horses. **Rolled Oats:** Plump even squashed with some exposed kernels and free fibrous husks. Dust and mold free.	Standard - Good quality whole feed oats weigh between 30-32lb per bushel or 4lb per gallon (about 500g/liter). Crushed, steam or other processed oats usually weigh less. Heavy oats weigh 40-48lb per measured bushel.	**Seasonal Variations:** Protein content grown in wet seasons about 6-7%, dry seasons up to 12-13%. **Newly Harvested Oats:** Contain high non-protein volatile nitrogen content (NPN) of about 36%, which is poorly digested and can cause skin bumps or diarrhea. Storage for 3-4 months lowers NPN to safe level of less than 20%. Store for 2-3 months before use. Avoid by mixing new season's grain 1:4 parts with old oats. Alternatively spread out in sun for 3-4 hours to reduce NPN.	**Size:** Prime oats are full and heavy. **Smell:** Sweet and dry. Musty smelling oats should be avoided. **Weight:** Drop handful into bucket of water. If prime quality, 95% sinks to bottom, more seeds float as quality decreases. **Dust:** Blow over a handful of oats or pass from hand to hand to check for dust. **Foreign matter:** Spread out on palm of hand or white paper - check for weed seeds, flat oats, mice droppings, ergot oats. **Weavils:** Sticky webs/strands in oats, weevils present.
Corn	**Whole Corn:** Top quality corn is plump, clean, firm and separated. Bright yellow color, with a sweet corn smell. **Cracked Corn:** Free flowing, not oily, low flour or corn dust content. **Corn on Cob:** Tightly packed, plump kernels are prime quality. Normally feed whole fresh or dried chopped. Greedy horses may choke - avoided by crushing.	Good quality whole corn weighs about 56lb per bushel or 6½lb per gallon (about 800g/liter).	**Storage:** Exposure of cracked corn to air and heat will release oil content, which will turn sticky and rancid. Store in bag or air tight container - not plastic bag to avoid sweating and musty smell. Fold down top after each use to exclude air.	**Size:** 80-90% are large plump yellow kernels. **Smell:** Fresh, sweet smell - no musty odor. **Dust:** Blow over handful to check for dust in cracked corn. **Spoil:** Spread handful out on palm - insect damage seen as holes in kernel; mold as black spots or musty smell. **Taste Test:** Taste cracked corn - sweet. **Dig Test:** Dig hand into cracked corn - sticky or oily feel indicates rancidity of too long or poor storage.
Barley	**Whole Barley:** Top quality is plump, dust free and sweet smelling with short sharp awns. **Steamed Rolled:** Flattened seed, most kernels exposed, few broken up - no dust. **Boiled Barley:** Plump, soft, damp, sweet smell - not wet or musty.	**Whole Barley:** Good quality barley weighs 48lb per bushel or 6lb per gallon (about 650g/liter) **Rolled Barley:** Average weight about 15% less. **Boiled Barley:** Depends on moisture content; cook with minimal water.	**Whole Barley:** Dry barley not very palatable to horses; may be softened by soaking; or mixed into damp feed for 1-2 hours before feeding, or spread out on wet bag (folded over) for 1-2 hours. **Rolled Barley:** Steam rolled barley flattens more evenly but may go musty if steamed and stored damp. Dry roll - grain broken and brittle, and less palatable. **Boiled Barley:** Boiling reduces oil content and natural vitamins, but changes the type of carbohydrates which may make horses less hot tempered and playful.	**Size:** Seed should be plump and free flowing. **Smell:** Dry - not musty. **Weight:** Rolled barley pour from one hand to other - lightweight kernels will float in air, and miss hand. **Dust:** Pour from one hand to other - dust should not drift away - blow over sample on palm of hand - no dust or light rolled kernels. **Foreign Matter:** Spread out on palm - check for weed seeds, weevil damage and dark edges on grain.
SOYBEAN MEAL (Example of Protein Meal)	**Solvent Extracted Meal:** Good quality solvent extracted meal with hulls is free flowing, even in color with a fresh soy smell. **Extruded whole full fat bean meal:** Golden in color, with a toasted aroma, free flowing and slightly oily feel.	Good quality soybean meal weighs approximately 2½oz per teacup (about 75g/120ml).	**Raw Soybeans:** Contain allergic, goitrogenic and anticoagulant factors, as well as an inhibitor that prevents trypsin digestion of protein. Must be heat treated by toasting, cooking or extrusion to destroy those factors for horses. Over-cooking destroys lysine, under-cooking reduces methionine uptake. **Solvent Extracted Meal:** Safe and good quality protein source for young and older horses.	**Solvent Extracted Meal:** **Smell:** Soybean smell, no rancidity. **Taste:** Bland to slightly bitter taste. **Spoil:** Not rancid or caked. Free from insects. **Dust:** Free flowing, no dust, not oily to feel. **Full Fat Extruded Meal:** **Smell:** Toasted aroma. **Taste:** Pleasant cooked taste. **Spoil:** Not caked or greasy to touch. **Dust:** Oil content on outside of granules eliminates dust.

FEED	DESCRIPTION	WEIGHT	OTHER INFLUENCES	SIMPLE TESTS/HINTS
Alfalfa hay Alfalfa pellets Alfalfa cubes Alfalfa dehydrated meal	**Hay:** High quality is dense green, evenly cured, not bleached on outside. Open bale should smell sweet, no mold dampness or foreign plants or material. **Pellets:** Pure leaf, finely ground; hard pellets, no dust. **Cubes:** Compressed cubes 2" x 2" x 1-3" - more fiber. **Chopped Hay:** Good quality is bright green, some flower heads, high leaf content, low dust and free flowing with a sweet smell. No weeds or prickles, or clumps in matted particles.	**Hay:** Bale weights range from 40-150lb depending on moisture content and compression. A single slice will weigh between 3½-4lb (1.5-1.8kg). **Pellets/Cubes:** Weight usually uniform. Store in dry conditions in high humidity areas.	**Harvest Time:** Mature hay will be shiny, stemmy, brittle, with numerous flower heads. This increases fiber content relative to protein and is less suitable for growing horses or racehorses. Stemmy, shiny hay is usually less dusty and is selected for horses with dust allergy. Dampen or soak prior to feeding. **Curing/Storage:** Poorly dried or badly cured hay will often heat in the bale, releasing smokey, pungent fumes, and develop mold - may ignite and burn. **Storage:** Long term storage of hay reduces Vitamin A activity particularly during summer conditions. Hay stored in wet conditions - moldy and blackened. **Pellets:** High leaf content, lower fiber increases incidence of wood chewing with pellets, but up to 32% higher than loose alfalfa hay. **Cubes:** More fiber, no wood chewing. Better digestibility than loose hay. **Dehydrated Meal:** Greater digestibility of fiber and energy than loose hay.	**Hay** **Weight:** Bale should be more than 90lb (40kg) compacted with green color. **Quality:** Tease out sample of hay and shake to assess leaf loss and dust. If brittle and dusty, can rehydrate before feeding. Rub a small amount between hands - soft, resilient feel with little leaf loss, more palatable and higher protein content. **Smell:** Sniff a sample - should smell sweet and fresh - no musty odor or fumes. **Foreign Material:** Tease out sample and examine for grass, sticks, stones and weeds. **Insect Attack:** A blackened sugary appearance with sticky feel indicates aphid damage - can lead to diarrhea. Should not be fed to horses. **Meal:** Free flowing, no caking, low dust. **Pellets/Cubes:** Alfalfa aroma, shiny outer surface, free flowing, low crumble, dust free.
Wheat Bran	Flakes are fluffy, separated, free flowing with minimum dust - no clumps or cobweb weevil strands.	Weight of about 3½oz per pint (180/liter) or 4oz (115g) per double adult handful.	**Processing:** Course middlings - even range of flake size. Small flake size usually contains more dust.	**Quality:** Pour a handful from one hand to another - free flowing, no weevil cobwebs, low dust, appetizing smell - dampen and taste - sweet, smooth taste - not bitter.
Custom Feed Mixes, Sweet feeds, Pelleted feeds, Meals	Wide variation in grain content and relative energy content to suit purpose. Generally should smell palatable, free flowing, minimal dust. Analysis should be on bag or on ticket sewn into top flap.	Weight depends on proportion of grain, moisture content and ratio of protein meal. Uniformity of pelleted feeds guarantees standard weight and consistency.	**Seasonal/Locality Variations:** Proportions and selection of ingredients change from season to season depending on availability and cost of ingredients. **Purpose:** Type of feed mix should be selected to match exercise level, climate, temperament and general condition. **Ingredient Range:** Some mixes contain minerals and vitamins to meet needs of target horse group. Long term storage of processed feed ingredients, particularly damp sweet feeds, will reduce potency of vitamins A, D & E and may bind calcium and trace minerals. Additional supplements usually necessary to ensure best condition or performance.	Spread a representative sample out on a white sheet or paper - read the label of ingredients and attempt to identify major components. **Grain Content:** Check for quality of individual grain, whole or cracked grains (see grains and base). **Roughage Content:** Check for content of fiber in complete custom mixes. **Protein Meals:** Check for types of protein seed/meal used, including whole or cracked kernels. **Dust Content:** Blow over a handful and check dust content. **Salt Content:** Taste for salt. **Sweet Feeds:** Taste for sweetness.

SELECTION OF COMMERCIAL PREPARED FEEDS

Stock feed companies have researched and formulated a large variety of sweet feed concentrate mixes, custom complete feeds, and pelleted concentrate or complete feeds to match the needs of all types of horses. The sales of commercial mixes have increased over the past 20 years, and horse owners find them convenient, time saving and in some cases, less expensive to feed than mixing the traditional grains, protein meals and other ingredients used in home mixed rations. Many owners feed home mixed feeds in the morning, using commercial sweet feeds as a convenient evening feed.

There are State and Federal laws that regulate the formulation, label formats and claims, distribution and sale of compounded commercial feed. The guaranteed analysis of Minimum Crude Protein; Minimum Crude Fat, and Maximum Crude Fiber must be included on the tag or label, as well as a list of common names or groups of all ingredients used to compound the feed.

When choosing a commercial feed, assess the feed using the following guidelines:

	Check	Comments
1	Is the feed formulated as a concentrate or complete feed - check ingredient groups on label?	Concentrate feeds are formulated for addition to a roughage base, either as an energy, protein or combined feed. Complete feeds usually contain roughage components such as hulls, straws, husks and corn cobs.
2	What is the protein and fat content guaranteed on the label?	Choose a protein level that is suited to the type of horse you are feeding. A growing horse will require more protein than a mature horse and higher protein feeds are generally more expensive. Less protein is needed when alfalfa or clover hay is used for roughage rather than a grass hay base.
3	Does the feed contain minerals and vitamins?	Many complete feeds contain a vitamin and mineral package. Unless they claim to be a feed supplement, only the ingredients need to be listed and not the amounts. Where concentrate feeds are used for racing, performance, growing and breeding horses, then the intake of vitamins and minerals is related to the amount of feed included in the diet, and an additional supplement source may be beneficial to overcome inadequate levels in the roughage base. Minerals such as iron and copper may also react to degrade vitamin potency during storage of compounded feeds prior to use, so additional supplements of trace minerals, vitamin A, vitamin E, and B-Complex may be beneficial in hard working, growing or breeding horses. NOTE: Unless the feed is claimed as a vitamin and mineral supplement, with individual amounts listed on the label, it is unlikely that it will meet the full needs of every class of horse.
4	What is the comparative cost per unit weight for similar formulations?	A wide selection of commercial feeds are often available as a choice from a local feed store. At first purchase of a compound feed, check prices per comparative sized bags as you may be able to save money. However, avoid changing brand names or types of feed once your horses are accustomed to one particular blend or taste. If a change is necessary due to unavailability, or budget constraints, change over 5-7 days in a step-wise manner to the new feed.
5	Will my horse accept the feed?	If you decide on a particular brand or blend, ask other customers or horse owners in the store as to the reliability of supply, palatability and results obtained of a particular feed. You may need to purchase a bag to try it. Not every horse will accept the same feed - some feeds are better accepted than others - you may need to purchase another brand or type of feed for a particular horse that is a picky eater or poor doer. Be prepared to add extra oats, corn, or even fat to the feed to increase the energy level in hard working horses.
6	Does the feed company have a good reputation for quality and consistency of its feed?	Many companies formulate on least cost principles based on computer controlled blending of feed ingredients to achieve a least cost product. Most companies take particular care to choose high quality ingredients from contract growers or suppliers, and have high standards of quality control.

ELECTROLYTES

Electrolytes, or body salts, are becoming more widely recognised as important additives to the diet of equine athletes. Recent studies have linked the loss, deficiency and imbalance of body salts with certain clinical signs and poor performance in working and racing horses. In working horses, loss of electrolytes in sweat is a major cause of electrolyte imbalances in the blood, particularly when the diet is low or contains inadequate amounts to meet these losses. Electrolytes are also secreted in saliva, but reabsorbed 3-6 hours after feeding as the food mass is digested.

The electrolytes that play an important role in muscle and nerve function, metabolism, acid-base and fluid balance in the body include sodium, potassium, chloride, bicarbonate, magnesium and calcium. Horses at pasture with a light workload should obtain adequate electrolytes from green pasture and good quality hay. However, once horses are worked fast or exercised for extended periods, extra electrolytes may be necessary to match specific demand or replace increased losses. Concentrated diets containing grains are deficient in many electrolytes, so a horse on a racing or performance ration will often require supplementation with electrolytes to overcome low feed levels.

Studies have shown that body salt requirements and losses are influenced by type, speed and duration of work, climatic conditions and relative sweat output. The following table summarizes the relative electrolyte needs for exercising horses.

Type of Work	Duration	Speed	Sweat Output	Ambient Temperature	Major Changes	Symptoms	Replacement/Action
Fast (Cantering/Galloping) Racing, Polo, Eventing	1-10 minutes	Above 450 yards (400 meters)/min Anaerobic	Light: up to 1 gallon (4 liters)	Below 85°F. (30°C)	Lactate accumulation in muscles and blood (Acidosis)	Stiff and sore in muscles in unfit horses. Loss of appetite, sour, bitchy. (See page xx)	Adequate cool down exercise as initial one minute walk, then trot 3-4 minutes. Alkaline salts (eg citrate and bicarbonate) may be administered.
	Up to 60 minutes	Mainly above 450 yards (400 meters)/min	Medium: up to 3 gallons (12 liters) total daily	Below 85°F (30°C) Hot, humid.	Lactate as above. Loss of sodium, potassium, chloride and fluids.	As above, also dehydration due to fluid loss. Loss of performance. Thick in wind, spookiness can develop in 4-6 weeks.	As above. Salt 3/4oz (21g). Extra potassium and chloride may be beneficial to replace sweat loss.
Slow (Walking/Trotting) Hunting, Stock, Hacking, Jumping.	Up to 60 minutes	Mainly below 450 yards (400 meters)/min	Medium, up to 3 gallons (12 liters) total daily.	Below 85°F (30°C)	Loss of sodium, potassium, chloride and fluids.	Dehydration due to fluid loss. Fatigue.	Salt 1oz (30g). Extra calcium, potassium magnesium and chloride to replace sweat loss.
	60-180 minutes	as above	Medium-heavy up to 4½ gallons (18 liters)	Below 85°F (30°C)	Loss of sodium, potassium, chloride, calcium, magnesium, iron and fluids. (More potassium and chloride los.)	Dehydration due to fluid lss. Thick in wind, spookiness can develop in 4-6 weeks.	Salt 1oz (30g). Extra calcium, potassium, magnesium and chloride to replace sweat loss.
	More than 180 minutes	as above	Heavy up to 6 gallons (24 liters)	Above 85°F (30°C) Hot/Humid	As above	As above	As above - increase amounts by 50%. (Multiply by 1.5)
Endurance exercise [Endurance riding 60-100 miles (100-160km)]	More than 180 minutes	Below 450 yards (400 meters) per minute	Very heavy, up to 10 gallons (40 liters)	Below 85°F (30°C)	Loss of sodium, potassium, chloride, calcium, magnesium, iron and fluids. (More potassium and chloride lost.)	Dehydration, fatigue. Poor recovery, thick in wind, spookiness.	As above, increase by 75% (Multiply by 1.75)
			Extra heavy, up to 15 gallons (60 liters)	Above 85°F (30°C) Hot/Humid	Higher quantities than above	As above	Increase by 100% (Multiply by 2)

MONITORING OF FECES AND URINE OUTPUT

Many horse owners consider that the form, consistency, ease of voiding, color and odor of the feces and urine are a useful guide to the digestive efficiency and general health of their horses. Daily observation of the excretory behaviour and output can monitor these parameters, particularly where changes in color, consistency and smell occur. The following table provides a practical guideline on the major influences of diet on the physical appearance of feces and urine in adult horses. It is by no means an exhaustive guide to all conditions. If you are concerned with the significance of the changes, consult your vet for advice.

FECES

	Normal	Possible - Feed Influences
CONSISTENCY/ FORM	**Normal** - A healthy horse will pass about 50% more manure than the weight of feed it consumes as feces pass about 50-60% moisture. Feces are normally freely passed as well formed balls without a straining or expulsive manner, or undue discomfort or anal dribble.	**Soft Fluid Feces** (cow pat form) - unaccustomed intake of green or wet pasture, playing with waterer, excessive electrolyte intake, excitement of transport or competition, bowel irritation from heavy worm burdens such as seasonal release of hypobiotic Small Strongyles, high grain diets without adequate roughage. **Hard, Dried out Feces** - Dehydration - mucus covering, smaller fecal balls due to heavy sweat output and inadequate volume or access to drinkable water. Introduction to dry hays and concentrate in newly stabled horses.
COLOR	Color is dependent on the type of feed mix and content of green forage in the diet. **Dark green colour** - high legume content in diet from hay or pasture. **Mid-green color** - balanced grass hay or mixed hay and concentrate diet. **Light green yellow color** - Grass hay and grain concentrate diet 50:50 maximum ratio.	**Very Dark Green, soft consistency** - high legume pasture content, heavy worm burdens in pastured horses. **Very light green** - high grain intake relative to roughage, increased grass hay, eating straw bedding. **White, pasty color** - excessive grain intake; fermentation abnormality due to loss of bowel flora.
ODOR	A balanced roughage and concentrate diet will result in a well formed ball with a fine texture and pleasant, not offensive smell.	**Increased odor** - high legume diets with darker fecal color. **Sour, pasty fluid feces** - excess grain intake in proportion to roughage, fermentation abnormality. A "rotting" smell may be associated with bowel infection, heavy worm burdens, sudden introduction of 1-2 cups of fat to diet.
TEXTURE	Finely macerated grass and grain particles into a well formed fecal ball. Break manure balls with a stick to check texture. Check for sand content on sandy soils as a guide to sand uptake and risk of sand colic.	**Long straws** - more than one inch (2.5cm) - sharp edged molar teeth, greedy horses. **Whole grain** - sharp edged molar teeth, feed bolter. - high whole grain diets above 10lb daily.

URINE

	Normal	Possible - Feed Influences
COLOR	Horse urine is normally an off-white to yellowish color, with a syrupy thick consistency due to mucus content, easily passed.	**Dark color** - high legume content in pasture, muscle breakdown pigments after fast exercise, particularly if horse tied-up. - Dehydration - more concentrated urine, thicker syrupy consistency, passed in small amounts - check water intake, provide electrolytes and free access to water. **White, creamy color** - high alfalfa or high protein meal content in diet. (If smelly, could indicate bladder infection). **Thin, straw colored** - excessive intake of water, playing with waterer, following saline drenching, or kidney disease.
ODOR	Urine has a bland urine like odor - not excess ammonia smell.	**Excess ammonia smell** - high protein content in diet, lack of adequate water intake. **Dank, sour smell** - bladder infection, occasionally high grain diet. **Abnormal odor or color in grazing horses** - eating plants with pigments or aromas.
EASE OF URINATION	Healthy horses with a normal fluid balance freely pass urine several times per day.	**Reduced volume, concentrated urine, slow to pass** - dehydration due to heavy sweat loss or inadequate water and electrolyte intake. **Passed in small frequent amounts** - seasonal cycles in mares, urinary infection (all horses). **Reluctance to stretch out** - fatigue after hard exercise, muscle soreness, lack of water/dehydration.
URINARY RESIDUE	Normal urine soaks into ground leaving a small amount of mucus and salt residue.	**White, crystal crusty, residue** - dehydration and high mineral content in diet. Large amounts of alfalfa hay with high protein and calcium content, or well water with high mineral content. **Dark residue** - high legume content, muscle pigments after fast exercise, particularly if horse tied-up.

STORAGE AND USE OF VITAMIN AND MINERAL SUPPLEMENTS

Various vitamin and mineral supplements are recommended to correct deficiencies, imbalanced diets and to meet requirements of performance horses under stress.

Exposure to heat, light, moisture and contact with air, alkaline mixes or certain minerals can reduce the potency of vitamins added to horse feeds.

A few simple storage and mixing rules will ensure your horse will accept and obtain full benefit from vitamin and mineral supplements.

DO's

1. Choose supplements that have been scientifically formulated to ensure potency is maintained during storage and use.

2. Take time to read directions carefully before adding supplements. Use measure supplied or suggested, at all times. Replace lid and reseal container tightly after use.

3. Thoroughly mix supplements into the feed. When introducing new supplements to the ration commence on a lower dose and increase to the recommended dosage over a week or so to help ensure acceptance.

4. Store supplements in a cool, dry place below 75°F (25°C). Avoid storing against iron walls, window areas or in direct sunlight. Refrigerate liquid and paste preparations during hot summer conditions, or for periods of prolonged storage.

5. Purchase the appropriate size of the container that can be used in 50-60 days, to reduce deterioration of vitamins once container is opened.

   Generally, larger containers reduce cost per dose. Refill larger packs [eg 40lb (18kg) drum] into smaller container [5½lb (2.5kg) tin)] for daily use for one or two horses, whilst ensuring the bulk supply is well sealed and stored in a cool, dry place.

   Try to ensure the supplement is used before the "Expiration" or "Use by" date.

6. Try to avoid over-supplementation. Select supplements to avoid "overlapping" to get maximal nutritional benefit at an economical cost. Use extra vitamins where necessary during times of stress.

DON'Ts

1. Avoid mixing supplements containing Vitamin E and Vitamin C into feeds containing supplements of iron or copper as these minerals can interact and destroy these vitamins.

2. Avoid storing damp feed with added minerals and vitamins (eg Vitamin E and iron) for more than 3-4 hours, as some of the vitamins may be destroyed by interaction with minerals in the moist environment.

3. Do not mix vitamin supplements directly into warm feeds (eg bran mashes, hot boiled barley or linseed) until they have cooled to room temperature. Mix in just prior to feeding.

4. Do not add mineral oils to the same feed as supplements containing Vitamins A, D and E as they will be absorbed into the oil and be less available to the horse.

5. Do not mix vitamins into feed containing alkaline electrolytes (particularly bicarbonate of soda) as some may be destroyed before the horse consumes them, particularly in a damp feed.

6. Do not rely on vitamin injections as the sole form of vitamin supplementation. Provide oral forms daily as a basic routine supplement, particularly to horses under stress of hard work and racing.

7. Do not mix calcium into pure bran mashes, as the calcium may be bound-up and made less available to the horse. In normal rations containing up to 10% bran, absorption of calcium will not be significantly reduced.

METHOD OF RATION FORMULATION

All suggested rations in this book have been formulated in accordance with National Research Council *(NRC)* (1989) Guidelines, the internationally recognised authority on nutritional standards for domestic animals and horses. The calculations take into account the type or class of horse, exercise demands, requirements for growth, pregnancy and lactation, as well as appetite limit, ingredient substitution and palatability of the ration based on my own practical feeding experience. The recommendations for each class of horse have been computed for the average horse.

The bodyweight ranges for each class of horse recommended on the ration guidelines are based on the breed, or typical type of horse used for each activity or horse sport. Some practical adjustments to the ration intake may need to be made to a bodyweight basis. However, in most cases, these variations from the guidelines would not exceed 10% under practical conditions, and little adjustment, if any, will be required.

Obviously, the ration guidelines may need slight adjustment to suit bodyweight, condition, temperament, feed preferences and appetite of individual horses, as outlined in the hints on nutritional management following each ration.

Feed nutrient values for average to good quality feeds have been taken from the NRC (1989) Guidelines, and other references.

The nutritional benefit of pasture in working horses on full concentrate feed, is believed to be minimal, although paddock exercise and grazing is psychologically beneficial to horses. Access to pasture is considered a bonus, as most stabled horses need to consume all the feed offered to meet their exercise requirements.

Most rations have been calculated to provide 100% of the daily nutritional requirements for working horses. Young growing horses, breeding mares, spelling horses, ponies and horses at rest usually have access to better quality or improved pastures, and hence have less need for concentrated grain diets. Where grazing horses are supplemented with concentrate feed, rations were formulated to provide approximately 75% of the daily nutritional requirements for these horses.

WEIGHTS AND MEASURES

Where possible, weights are given in pounds and U.S. pints, with the equivalent metric measure in brackets. Other volume measures refer to level teacups, (120ml), teaspoons (5ml), tablespoons (15ml), or scoops (supplements).

All grains and hays are measured by weight, as volume is influenced by quality of feeds. However, oils, molasses and powdered supplements are measured for convenience by volume as they are less variable in quality and density.

SUPPLEMENTARY READING LIST

In the preparation of this book, I acknowledge the scientific and practical information provided by the reference books and authors listed below. They form the basis for supplementary reading by teachers, students, and all horse owners.

Boillotat, S.B., Polocrosse - Australian Made, Internationally Played, Belcris Books, Sydney. 1990.

Choice, Amanda, Polocrosse A Practical Guide. A. Choice, Armidale NSW Australia. 1992.

Clarke, A., Air Hygiene and Equine Respiratory Disease, in Equine Practice, Bailliere Tindall, London 1991 p.59-79.

Cunha, Tony J., Horse Feeding and Nutrition, Second Edition, Academic Press, San Diego, California 1991.

Evans, Borton, Hintz and Vleck, The Horse, W H Freeman & Sons, San Fransico, 1977 p241-244.

Frape, David, Equine Nutrition and Feeding, Longman Scientific and Technical, Essex, England 1986.

Hintz, Harold F., Horse Nutrition: A practical Guide, Acro Publishing Incorporation, New York, USA 1983.

Hungerford, T.G., Diseases of Livestock (9th Edition), Angus and Robertson Publishers Pty Ltd, Sydney, NSW, Australia 1990.

Kerrigan, R.A., Practical Horse Nutrition (2nd Edition), Griffin Press Ltd., Adelaide, South Australia 1989.

Kerrigan, R.H., Horse Feeding Simplified, Kerrigan, Maitland, Australia. 1990.

Kohnke, J.R., Health Care and Common Problems of Horses, Birubi Pacific, 1992.

Lewis, Lon D., Feeding and Care of the Horse, Lea and Febiger, Philadelphia, USA 1982

Merck Veterinary Manual (7th Edition) Merck & Co., Rahway NJ 1991 p.1225-1239; 1700-1719.

Morrison, Frank B., Feeds and Feeding, The Morrison Publishing Co., Iowa, USA 1961.

Naylor, Johnathan M. and Ralston, Sarah L., Large Animal Clinical Nutrition, Mosby Year Book, St. Louis, Missouri, 1991 p.407-445.

Nutrient Requirements of Domestic Animals No.6 Nutrient Requirements of Horses (Fifth Revised Edition), National Research Council, National Academy Press, Washington DC, USA 1989.

Oehme, Frederick W., Plant Toxicities, Current Therapy in Equine Medicine 2, Edited by N.E. Robinson, W.B. Saunders, Phil 1987, p.672-681.

Raisbeck, Merl F., Feed Associated Poisoning, In Current Therapy in Equine Practice - 3, Edited by N.E. Robinson, W.B. Saunders, Phil. 1992, p.366-380.

Savage, C.J., Nutrition to Avoid Skeletal Growth Abnormalities, Proc. 181 Post Grad. Comm. in Vet. Science, Univ. of Sydney, Canberra, Dec 8 1991, p.25-29.

Snow, D.H. and Vogel, C.J., Equine Fitness. The Care and Training of the Athletic Horse. David and Charles, Newton Abbot, London 1987 p.210-230.

Veterinary Clinics of North America, Clinical Nutrition Equine Practice, Edited by Harold F. Hintz, W.B, Saunders, Phil Vol.6 No.2 Aug. 1990.

INDEX

Extra coupons for extra copies!

 Call 1-800-435-8188 with credit card details to
have your copy sent today. Or mail/fax the coupon below.
Price includes handling, postage and tax.

Mail to: Vetsearch International, c/o American Book
Centre, Brooklyn Navy Yard Bldg #3, Brooklyn NY 11205

Or fax to: (718) 935-9647

Yes, please RUSH me "Feeding & Nutrition"

Name _____

(Please Print)

Address _____

_____ State _____ Zipcode _____

I enclose Check ☐ Money Order ☐ for ☐ Softcover copies at $19 each.

Total $ ☐ Please charge my Visa ☐ MasterCard ☐ Amex ☐

☐☐☐☐☐☐☐☐☐☐☐☐☐☐☐☐

Signed _____ Expiry ☐ / ☐

Mail to: Vetsearch International, c/o American Book
Centre, Brooklyn Navy Yard Bldg #3, Brooklyn NY 11205

Or fax to: (718) 935-9647

Yes, please RUSH me "Feeding & Nutrition"

Name _____

(Please Print)

Address _____

_____ State _____ Zipcode _____

I enclose Check ☐ Money Order ☐ for ☐ Softcover copies at $19 each.

Total $ ☐ Please charge my Visa ☐ MasterCard ☐ Amex ☐

☐☐☐☐☐☐☐☐☐☐☐☐☐☐☐☐

Signed _____ Expiry ☐ / ☐